Are you really pro towards your phy strength goals?

D1220237

If you're not, *more of what didn't help you over the last few months will not help you over the next few.* No matter how well you may think you're satisfying all the factors involved in bodybuilding and strength training success, if you're not progressing, all is *not* well.

This book's purpose—like that of its companion texts—is to teach you how to achieve *your* drug-free potential for muscle and might. FURTHER BRAWN doesn't, however, promote conventional training methods because most of them simply don't work well for most people.

Today is the start of the rest of your life. You'll never be as young as you are now. There'll never be a better time than today to start getting your training-related life in perfect order. *So start today to get in charge of your physique!*

But where are the photographs?

There's no shortage of photographs in the training world. But there *is* a shortage of training instruction that's 100% relevant to the training masses. Most photographs used in the training world are for decorative purposes and/or to attract buyers, but *not* for instructional value. Photographs are, however, vitally important for teaching exercise technique, and nearly 250 of them are included in a companion text—i.e., THE INSIDER'S TELL-ALL HANDBOOK ON WEIGHT-TRAINING TECHNIQUE—which focuses on correct exercise form.

Further BRAWN

OVER 230 QUESTIONS & ANSWERS ON HOW TO BUILD MUSCLE & MIGHT

Stuart McRobert

CS Publishing Ltd., P.O. Box 20390, CY-2151 Nicosia, Cyprus
tel + 357-233-3069   fax + 357-233-2018   email: cspubltd@spidernet.com.cy
web site: www.hardgainer.com

US office: CS Publishing Ltd., P.O. Box 1002, Connell, WA 99326
tel 509-234-0362   fax 509-234-0601   email: info@hardgainer.com
web site: www.hardgainer.com

Cover illustration by Stephen Wedan copyright © 1998
Cover design by Nicholas Zavallis

Printed by J. G. Cassoulides & Son Ltd., Nicosia, Cyprus
Reprinted in 2002, with minor revisions and corrections

Publisher's Cataloging-in-Publication
(Prepared by Quality Books, Inc.)
McRobert, Stuart
   Further brawn : over 230 questions & answers on how to build muscle & might / Stuart McRobert. -- 1st ed.
   p. cm.
   Includes index.
   ISBN: 9963-616-14-3

   1. Bodybuilding--Training--Miscellanea.   2. Weight training--Miscellanea.   I. Title.

GV546.5.M37 2001   646.7'5
                          QBI00-740

Contents

Acknowledgments

Without the publicity arising from being published in newsstand bodybuilding magazines, the interchange with the authors and readers of HARDGAINER, and feedback from readers of my articles, other books and the web site www.hardgainer.com, this text would not exist.

I specifically want to thank John Christy and Dave Maurice for providing feedback on a draft manuscript during the production of this book, and Efstathios Papadopoulos, DC, for his input on answers that concerned chiropractic. I also want to thank John Leschinski and Webby Webmaster for running www.hardgainer.com, from where some of the questions answered in this book originated.

Debts of appreciation are also owed to Carolyn Weaver for the index, Stephen Wedan for the cover illustration, and J. G. Cassoulides & Son for its dependability and expert printing and binding.

Trademarks

All terms mentioned in this book that are known to be trademarks have been marked as such. But CS Publishing Ltd. can't attest to the accuracy of this information. There may be unintentional omissions in acknowledging trademarks. The publication and use of this book does not affect the validity of any trademark or service mark.

> As far as instruction goes, there's very little that's truly new in the weight-training world. Here's how I expressed this point in BRAWN: "Charles A. Smith, over the time I knew him before his death in January 1991, used to remind me that what we have today we owe to the past. How right he was. As Chas used to put it, 'It's upon the pioneers' shoulders that we have to stand in order to be as tall as they. We're merely the heirs of those who have gone before us.'"

Introduction

Thank you for buying FURTHER BRAWN. This book was based partly on the 1999 answers I wrote for the "Questions & Answers" column at www.hardgainer.com. The answers from that column which are published here have been revised and improved (and indexed). But many of the answers in this book were never put on the web site.

The questions originated primarily from readers of one of more of HARDGAINER, BRAWN, THE INSIDER'S TELL-ALL HANDBOOK ON WEIGHT-TRAINING TECHNIQUE, and BEYOND BRAWN. As comprehensive as the information in those publications is, it's not exhaustive. The purpose of FURTHER BRAWN is largely threefold: to provide new material, give expanded or additional explanations on some topics already covered in the other texts, and supply the reinforcement and encouragement many readers of the other works need to *keep them* on the training straight and narrow. The emphasis is on how *to apply* knowledge to individual situations—to teach you to become *your own* expert personal coach.

You'll get the most out of this book if you've already read BEYOND BRAWN and THE INSIDER'S TELL-ALL HANDBOOK ON WEIGHT-TRAINING TECHNIQUE. Those two books provide the extensive background information this text builds upon. But even if you haven't read those other two books, this text alone provides a wealth of practical information that will help you realize your physique and strength goals, while improving your health *and* accommodating a busy working and family life.

As a teenager I wanted a great physique more than anything else. But passion wasn't enough. It needed to be married with good instruction and discipline. I had the discipline, but not the good instruction. I wasted much of my life by training incorrectly. The mistakes I made are being made by legions of trainees today, of all levels of experience.

Don't waste years of your life, and thousands of workouts, before finally grasping the fact that abbreviated weight training is the only way to go for the huge majority of bodybuilders and strength trainees. It's *also* a better way to train *even for the minority of people who can gain well from conventional routines*, because they can gain the same results, or perhaps *better* results, from much less training, thus freeing time for other activities.

Learn this truth now, apply it, and then get on with developing a terrific physique and strength level. If you ignore this truth, you'll follow the same path of frustration and extreme disappointment that I did, and millions of others too. Bodybuilding and strength training are wonderful activities, *but only if you train effectively.*

I wish a wise mentor had grabbed me by the scruff of my neck as a beginner, and *forced* me to follow simple and abbreviated training programs, with the priority goal being to increase my exercise poundages while always using *impeccable* form. I wish that mentor had ensured I never wavered from the sure way. Had this happened I'd have developed a better physique by age twenty (after five years of training) than most drug-free bodybuilders the world over. As it happened I gave my absolute all to bodybuilding for five years, but had little to show for it. Appropriate training instruction is essential. No level of dedication and motivation can make lousy training programs work.

Self evaluation

Are you stronger now than you were a month ago? If you're not, your training is not working (assuming you're striving for muscle and might). Are you carrying any injuries? If you are, you're not training properly. Are you full of excitement for each workout? If you're not, you're probably overtrained—and overtraining won't develop bigger muscles.

Are you feeding on quality food every three hours or so? If you're not, you're not supplying the regular nourishment you need. Are you consuming enough calories to gain on? If you're not, how can your muscles grow? If you're cutting corners with your diet, your body will cut corners with its recovery and building processes.

Are you providing the rest and sleep your body needs? Are you getting eight or more *quality* hours sleep each night? If you're not, how can your body recover optimally between workouts? Unless you're fully recovered between workouts, you're not going to develop a much better physique.

The components of successful bodybuilding are simple enough, but putting them into consistent practice is something else. This book will teach you much of what to do to make your training a success, but actually *doing it* is where *you're on your own. You* have to stay clear of other approaches to training. *You* have to ignore the liars, cheats, fools and unadulterated bull that abound in the training world. *You* have to avoid distractions. *You* have to discipline yourself to *always* use good form. *You* have to push through the tough reps. *You* have to ensure you feed every three hours or so. *You* have to ensure you rest well between workouts. *You* have to ensure you go to bed early enough so that you get your required eight or more hours of quality sleep each night.

Distraction attraction

Beginners in particular are easy prey for the many distractions that flourish in the bodybuilding world in particular, and training world in general. Beginner or otherwise, to protect your own best interests you must have the discipline to avoid getting caught up in the hoopla, hype and razzmatazz of the training world, especially bodybuilding.

You must have the discipline to stick with sensible training methods. Even good progress is usually slow, *but steady*. You must have the *patience* to keep at it. Slow and steady for a few years adds up to *very impressive* progress. Trying to get there quickly nearly always ends up in failure, and often even regression because of injuries sustained.

Training programs are not exciting. What's exciting is the progress that accumulates from training. Training is merely the tool used to bring about the end product. Most trainees change their training programs far too often. Substantial progress doesn't happen in just a month or two. A program has to be stuck to faithfully for enough months to deliver noticeable improvement. Chopping and changing programs yields nothing but frustration and disappointment. *But sticking to a poor program is no good. It has to be a good program.*

If I'd had the imaginary mentor I referred to earlier in this introduction, and had he been an uncompromising dictator when it came to the use of *perfect* exercise form and *abbreviated* routines, and belligerently insistent on the need *to keep adding a little iron to each big exercise every week or two*, for year after year after year, I'd have made gains so consistently, and without injuries, that I'd have thought I was an easy gainer.

I'd have been adding a tad of iron every week or two *without* any perceived increase in effort needed, such would have been the gradual and intelligent nature of my progression. I'd have accumulated gains on an almost linear basis for year after year. Having discovered *The Golden Fleece* I'd have been scratching my head wondering why so many people had trouble developing bigger muscles.

I didn't have such a mentor. I had an abundance of inappropriate, absurd, often dishonest and frequently conflicting information, mostly from bodybuilding magazines. So I wasted many years of my life learning the hard way. The wasted years were not just during my teens.

Through my books, and HARDGAINER, I've tried to publish the next-best alternative to the mentor I wish I could have had. Together they don't provide *all* the practical information you can use for building muscle and might, but they supply enough to get the job done for anyone who has the requisite desire, dedication and determination to build a terrifically developed and strong physique, *drug free.*

A few years of dedicated effort to *The Golden Fleece* may seem a long time, but it will soon go by. If you're into the usual pile of routines that overtrain 99% of drug-free people, you're going to waste years of your life. After a few years of that you could look back and think, "Heck, if I'd followed the down-to-earth, sensible, gradual and steady approach, I'd actually be big and strong by now."

After a few years of the usual overtraining routines you won't be significantly stronger or better developed than you are now, but you may have accumulated a collection of injuries from having persisted with hostile exercises and/or techniques. So get on track now, and put into practice what this book teaches. It's never too late, and the best time is always now. You'll never be younger than you are now.

To your training success,

Stuart.

Stuart McRobert

P.S. The questions and answers have been divided into several categories. In some cases the grouping is loose because quite a few questions and answers deal with multiple subjects. To find answers dealing with specific topics, please use the index.

To make the index as user friendly as possible, paragraph indexing was used for most of this book. For example, 51(T2.3) refers to page 51, paragraph T2.3, i.e., *Training* section, answer 2, paragraph 3.

What gives me the right to preach to you?

I've dedicated my working life to exposing the bull, lies and other major shortcomings of the exercise world, and to providing an alternative. I've done this in order to teach people how to exercise responsibly, safely and effectively for building muscle and might.

Born in 1958, in England, my "credentials" include over 25 years of training, over 350 articles published in newsstand magazines, having authored four other books on training, having published and edited an *independent* training magazine since 1989, and having always been independent of food supplement companies. Because I'm genetically average, have never used performance enhancing drugs, have an extremely demanding job, and am a family man too, I can totally relate to the lot of the average person.

I'm not part of the weight-training establishment. Though I've written many articles for the mainstream bodybuilding press, I've hammered away at my central themes, albeit limited by editorial constraints. *Few people in the training world who have any visibility speak on behalf of the true interests of typical grassroots trainees.* Most people with visibility speak on behalf of the training establishment, and therefore have to peddle the usual "company line."

But I'm no armchair athlete or theoretician. I've deadlifted 400 pounds for 20 consecutive rest-pause reps, and I've been an inveterate muscle and strength buff for most of my life.

What I teach isn't the only way to train; and what I teach isn't unique to me. But when properly put into practice, it *is* a practical, safe, realistic and super-productive way to train. I just happen to be the person who invested the time and effort needed to put the entire package of information together into a comprehensive set of interrelated books, and a magazine. While no set of materials can ever be exhaustively comprehensive, I've given my pound of flesh to try to get close. Of course, I'm not infallible; and I'm still learning.

I promote training methods that are more conservative than those of most coaches. I explain possible if not probable dangers of certain methods or techniques, rather than ignore them and hope that readers don't find out about them the hard and potentially disastrous way. And I strongly promote the importance of individual variation. But I get overwhelming feedback that this produces much better results for many more people, *and* greater training longevity, than does the non-conservative little-or-no-caveats approach that doesn't fully consider individual variation.

Striking a balance...

Being realistic isn't negative. Though typical trainees can't develop an awesome physique by today's drug-distorted standards—240+ pounds at average height and no more than 5% bodyfat—that doesn't mean you can't become "big." It's just that "big" is a relative word. Though typical trainees will never bench press 500 pounds, that doesn't mean you can't be "strong." It's just that "strong," too, is a relative word.

How muscularly big and strong you can become, only you can know by actually achieving your potential. On-paper concerns are just that—on paper, and academic. What matters most is what you *actually* do. With the 300-400-500 numbers (bench press, squat and deadlift) I didn't set ceilings, though in truth most trainees will never get to those numbers due to age, structural or health limitations, or plain lack of the requisite dedication and commitment. The 300-400-500 numbers are targets which are very challenging for most trainees, but which most trainees not limited by age, structural or health concerns *can* realize *if* they deliver the requisite dedication and commitment.

Even outstanding achievements are produced by knocking off lots of little bits of progress. Just focus on getting today right, this week, next week, and then the week after that. Do that for a few years and you'll be so big and strong that you'll be impressive by any standards other than today's drug-fed excesses.

I believe in training dedication, hard work and the discipline to maintain good form *even while working very intensively*. In BEYOND BRAWN I paid far more time to matters of safety and injury prevention than I did in BRAWN. You'll never realize your size and strength potential if you repeatedly get injured. Staying free of injuries is essential. Being safety conscious, training with discipline, and never letting bravado get the better of you, are essential components of successful long-term training.

To make the best of what you've got, you must respect structural and recuperative limitations. While respecting limitations, *don't* set ceilings. *Strike the right balance.* Then keep knocking off the bits of progress for as long as you want to get bigger and stronger. Then you'll develop a physique that, relative to your age, will make most people stare in admiration when they see you for the first time.

Be challenged by the call to arms to stand firm against the stench of drugs, lies, bull, fraud and irresponsible training advice that besmirch the Iron Game. Together, we really can make a difference.

Bull, Deception and Dishonesty

A number of questions gave rise to a series of answers which I blended into a short book and initially published in electronic format entitled WHY CONVENTIONAL BODYBUILDING METHODS SUCK...AND THE ALTERNATIVE APPROACH THAT REALLY DELIVERS. That short book can serve as an appropriate introduction to FURTHER BRAWN because it details much of what's wrong with the training world, and explains how you can avoid falling foul of the same bull, deception and dishonesty that millions already have. As most readers of FURTHER BRAWN will not have read the electronic edition of SUCKS (available at www.hardgainer.com), here's a revised version:

What follows is a scathing report on conventional bodybuilding methods. This may seem very negative, but out of a negative you'll discover a huge positive.

The basic problem is that conventional bodybuilding dogma dominates the training world, despite this dogma being a total sham.

To discover the greatness of bodybuilding, and strength training in general, you first need to understand what's wrong with the training world. Then you'll be informed enough to be able to cut through all the crud. So out of a negative you'll get to a positive, and discover how to build the physique that conventional training methods deny you.

Anyone who thinks that the contents of this section are alarmist, or that I'm exaggerating, is out of touch with reality; or he has his head in the sand, is living in a make-believe world, or is promoting a lie.

I'm exposing the squalid mess to help prevent people from getting caught up in it themselves, and to educate them on how to exploit the marvellous potential benefits of intelligent training.

With influence comes the responsibility to wield power in a socially accountable way. Many influential figures and companies in the mainstream of the training world have been utterly irresponsible, to put it mildly. Millions of trainees have put their trust in various individuals, publications and institutions, but have been betrayed, and at great personal cost.

I'm a diehard training and bodybuilding buff, but I belong in a different camp to that of most of the mainstream. I've no time for the bull, deceit, fraud, drugs, lies and absurd training practices that are rampant in the mainstream.

The way that much of the training establishment has deceived the masses is akin to how the tobacco industry has spun its wicked web over the years. A glossy picture is presented in order to hide the squalid abuse of economic power. This is a strong statement, but read on and you'll see that my words are not mere rhetoric.

Sure I'm a rebel, but a rebel with a cause. You need a rebel's perspective; otherwise you're going to fall prey to the training mainstream due to ignorance. You're never going to get this rebellious but liberating perspective from the mainstream, because the establishment isn't going to go out of its way to undermine its power. That many magazines and books give similarly irresponsible and even harmful advice will never make that advice right. While repeated hammering away at the same lies and deception does make many if not most readers believe they are being given good advice and information, no degree of repetition of deceit and nonsense will ever produce something of truth and value.

Learn from the costly experiences of those who've been through the mill of desperate frustration with conventional training advice. Like my other books, FURTHER BRAWN is not based on only one man's journey. It's a distillation of the acquired wisdom of *generations* of people *but which has been largely hidden or ignored by the training mainstream.*

Once you apply radical changes to your training program you'll be totally out of step with what most people do in the gym. Have the courage to swim against the training tide. Always keep in mind that popular training methods simply don't deliver the goods for most people. So why would you want to use popular training methods? Life is too short to waste any of it on useless training methods.

Because I'm only interested in drug-free training, and primarily concerned with satisfying the needs of the hard-gaining masses, most of the values and methods promoted in this book are heretical relative to what's customary in most gyms today. There's no other approach to take if training methods that are practical and helpful for drug-free typical people are to be promoted.

Anyone, anywhere or anything that promotes training routines that only work well for the genetically gifted and/or drug enhanced, or offers how-to information on drug abuse (or carries ads for books on the same), or promotes absurd expectations and role models, or teaches high-risk or impractical training practices, or is a food supplement catalog in disguise, simply doesn't have your best interests at heart. If you follow the "instruction" found there you're going to tread the same path of frustration and even despair that millions already have.

Is your training working?

Do you *really* have some progress in muscle and might to show for your efforts over the last few months? More of the training approach that didn't work over the last few months isn't going to work over the next few months.

Before you can take charge of your own training and physique, you need to understand *why* conventional training methods not only won't help you *but may actually harm you.*

Conventional bodybuilding methods are useless for most people, and their promotion has grossly misled the training masses. Look around almost any gym and you'll see few drug-free people who have good physiques. And consider how many people have been gym members at one time or another, but gave up due to dissatisfaction with the results.

The enormous failure rate of conventional training methods isn't publicized by the mainstream, because the mainstream has a vested interest in the maintenance of the status quo.

Weight training is a wonderful activity, *but only if it's working.* When it's not working it's a massively frustrating and disappointing activity. To increase the success rate of weight training, an approach is needed which is radically different to that promoted by the mainstream.

What *is* conventional bodybuilding?

Conventional bodybuilding methods are largely the training practices of "elite" male and female bodybuilders and strength athletes—practices which are vigorously promoted in most bodybuilding magazines and books, and even on television too. They involve weight training on 4–6 days per week, multiple exercises per muscle group, and usually at least three work sets per exercise *in addition* to warmup work.

Most of the "elite" of the bodybuilding and strength worlds are phonies because without their drug support they'd be shadows of themselves. So "elite" is being used here purely as a collective description, not as a suggestion of any sort of superiority. Drug-fed bodybuilders and strength athletes are shams.

Conventional bodybuilding methods aren't just what any specific magazine, book or publisher has to say. It's a collective thing arising from many authors, publishers, books, magazines, organizations and gyms. It's the whole shebang of excessive and impractical routines, and the presentation of the competitive "elite" as gurus and role models.

Consider some of what conventional training methods promote, and see how it's a travesty of useful instruction:

1. Conventional training methods overtrain everyone other than the genetically gifted and drug abusers, but overtraining won't help you.

2. Conventional training methods promote some high-risk exercises that injure many people. Getting injured won't help you build the physique you want.

3. Conventional training methods often promote specific dangerous techniques for otherwise good exercises, and those specific techniques injure many people. Again, getting injured won't help build a good physique.

4. Conventional training methods promote a volume and frequency that are impractical for busy working and family people. But even sacrificing work, family, education and a balanced life won't make conventional training methods work for typical people, so there's no value in extreme measures anyway.

5. Conventional training methods place exaggerated importance on food supplements. Supplements can't make lousy training programs work.

6. Conventional training methods promote exaggerated expectations, and invariably use drug-fed genetic freaks as gurus and role models, neither of which will help *you* to realize *your* potential.

7. Conventional training methods complicate training, and confuse people. Complication and confusion can't help.

8. Conventional training methods are not personalized to meet individual needs, limitations, lifestyles and goals. This produces overtraining, injuries, frustration and giving up—i.e., failure.

9. Conventional training methods actually *encourage* drug abuse, because without the drug assistance those methods just don't work for most people.

Much of the mainstream of the training world, and the bodybuilding dimension in particular, plays down the drug problem, or pretty much pretends it doesn't exist, and does nothing of substance to help put an end to drug abuse.

That much of the establishment panders to the drug abusers, glorifies many of them, has made a few of them into icons, and presents them as role models, has played a major part in encouraging drug abuse and the accompanying chaos.

The drug problem in the bodybuilding world in particular is bad beyond belief. This has brought great ignominy upon mainstream bodybuilding.

But there's another side to bodybuilding, and strength training in general. It has nothing to do with the drug abusers or their lackeys. The other side of the coin is clean, honest, truthful, productive, practical, healthy and life-enhancing.

As a youth, when searching for training instruction I was heavily swayed by appearances. What looked the best (to my gullible eye), had the most striking photos, and the most hype to really spike my expectations, was what grabbed my attention. That it presented useless and even harmful training instruction didn't dawn on me until years afterwards, by which time I'd been robbed of some of the best training years of my life. Nothing has changed on this score over the years. The same shambles continues for today's novices, and will continue in the future.

The "information" most responsible for misleading trainees is not isolated to some specific and famous individuals and publications. It's everywhere, and even includes most non-mainstream publications *and* a plethora of internet web sites.

My motives
It cost me nearly half of my life, a great deal of suffering, and an enormous waste of time, effort and money before I learned the real deal on how to improve one's physique safely and efficiently. I want to spare others from learning in the same extremely expensive way, or from giving up training due to frustration with lousy results.

In my youth, being a naive and trusting lad, I followed conventional bodybuilding methods hook, line and sinker—just like millions of people have over the years. And just like almost all of those millions, I found that conventional bodybuilding methods suck.

Whereas just about all of those people moved on, disillusioned and frustrated at having not realized their exercise goals, I stayed in the weight-training world and made a career out of teaching others to avoid falling foul of the same perils that I and millions of others already have.

My views challenge the mainstream of the training world. In my defense, consider these questions:

1. Is it wrong to want to stop people from committing training "suicide"?

2. Is it wrong to want to prevent people from wasting years of their lives training incorrectly?

3. Is it wrong to want to spare people from suffering injuries from using high-risk exercises and specific techniques?

4. Is it wrong to teach people that they don't have to spend a great deal of time in the gym to realize their strength and physique potentials?

5. Is it wrong to teach people how to realize their exercise goals while maintaining a balanced life—*without* sacrificing work, personal and family lives on the altar of excessive time spent in the gym?

6. Is it wrong to want to spare people from wasting money on food supplements that don't deliver what the ads promise? Is it wrong to let people know that some food supplements simply don't contain what the labels list? Is it wrong to let people know that lies and massive exaggeration are used to promote food supplements?

7. Is it wrong to expose the drugs, lies and deceit that are rampant in the training world?

8. Is it wrong to promote training routines that work without drugs?

I'm not anti conventional training methods for the sake of it. I'm just against anything that deceives the masses, or promotes useless, harmful or impractical training methods. Conventional training methods work well for hardly any drug-free people, so why promote them?

The benefits of a responsible exercise program are great, but you won't experience any of them if you get cheated like I was and millions of other people too.

Conventional training instruction is in a colossal mess, and it's outrageous how so much bull and deception are promoted in gyms today. Inappropriate, impractical, non-personalized and dangerous instruction won't do. There's an alternative approach—one that's appropriate, practical, personalized, safe, healthy *and* super productive.

What's wrong with the training world?

Primarily the promotion of impractical and inappropriate training methods that only work well for people who've been blessed with great genetics, or for drug abusers. As a result, most people don't get the results they want.

The training world is built on huge success for a few people, and minimal or no results for the majority. What I promote is different to what the mainstream churns out because I teach healthy, real-world training for real people with busy lives and a sane *drug-free* mentality. My concern is with the training masses, not the competitive "elite."

What most mainstream articles and books don't tell you is that the featured role models are usually genetic super people and/or are taking so many drugs that they make themselves super people until, that is, their health crashes. As super beings they can prosper on training methods that the average person can't. Someone who doesn't share your drug-free genetically "normal" condition is in no position to lecture you on how to train for your best results.

With few exceptions, it's true that mainstream books and articles don't give how-to advice on drug abuse. But by promoting routines that only work well for drug abusers, and by revering people who are drug abusers, that's tantamount to drug endorsement at worst, and outrageous hypocrisy at best. And it's a travesty of responsible behavior.

The calamitous fallout

The rampant use of muscle-building drugs is the worst calamity that has ever hit the training world. Drugs have produced dishonesty of untold proportions. *The first casualty of drug abuse is the truth.*

Most modern-day training magazines and books reek of lies and dishonesty because of rampant drug abuse by many if not most of the men and women featured in those publications, and used in advertising.

Some bodybuilders and strength athletes who only got to the top because they had drug assistance are *still* claiming that they never took chemicals. Usually they are dishonest because they are ashamed of their drug abuse, and don't want to tarnish their clean public images. And some even promote the charade that they were hard gainers.

While the harm to health that the chemicals have wreaked is a huge problem, as are the criminal implications of illegal drug use, these are nothing relative to the colossal harm done to the drug-free training masses.

Rampant but generally secretive drug abuse since the early sixties, when steroid use really took off, led to drug-assisted training methods being almost universally promoted as appropriate even for the drug-free training masses. But these conventional training methods don't work for drug-free genetically typical trainees. Because these methods are so unproductive, most people who try them are propelled into a well of frustration and disappointment.

To make conventional routines work well, harmful anabolic chemicals usually need to be used. Dissatisfied bodybuilders looking for quick fixes to their training frustrations and disappointments have produced huge markets for drug pushers. *But the drug route is not the only solution for training woes!*

If people would train based on the principles promoted in this book, they would get results that would astound them. They wouldn't experience the frustration and disappointment that are usually standard when using conventional training routines. Then they wouldn't feel pressured to take dangerous drugs in order to make their training work.

Out-of-this-world strength and Mr. Universe-type muscular development are only possible for genetic phenomena who are stuffed with drugs. Forget about comparing yourself with drug-fed genetic phenomena, because that's the route to despair, frustration and drug abuse. What matters is what *you* do with *your* physique, not what others do with theirs under extraordinary circumstances.

While it's true that the approach I promote won't make you into a Mr. Universe, *it will take you a darn sight further than conventional training methods would.* There's no comparison!

Keep your integrity, sanity and health. Absorb with every atom of your being the paramount fact that your health is your most important possession. And your integrity is not far behind in importance. Train drug-free, always!

Anyone who says that bodybuilding drugs are safe to use, is full of bull. Some of the people who give you the "bodybuilding drugs are safe" spiel happen to sell how-to books on drug abuse. A few of the "experts" are dead, partially if not wholly due to their own drug abuse.

Bodybuilding drugs are dangerous, and should be avoided like the plague. As Charles A. Smith told me shortly before his death in January 1991, "You never know how important good health is until you no longer have it." Think about this. Dwell on it. Make it one with you while you still have your health, *not* when it's too late. Avoid all harmful habits, activities and environments. *Look after yourself!*

Train like a champ to become a champ? No way!

"Train like a champion to become a champion" has long been the message promoted by the weight-training world, especially bodybuilding. This message has been trumpeted in one form or another by almost all the magazines and books in the field—both mainstream *and* "sidestream"—and by most trainers and gyms too. The motive is simple—it attracts great interest and sells magazines, books, courses, food supplements and gym equipment.

While it's been a big commercial success in some respects, it's been a disaster for the training masses.

The promotion of the "merits" of copying—wholly, or partially—the training methods of the "champion" bodybuilders and lifters is one of the most costly frauds in the exercise world. Despite millions of trainees having failed to meet their exercise goals in spite of putting into practice the methods used and promoted by the "champions," the fraud continues. The failure of the training masses to achieve their goals is *not* publicized by the mainstream. The successes of a tiny minority—the "champions"—dominate the mainstream press and hide the real state of affairs in the training "trenches."

Many years ago I used to be a big fan of a number of very famous, "elite" competitive bodybuilders. They were heroes of mine *until* I found out about the immense harm they were responsible for. I was just one of the millions who, over the years, were grossly misled by these men.

The following is a statement of what these men were really responsible for; and what bodybuilding orthodoxy prefers to keep hidden, in the hope that by keeping it suppressed people will actually believe that competitive bodybuilding is healthy and full of decent and honest people worthy of emulation. This suppression is necessary in order to keep the "train like a champ to become a champ" mentality alive and kicking.

The real champions of the training world are not the drug-enhanced genetically blessed competitive "elite." The real champions are the unsung heroes who applied years of dogged determination in order to build themselves up against the odds, without ever using drugs, without seeking or finding publicity, and without divorcing themselves from the rigors and responsibilities of everyday working and family life.

Genetically gifted and drug-enhanced super achievers who have near-perfect training conditions and lifestyles can't hold a candle to the real heroes of the training world.

I started weight training in 1973, age 15, when a handful of "legendary" bodybuilders were in their prime. I know from first-hand experience the impact such men have on ignorant and gullible neophytes. Their training methods were promoted to the training world with no caveats. This was done via numerous magazines from many publishers worldwide, and several books. The format was basically, "Here's how the champions did it, and if it was good enough for them it's certainly good enough for you. Train, eat and take food supplements like the champions do, to be like the champions!"

When I started bodybuilding I was consumed with dreams of building a great physique. I wanted to be as good as the most famous men of the time. I trained with the same dedication. I trained as their articles said I should. And I didn't neglect the mental aspects—I imagined my biceps as mountains, and I had a hugely positive mental attitude.

I was at high school at the time. I took on jobs to earn the money needed to buy the food supplements and extra food I had to have, along with as much training literature I could get ahold of. Everything in my life played second fiddle to bodybuilding. I became a recluse. I was antisocial. All I wanted to do was train, and then apply myself to fully satisfying my recovery needs, which meant getting lots of sleep and avoiding social activities. I was as dedicated as possible. Because I had the extreme level of dedication supposedly needed to become a "champion," and because I knew I was delivering on the dedication front, and was training harder than anyone else at the gym, and I ate a lot and slept plenty—going to bed earlier than my peers—I couldn't understand why I wasn't making good progress. In fact, I wasn't making *any* progress for a long while.

It was only many years later that I understood why I wasn't making any progress—I didn't have the extraordinary genetics the "champions" had, and I wasn't "supplementing" with drugs. I used to believe that the only supplements the "champions" took were of the food type.

I didn't build a physique like the "champions." Not only that, but I didn't even get close. In fact, the methods they followed and advocated *set me back*.

When I got to know of the drug component, I was disciplined enough never to use bodybuilding chemicals. Had I not had this discipline, however, I'd probably either be dead by now, or a physical wreck. Not having the genetics to be able to build huge muscles naturally, almost certainly meant that I'd never have had the physical robustness needed to withstand heavy drug abuse.

I wish someone had grabbed that young, gullible and oh-so-enthusiastic bodybuilder I was, and *insisted* that I trained in a way that was appropriate for me. Then I'd have made more gains over just a few months than I did from years of the conventional approach of four or more days of training each week, multiple exercises per bodypart, and many sets. I was robbed of the best training years of my life through deception and utterly irresponsible instruction.

Train like a modern-day "elite" bodybuilder and you'll never develop a terrific physique *unless* you're one of the very few who have fantastic genetic potential. Don't waste years of your life before you learn this lesson. Learn it now!

The "instruction" found in most articles from/by "elite" bodybuilders has no practical relevance for typical people.

Almost all bodybuilding magazines throughout the world have, to varying degrees, promoted the "train like a champ to become a champ" maxim. For an illustration, consider a 1998 article in a major newsstand bodybuilding magazine on the chest training of one of the most famous bodybuilders of all time. A five-exercise 24-set chest routine twice a week is training suicide for the typical drug-free trainee. That's how it is. This is not sour grapes, or mean spirited.

There were no caveats accompanying the article pointing out the need for superior genetics and drug assistance to make the routine work. What relevance has that article got for the typical trainee with average genetics and the good sense not to use drugs? But the typical youngster is going to copy it, and thus suffer as I did when I was very young.

Countless others suffered the same way I did, and still are today, because the same sort of irresponsible training nonsense that misled me in the seventies is being reprinted or rehashed today.

Not only did the "champions'" methods not help me, they caused injuries, gross overtraining, and sickness. So they *harmed* me. Millions of others have been affected in an adverse way, though you'll never read about this in the mainstream publications. Despite all of this, the "elite" are almost deified by some people and publications.

Just about every "champion" bodybuilder since the steroids era began has been guilty of promoting overtraining and impractical and often harmful training methods, destroying the dreams of countless people, and giving weight training a bad name.

Some "successful" but scurrilous bodybuilders have claimed to have been hard gainers. Steroids were what "fixed" their perceived "hardgainingness," and enabled them to train six days a week; but never was that mentioned in the magazines and books. Food supplements, "better" training, and more dedication were the "secrets," *so we were told.*

The promotion of the training methods used by drug-assisted and genetically gifted men wreaks havoc, despite these men being presented as demigods in the bodybuilding world. Sure they have inspired millions, but at the same time they have misled millions; and their "instruction" has robbed millions of people of the best training years of their lives.

The ensuing desperation drove many people to steroids, to try to make the pseudo training advice work. Lousy instruction fuels drug abuse because without drug assistance those methods don't work for most people.

Though people who've suffered from the "train like a champ to become a champ" nonsense know the real score, endless newcomers to bodybuilding don't, and they are going to tread the same well-worn path of frustration that millions of people already have.

The legacy of many "stars"
When sizing up the contribution to bodybuilding of modern-day physique "stars," consider the following:

1. They were presented as role models for others to follow, with the implicit or explicit mantra of "train like a champ to be like a champ." Millions of people tried exactly that, in good faith. But they didn't get the full story. The roles of genetics and drugs weren't disclosed, and the utter inappropriateness of the "champions'" methods for typical trainees wasn't pointed out, so the training masses were deceived big time.

2. Many people dedicated their lives to bodybuilding, to imitate the "champions," and sacrificed education, careers and balanced family lives, and all without even getting close to what the "elite" achieved.

3. Food supplements were often touted as the "missing ingredient" for training success. Millions of dollars have been made by selling overpriced food supplements that didn't deliver what the hyped up claims said they could. Drug-fed supermen endorsing food supplements was a powerful commercial success for the companies involved, but again, the whole story was held back. As a result, many if not most readers really believed that the food supplements played a major role in the bodybuilding success of the men providing the endorsements. That drugs were *the* big "supplement," and food supplements were neither here nor there relatively speaking, was kept quiet. So again, the bodybuilding masses were hoodwinked.

4. What has gone wrong in the past is still happening today. There are millions of newcomers to bodybuilding who will get sucked into the same mess that I did and millions of others too. So the fraud continues.

5. Many people discovered that the "champions'" training methods do work to a degree *if* you take enough steroids. So indirectly, the failure of those methods to yield results for the masses, promotes drug abuse.

6. The drug abuse has caused deaths, countless health problems, crime, jail terms, ruined relationships, and devastated families. This is a hideous state of affairs.

It's a strange world that glorifies many drug abusers who have deceived millions of people and caused so much dissatisfaction, frustration and downright misery.

The claim that the "elite" are healthy

Some magazines and books which supposedly promote a healthy lifestyle are packed with physiques that are pumped to their gills with drugs. A few of those physiques have subsequently died largely if not wholly due to drug abuse. That's hardly in line with a healthy lifestyle.

When I started out in bodybuilding, and for quite a few years, I believed that the "champions" followed the healthy lifestyle the magazines boasted. I believed that the "champions'" success was a result of their dedication, hard work and "clean" living, and that I should follow their example. In my ignorance I followed their training advice, like millions of other have and still do.

These people didn't spill the beans about the whole story behind their ability to grow on routines that were training suicide for me and other clean-living and principled people. I was just one of the millions who were deceived.

I wish I'd known the full picture in my teens, and had trashed any advice coming from anyone on drugs. But the mess related to drug abuse back then was low-key relative to the extent of the squalor today. How do you know who is and who isn't on drugs? Just about every "champion" competitive bodybuilder since the early sixties has been into the juice, and not just steroids in most cases. It's not a case of "if" so-and-so abused drugs, it's more a case of "how much?"

It's not just the bodybuilding dimension of the weight training world that has a lot to answer for. Drugs are a mess in all aspects of the Iron Game, but more so in some aspects than others. Of course, drugs have provided huge problems in almost all athletic endeavors.

The old-timers were clean, weren't they?

The pre-steroids old-timers did it drug free, but steroids go back to before the early sixties, which was when their use really started to take off. Some old-timers were taking steroids before the stench of drug abuse became widespread.

If you look at bodybuilding magazines since the forties, the sudden jump in the standard of physiques in the sixties, and the number of people with very "high" standards of development, is striking. It wasn't a result of "better" training, supplementation and nutritional habits, like some people would have you believe. Additionally, there was far more frequent promotion of absurd training routines once steroids became widespread—working out six days per week, even twice a day in some cases.

Steroids enabled the "champions" to train to a far greater extent and *still* progress, and those methods were promoted to the masses *without* the caveat of the need for steroid use to make the methods work. Instead, the "champions" were promoted as demigods who were dedicated to a greater degree than other people, and that was why they became "great." As I've said before, and I'm sure I wasn't the first to have said it, "The first casualty of steroid use is the truth."

Bill Pearl is a very big name who misled the masses for many years. To his credit, he did come clean about his use of steroids, and spilled the beans to some extent. As a genetic superman bolstered with drugs, Pearl was light years away from being a role model for the genetically typical and drug-free masses. He was one of the big names who seriously misled me—one of the men promoted as a demigod by the bodybuilding world.

My parents bought me Pearl's courses, as a Christmas present when I was about 17. Their instruction was useless for me. There was no mention of the role of genetics and drugs in Pearl's achievements. No mention of drugs, that is, until I read his 1986 book GETTING STRONGER. Then I started to appreciate that Pearl was an example of a tremendously gifted man who was *further* enhanced by drug abuse. Yet for many years he'd been offering advice to the drug-free genetically typical masses. No wonder his routines were so far off the mark. Here are some of Pearl's own words, from GETTING STRONGER, and he could probably have spilled a lot more of the beans had he chosen to:

> My first experience with steroids was in 1958. I had won the Mr. America and Mr. Universe contests and was in Florida making a movie with Arthur Jones, a thoroughly unorthodox and eccentric friend (who would later revolutionize weightlifting with the invention of the Nautilus machines). Arthur told me about a new chemical the Russian weightlifters were using. When I returned to California I did some research.
>
> At the University of California at Davis I met a veterinarian who told me that steroids were being used with good results to develop strength and growth in cattle. The name of the drug was Nilivar and the daily recommended dosage for humans was 10 mg.
>
> Now it might seem extreme for someone with no more information than that to begin using the drug, but that's what I did. Good enough for a bull, good enough for me! It never even occurred to me that there could be anything harmful in the drug or any side effects...
>
> Two years later I decided to enter the 1961 Mr. Universe contest. By then, steroids were out of the experimental stage and well-known to most competitive bodybuilders. They were no longer an underground item. I remembered the fast progress I'd made using them and decided to do so again...

Most of the old-time bodybuilders will not touch steroids now, but probably used them at one time or another.

While Pearl came clean, at least to a degree, few of the other big names did—at least not in public. So training methods that only work for drug-fed genetic supermen have been drip fed to the masses since about 1960. The training masses have been led asunder, and the only way for most people to make those training methods work well was to take steroids. This is no way to promote "healthy" bodybuilding.

There wasn't a golden age of training instruction in the pre-steroids era. I've a library of training publications going back a hundred years. Training volume inappropriate for most people, exercise techniques that cause problems for many people, high-risk exercises, non-individualized training, and dreadfully deceitful ads have been promoted to the masses for a century. Though there's nothing new here, modern-day big business and the drugs problem have made matters far worse.

The bodybuilding world is stuffed with people who lie freely and sell fraudulent products. A few of them have been hailed as icons of the modern world, and given numerous awards for business "excellence" or "contributions" to the training world.

Want creation
The "follow the champs to become a champ" maxim is used to create demand for innumerable training-related products.

Why is there so much attraction in the training world to matters that are insignificant, useless or even harmful? Because there's not much money to be made out of getting people to just deliver on *the package*—hard training on basic exercises along with plenty of milk and knife-and-fork food (to produce a caloric and nutrient surplus), bags of rest and sleep, and gearing *everything* to generate the progressive exercise poundages (in *perfect* form) that produce bigger muscles.

To produce enough income to satisfy the demands of a plethora of interests, money has to be made out of selling "improvements" to *the package* in terms of "better" programs and equipment, and "add ons."

There needs to be a great industry of want *creation*, and never mind the uselessness of many of the products that demand is created for, or the fraudulent nature of the promotional techniques. This industry of want creation is largely what the bodybuilding establishment exists to produce. *And how well it has produced it.*

The most profitable "add ons" are food supplements, because they are mass produced, consumed quickly and need to be "renewed" often, yielding lots of repeat sales.

Food supplements offer huge potential for repeat sales. A barbell set can last a lifetime, as can a good book on training know-how, but a can of protein powder only lasts a week or few. The profit margin on food supplements is large, and the scope for hype and lies in marketing material is unlimited.

Because bodybuilders and strength trainees are made so gullible by the mainstream literature, there's an unlimited market for selling food supplements. So the supplement hawkers are going to keep ramming their often criminally dishonest claims down the throats of muscle mag readers.

Some food supplement companies publish bodybuilding magazines (or are very closely intertwined with the publishers), and use those magazines to promote their wares. It's no wonder that many trainees seem to think more about food supplements than their training.

Exaggerated claims, dishonest reporting, abuse of editorial responsibility in magazines and books, and utter nonsense are used to produce demand for large sales of supplements.

Ask around most typical drug-free gym members who have no vested interest in the sales of food supplements, and you won't find many who will tell you they experienced much if any significant increase in their rate of progress as a result of using bodybuilding food supplements. You will, however, find many who will tell you that the most significant results of their taking food supplements are the dents made in their bank balances along with increased visits to the toilet.

Because there's nearly always something "new" being hyped up, along with "improved versions," many trainees are willing to give food supplements "just one more try." Even when that "last one" bites the dust, as it usually does, something else comes along, with a sales pitch that wins the doubters over, and trainees give that one a shot. On it goes—the supplement marketing boys know what they are doing, and the bodybuilding world is ripe for the picking.

Some ads in the muscle magazines truly are criminally dishonest. The problem isn't a bit of exaggeration or promotional hype. The problem is so very serious that it's a damning indictment of the liars who put their names to "endorsements," and of the liars who write the fictional claims for progress made while supposedly using the advertised supplements.

I know that these scoundrels are full of bull, as do most seasoned trainees. But novices don't. It's not only the big guys used in the bogus ads who should be damned, but the companies putting the ads out. And those who allow the ads to reach the public are encouraging the liars and crooks.

Drinking a potion, or swallowing tablets or capsules, to try to help training and physique progress will always have a big appeal, largely because they are easier to deliver on than are consistently hard training, good eating and sleeping.

Promoting a training method that supposedly needs food supplements to make it work is a great marketing ploy to sell food supplements. But no food supplement will make a bogus training method work.

Off the record, some of the charlatans will tell you that you've got to get on the real "gear," namely steroids (not food supplements), to make their training methods work.

A reader of HARDGAINER called to let me know about a well-known "expert" (a man who has taken steroids for many years). Someone called the "guru" to complain that the "expert's" training methods weren't working.

The first question the "expert" asked was, "What are you on?" "Guru" assumed that the caller was already on drugs, but the wrong stack and dosage of the blasted things. Of course, the "guru" doesn't put the required drug usage in his articles; so people follow the articles in good faith, not knowing that they are only for drug-using fools. Thus, the "guru's" methods wreak havoc in the training world.

Such is the shambles of mainstream bodybuilding, and the criminal activities of some of its "experts." Truth be told, those "experts" should be put behind bars.

The "improvements" and "add ons" of the training world have to be hyped up *way out of proportion* to what they can really deliver (or even be promoted with a pack of lies), due to the commercial imperative of *creating* a demand.

The great attention placed on all the "extras" inevitably produces a huge distraction from the *priority issues*, along with a great deal of bull and deceit, including bogus and even harmful products. So the training masses are cheated, and denied the progress that should be theirs.

Get *the package* in good consistent order, and you'll go far—a darn sight farther than all typical trainees who get caught up in the hoopla and bull of the modern training world.

Wreaking of havoc in other ways

Genetically gifted, drug-fed, pro or semi-pro athletes are a different breed to the rest of us, and what can work well for them can wreak havoc on us. For example, training techniques that work for them can ruin the joints of typical trainees. Despite this, many of those harmful training practices are promoted to the masses without any cautions or caveats.

Presenting some outstanding success stories as men who once were "ordinary" hard-gaining people is a travesty of the truth that has been used many times. The truth is that these people are usually genetically gifted and, at least during the last forty years or so, drug assisted.

I'm not calling all trainers and coaches liars. Neither am I saying that all examples of stellar results are from genetic standouts and/or drug abusers, but I can confidently say that most are. Only part of the truth is usually used in promotional writing, in order to increase the trainer's status and kudos, in order to kid the ignorant and gullible masses.

This method of conning the masses has been used for many years. But what you don't find out about are the failures from applying the methods that supposedly account for the success stories, and the injuries and damage that were produced among typical trainees.

Conning the training masses takes many forms, such as...

1. It's a fact that some people who've never used a given trainer's program actually endorse it and even claim to have used it.

2. It's a fact that some people who've never used the touted food supplements, endorse them.

3. It's a fact that some people who've been taking steroids for many years claim to be drug-free examples of what a certain coach's training and food supplement regimen can do.

4. It's a fact that "research" referred to by some people in the training world is fictitious.

5. It's a fact that the benefits of food supplements are usually exaggerated big time, or even made up.

I'm *not* saying that all claims are packs of lies, but I *am* saying that the bodybuilding world is notorious for exaggeration and deception, especially when food supplements are involved.

There are often facts that are hidden—perhaps the trainee concerned was coming back after a long layoff, perhaps he's a very easy gainer, perhaps he was on steroids, perhaps the time period involved was much longer than reported, or perhaps there's been some creative touching up of the photos concerned. I've seen the same head put on different bodies! But an expert *can* merge a head with someone else's body and *you would never be able to detect it.* There are *almost no limits* on what can be done today when working with photographs.

Some people and companies have no scruples, and will do whatever they can get away with in order to con people. This behavior is becoming even worse because an ever increasing number of individuals and companies are digging their hands in the coffers of the bodybuilding world.

Fraud and the commercial imperative

The "train like a champion to become a champion" mentality carries a great deal of marketing clout, and even works very well for the "elite" of the bodybuilding and powerlifting worlds. These people—who are often credited with having written articles and books—promote the sort of training that worked for them. They never had the experience of being bona fide hard gainers, so can never get in the shoes of typical trainees. So the training masses continue to be led astray.

Some of the ghost writers do know the real score, however, but because they are the lackeys of the big names they are writing on behalf of, they have to fuel the flames of bull, nonsense and fraud.

In some ways it's in the best interests of many companies that people fail in their training. This failure creates the reservoir of frustrated masses that produces the fodder for those making exaggerated or fraudulent claims for food supplements. The food supplement industry is where serious money is made, not the training instruction industry.

Most mainstream magazines don't exist to promote practical training information that works for typical trainees. They exist largely to maintain the high circulation figures needed for obtaining a lot of high-priced advertising. Also, keep in mind that some magazines are used as catalogs for the sister or master food supplement companies that are associated with those publications.

Sensible training information that works for the masses won't sell hundreds of thousands of copies of magazines or books. Photographs are the prime factor behind big sales of bodybuilding magazines and books.

In many cases, the more awesome the photographs, the better. This leads to glorification of drug-fed excesses, and a glaring contradiction with any espoused principles of good health.

The focus on the visual has also led to the presentation of as much female flesh as possible (whether trained or untrained), and as much use of sex as possible. Consider how often that word crops up in cover blurb. The use of the word "sex" seems to have greater importance than the word "muscle" on the covers of some bodybuilding magazines. This has nothing to do with training instruction, or the best interests of readers, but simply the commercial imperative of attracting buyers in sufficient numbers to make a newsstand magazine economically viable.

When numbers are the bottom line, publication content will be tailored to meet the primary need, *not* the best interests of readers. And that, in the bodybuilding world in particular, usually means a focus on the "elite," the freaks and the most awesome, along with as frequent as possible connections with sex. Of course, the use of sex as a sales technique is not unique to bodybuilding. It's used in many other fields too.

The failure rate of bodybuilding is enormous, and not just because of the lousy results that conventional training methods deliver for most people. The number of people who get turned off by the dishonesty, clear contradictions and nonsensical training advice that abound in most of the mainstream publications, is vast.

Additionally, the drug-fed muscular monstrosities (male and female) that some magazines publicize and admire, repel many people from bodybuilding, and make the activity a freak show and laughing-stock.

As long as there are plenty of gullible newcomers—usually young men— to replace the former "discarded" readers, all is well on the numbers front. And why change a proven formula? It has "worked" for decades.

The training mainstream is very adept at presenting bull, nonsense and deception as truth. Even people who are well educated and very discriminating in their professional lives often become utterly irrational in what they accept as truth in the training world; until, that is, they've invested a year or two of training and learned that conventional routines don't work well for conventional people. But by then most of them have given up, and written off bodybuilding (and perhaps exercise in general) as something that doesn't work for them. Thus they fail to obtain the wonderful benefits that accrue from a lifetime of regular exercise.

So continues the story of the training masses getting shafted by swallowing the mentality of "train like a champion if you want to become a champion."

There's quite a bit of information and advice in the mainstream that *is* accurate, but the promotion of accurate information is a vital part of the game of deception. An *illusion* of credibility is produced through presenting accurate information, and drawing upon people with *apparently* impressive academic qualifications and "reputations." This "softens up" the readers so that they are easily conned by the deceit and bull which are mixed in with the accurate material.

The current state of affairs

It's over 25 years since I started bodybuilding. But mainstream popular training instruction is no better now than it was back then. And in fact, it's worse. I am, however, only concerned with drug-free and genetically typical (and disadvantaged) trainees—i.e., the training masses. As far as the "elite" are concerned, it's a "better" world today—more drugs, more effective drugs, more competitions, more publicity and more money.

Part of me wants to wash my hands of the training world because of its nauseating deception, bull, dishonesty, hype and drugs. (I'm not just directing my comments at bodybuilding. Strength sports are riddled with the same mess.) But another part of me gets very angry at the hokum that's rampant in the training world, and drives me to make an effort to present some truth and honesty.

The word "success" is often used incorrectly. Kidding the masses, selling training misinformation, and leading people astray is not "success" no matter how many millions of items of "product" are sold, how much profit is earned, or how many tributes for business "excellence" are awarded.

Appropriate, practical and safe training instruction for typical trainees is what I'm into, and what *should be* the heart and soul of bodybuilding and strength training—mainstream and otherwise.

Photographs sell training magazines and books, not articles and workout instruction. In many cases the articles are just the padding needed to provide the spaces for photographs and ads.

For photographs to do the job of grabbing the bodybuilding masses—who, to their cost, are usually into a publication's appearance before its content—they need to be arresting. This inevitably leads to the publication of the most awesome physiques.

Today's most awesome physiques belong to the genetically gifted *and* drug-enhanced. They are *light years* away from what the genetically typical drug-free person can achieve.

But the drugs component is either understated or, more commonly, ignored—for reasons of not downgrading the physiques and reputations concerned, to avoid law suits, and to try to give bodybuilding a "clean" image.

The training methods used by the drug-fed genetic phenomena—which are often embellished with a hefty dose of fiction—are promoted without any caveats. *They should be accompanied by this sort of warning:*

"But these routines only work if you have phenomenal genetics or drug assistance, and preferably both in spades. Sane and genetically typical people must train in a totally different way. We only provide over-the-top instruction for entertainment and to attract buyers. Don't try to use the instruction yourself! What worked for the champions will not only not work for you, but may destroy your chances of achieving your potential. Not only that, but it will yield huge frustration and disappointment from so much time and effort being invested in achieving training failure, along with accumulating injuries that could scar you for life."

To finish "the current state of affairs," here's what a publisher of a foreign language edition of a big US bodybuilding magazine told me recently: "One [city]-based sports nutrition trader...has undertaken to publish a US bodybuilding magazine...The sole purpose of this project is clearly to use it as a promotion vehicle for nutrition products." The same can be said of some of the *original* US-published magazines. The job of the publication is to pull in readers, and then feed them information that "softens" them up for the sales pitches for supplements embedded in articles, or in the ads themselves. Training "information" and photographs are just the padding around which the supplements promotion is arranged. What hope is there for decent training instruction or objective nutritional information?

Bad beyond belief

I was recently leafing through a series of books from a famous bodybuilding author. The content was bad beyond belief. It was one awful book after another, preaching the same bull—training instruction totally inappropriate for the drug-free and genetically typical masses, "decorated" with genetic phenomena largely if not wholly bolstered with drugs to further enhance their already great advantages.

The naive, gullible and ignorant masses—especially young men—are attracted by the photographs in these books, buy the books, and follow the abysmal "instruction" that was used to fill the spaces between the photographs. These books are not published to help the average drug-free bodybuilder.

Relative to 1973 (when I started weight training), nothing has really changed instruction wise in the bodybuilding world other than a greatly increased number of photograph albums that pose as instruction manuals. So the mess is actually worse today than it was when I started out, and it was bad enough back then.

Even worse, and I'm not saying that this is intentional, but promoting training routines which simply don't work for the huge majority of trainees actually encourages drug abuse. Without drug assistance those training methods just don't work.

No matter how awesome something looks or is packaged, and no matter who says it or endorses it, never be persuaded that any workout instruction used by drug-fed genetic phenomena—even a watered-down version—has any real relevance to you.

Think things out for yourself, be true to yourself, and only follow routines that are *appropriate* for you, *practical*, and *personalized* to your individual situation.

If you don't do all of this you'll follow the same route of training misery that millions already have, and further millions will as they apply themselves to training methods that haven't a hope of yielding success *unless* drugs are used to compensate for the lack of phenomenal genetics.

Trading your soul and health for fleeting physical rewards from drug abuse is no sane way to go. Don't wait until you no longer have your health before you appreciate its priceless value.

Role models that mislead

In the pre-drug era, before I was born, the genetically super gifted, including the late John Grimek, were inspiring even though their achievements were out of reach for typical people. Their training routines, too, were out of line for "average" people.

But the physique achievements of today's drug-enhanced genetic freaks are *in a different world to the achievements of the super gifted of the pre-drug era.*

Even John Grimek in his prime wouldn't have been able to gain on what the modern crop of drug-fed mega achievers grow on. If a fantastically blessed superman like Grimek couldn't have gained on this modern stuff, what hope is there for regular mortals?

Drug-assisted *and* drug-free genetic phenomena don't have a clue how to train drug-free genetically typical people. But they know much about how to mislead and deceive. Always keep that in mind when you hunt for role models or help with your own training.

What about the legitimate drug-free "elite"? Aren't they worthy role models?

There are some *drug-free* top-level bodybuilders, though *not* as freakish as the drug-fed crop. While many of these elite "naturals" are as drug-fed as the monsters, there probably are a few who are clean (but *astonishingly* gifted genetically). Some of them even claim to be hard gainers. After all, they did struggle a bit to get from 18-inch to 19-inch arms. But anyone who could get huge without drugs was *never* a hard gainer. Even the elite's progress grinds to a halt eventually, and then they find gains hard to come by. But that doesn't qualify them as hard gainers. And just because they are drug-free doesn't mean they are genetically typical and therefore suitable role models for the rest of us.

Some of the near-freakishly developed "naturals" boast they are examples for what can be done sans drugs. Then they lay out a training program for readers to follow that even Schwarzenegger in his prime would have been proud of. (Schwarzenegger was absolutely no example of a drug-free hard gainer for typical trainees to follow.)

There's remarkably little difference between the elite naturals' routines and the drug-fed's routines. Perhaps the former need a bit more recovery time, and fewer sets, but still their training methods are far removed from what typical trainees need, such are the former's tremendous genetic advantages. So, paradoxically, the mainstream deception "machine" has found allies in some natural "champs."

No one—whether drug-free or drug-fed—who has great genetics for building muscle and might can *ever* get in the shoes of the typical hard gainer. Anyone who promotes long routines, and more training days than rest days, is promoting an approach that only works for the genetically gifted and/or drug fed. It never worked for typical drug-free trainees in the past, and it will never work for them in the future, *no matter how many food supplements are taken, or which brand name is chosen.*

Dedication, food supplements, attitude and hard work can't improve one's genetic inheritance. They are, however, essential for realizing one's potential, *but only if combined with a training program that's appropriate for genetically average people.*

Some food supplement companies use "tested" drug-free near-freakish physiques to endorse their products. A big thing may be made of the "drug-free" condition, but no mention of the *tremendous* genetic good fortune the men have. Supplements are promoted as the big "equalizer." So once again, the typical trainee gets shafted as the establishment hides truths, makes its own "truths," and distorts things to suit its own ends— ends which are *not* in the best interests of the training masses.

Why's nothing done to put things right?
With the bodybuilding world in particular being in such a mess— though you'd never realize it if you only read the mainstream magazines—you might wonder why nothing is done to put things right.

Despite drugs being so endemic in bodybuilding, and with the "elite" competitive physiques (male and female) being juiced up to the hilt, no serious action is taken against drug abuse. Instead the "stars" are presented as role models, given tremendous publicity and opportunities to line their pockets, and some of them are made into icons.

Drug testing, as scarce as it is, is pathetically inadequate. No serious action is taken against drug abusers because the consequences could be so dire for the powers that be. If a *legitimate* and *rigorous* surprise test was performed at a big contest, or on the big guys who endorse food supplements, they would all test positive for drug abuse.

If all the beans were spilled, that would rubbish the public "credibility" of the many organizations and companies that have built their success on the edifice of lies, drugs and deceit that makes up much of mainstream bodybuilding. There's simply no strong and principled leadership at the top to do anything about the problem. So the drug issue is largely swept under the carpet, and a pretense made that there really isn't such a big problem after all.

Stand up and be counted!

In my teens in particular I fell prey to the siren calls of those who sold fraudulent products and used scurrilous tactics to deceive the ignorant but gullible masses. Today the siren calls are even more attractive and deceptive.

I recently discovered some antics of a very big name in the world of competitive bodybuilding. Exploiting his fame, he's offering "personal" (and very expensive) training courses through correspondence.

Based on minimal information that can never get even close to understanding the strengths, limitations, goals, individual circumstances and lifestyle of the individual—all of which can hugely influence the design of a training program—Big Name provides a non-individualized "personal" training program along with supplement advice. It probably won't be long before he has his own line of food supplements, in order to pillage the market even more.

No mention is made to prospective "clients" of the freakish genetics *and* tremendous drug support Big Name has, and of how he's utterly unqualified to instruct typical trainees. His training philosophy for the masses is pretty much "train like I did to become like me."

Big Name has an accomplice for the scam—another juiced-to-the-eyeballs genetic marvel. What hope is there that this duo will offer responsible training for typical trainees? Zilch! These two scam artists are just two of many, such is the state of the training world. This sort of mess is not new, but there's far more of it around today than in the past.

That so many people are ripe for being ripped off is largely a reflection of the mainstream propaganda that intentionally misleads people, or at least hides the truth. This leaves the training masses prime prospects for ripoff merchants.

The mainstream misinformation and deception "machine" is wrong. But doing what's right isn't the bottom line for most mainstream interests—the numbers game and end-of-year financial statements are what count most of all.

Stand up and be counted by turning your back on what's wrong in the training world. Never mind if having scruples and doing the right thing is unfashionable in some people's books.

Rid yourself of all the crud that produces so much failure and exploitation in the training world; and rid yourself of those who propagate the crud. This means cutting yourself off from drugs, liars, cheats, hypocrites, and unrealistic expectations that can only be realized through freakish genetics and buckets of drugs.

Educate yourself, become your own expert personal trainer, take charge of your own training, never surrender control to another person (especially a drug-fed genetic phenomenon), train yourself safely, sensibly and productively, and accept that you can never match the drug-fed monsters.

Dedicate yourself to achieving your *own* potential, and knuckle down to years of consistent *intelligent* training that has been personalized to suit you. And always keep your health as your number one priority.

Do all of this and you'll achieve your own physical excellence, enjoy the journey there, and be a credit to the true and honorable standards of the Iron Game, and be a credit to yourself.

Be challenged by this call to arms to stand firm against the stench of drugs, lies, bull, fraud and irresponsible training advice that besmirch the Iron Game. Together, we really can make a difference.

The paradox...

Though the chronic failings of the training mainstream motivated me to write articles and books, and publish a magazine, it was the training mainstream that actually provided me with a degree of visibility from which I could present an alternative perspective. On the one hand there's *so much* to protest about concerning the training mainstream; but on the other hand, without the training mainstream I wouldn't have been able to provide an alternative voice to the extent I have.

While I actually have a vested interest in the shortcomings of the training mainstream—because I've made a career out of providing an alternative viewpoint—I'd *much* prefer that the mainstream hadn't been defective and deficient in the first place. Then the success rate from mainstream instruction would have been so wonderfully high that there would have been little or nothing to protest about, and no need for an alternative way.

Time to be frank...

Over recent months, have you really progressed towards whatever training and/or physique goals you've set for yourself? Do you actually have some *specific* goals? If you don't, you need to set some.

If you're not progressing, you *must* make some changes or else stagnation will continue. *More of what didn't help you over the last few months will not help you over the next few.* No matter how well you may think you're satisfying all the factors involved in bodybuilding and strength training success, if you're not progressing, all is *not* well.

For example, all may be well in the gym—hard work and perfect form on abbreviated and personalized training routines focusing on a handful of big exercises that suit you— but the problems may be out of the gym, such as insufficient food, not eating often enough, or not sleeping and resting enough. But most trainees have deficiencies in *and* out of the gym. Be ruthlessly analytical, objective and critical, find what's wrong, put everything right, *and then you can look forward to progress.*

Just acting on the content of this *single* box can make the difference between gains and no gains, and this alone will more than justify the cost of this book.

I've written this sort of "call to arms" before, but it needs to be repeated. Perhaps you've read it before elsewhere, but didn't act on it. Please act on it now *and end the stagnation once and for all.*

Whenever you think that it's tough to deliver on all the components for bodybuilding and strength training success, remind yourself that having the good fortune to be able to dedicate yourself to hard training, and everything that should go with it, IS A PRIVILEGE. Eventually you won't be able to train hard, or dedicate yourself to anything, so make the most of the going while it's good—no slacking, no corner cutting, and no excuses. GET TO WORK AND MAKE THE MOST OF YOUR WONDERFUL BUT NOT INFINITE OPPORTUNITY TO TRAIN AND ACHIEVE PHYSICAL IMPROVEMENT!

Training

My question concerns a training program. It's a two-day split routine—on Monday I do mostly lower-body work, and on Friday I do upper-body work only. Is this a good strength and mass builder?

MONDAY: squat, deadlift, calf raise, curl, ab and neck work

FRIDAY: bench press, dip, shoulder press, chin, row, ab and grip work

T1.1   Whether this program is a good mass and strength builder is not determined by a list of exercises, but by the effort and dedication invested in the gym, and the satisfying of recovery needs—rest, sleep and nutrition—out of the gym. Only if all of these factors are in good order, and the ability produced to add a tad of poundage to each big exercise every week or two, will the program be a good strength and mass builder.

T1.2   A program is a mere list of exercises, and training days. The same program can be implemented by identical twins with contrasting results. If one fully satisfies all the requirements—hard work, perfect form, excellent recovery and progressive poundages—and the other holds back in the gym, or cuts corners in his diet, rest and sleep habits, then the former will make good progress, but the latter will waste his time. But the program in both cases, and genetic factors, are identical.

T1.3   Many trainees are quick to change their training programs, because they assume that when they are not progressing it's the program's fault. So they try another program; but because they don't fix up their effort levels, don't use perfect form, and persist in cutting corners on the recovery front, they continue to make minimal or no progress. Even a "perfect" program won't work if the user doesn't deliver on all the "ingredients" needed for the program to work.

T1.4   Of course, if you're on a twice-a-day, six-days-a-week program, you're never going to get it to work unless you've got tremendous genetics *and* are foolish enough to stuff yourself full of drugs. The program you select needs to have *the potential* for producing gains, assuming that you deliver on the effort, form, rest, sleep, nutrition and progressive poundages fronts. Many programs have this potential, providing they are abbreviated.

T1.5   The questioner's program has the potential to be productive, so from that point of view it will suffice. But to make it better for most hard gainers, bench press *or* dip, and chin *or* row. Generally speaking, use the different but overlapping exercises in different cycles rather than mix them in the same program.

TRAINING 2
If I understand you correctly, you're saying that I should only do one major movement for each large muscle group. This would surely make my workouts *very* short. Is this correct? Could you elaborate on the proper amount of work per muscle group to perform for a week?

T2.1   I urge trainees to find what works for them. A few can progress well on volume training, but they are very few and far between—and almost non existent if you take out the drug component that's so prevalent in gyms today. My focus is on training for genetically typical and drug-free trainees. The approach best suited to these trainees just happens to necessitate abbreviated training. As a bonus it's also a practical way to train because you don't have to weight train on 4–6 days a week. But abbreviated training isn't only for hard gainers; it's also perfect for people who have very responsive bodies, i.e., easy gainers. Easy gainers respond to abbreviated training even better than do hard gainers.

T2.2   As long as you're truly training hard and seriously, and really are eating, resting and sleeping well, if you're not gaining well, then you're almost certainly overtraining. You need to find the amount and frequency of training that does the job of stimulating increases in strength and muscular size, but *without* exceeding your ability to recuperate. Some people need to abbreviate their training more than do others.

T2.3   Relative to the 4–6 weight-training workouts per week on a split routine, and the 8–15 (or more) sets per bodypart that's typical of mainstream instruction, abbreviated training involves short and few workouts. But that's exactly what you want—get in the gym, stimulate growth quickly, then stay out of the gym until you've recovered, and only *then* go back in. Hard gainers are usually best off weight training no more than twice a week, and may only hit each big compound exercise once a week. Not only can this produce terrific gains, but it leaves you with the time you need for a balanced life outside of the gym.

T2.4   What matters is what works. Most people train too much. So cutting back on training volume and frequency are the big steps most trainees need to take to start experiencing good gains.

TRAINING 3
I've read about a number of different ways to train in an abbreviated way, and I'm confused. How do I make sense of all the variation?

T3.1   Different people can respond in different ways to the same training approach. Individual variation can be dramatic in some cases. Always keep this in mind when you read of the success any one person has experienced as a result of a certain way of training. What works well for him may work for you too, but on the other hand it may not work for you and may even have negative effects. One person's meat can be another's poison.

T3.2   Warming up is a good example of the variation you can find among trainees. One person may prosper well on 20-rep squats, for example, while only needing minimal or almost no warming up prior to the work set. But some people need a very thorough and time-consuming warmup or else they will get hurt from the work set, or at least not be able to perform well at it. Some people can squat rock bottom and prosper very well on it. But others only end up with lower back and/or knee problems from squatting so low. Some people prosper on singles, while others only get hurt on them (even when perfect technique is used, and not-quite-limit singles). Individual variation can be considerable.

T3.3   You need to discover what *you* need. That's what should matter
        most to you. By all means consider what others prosper on—
        providing it's not clearly very risky or only suited to genetic
        freaks or drug users—and experiment in a sensible, conservative
        and *progressive* way to find what works best for you. Don't
        throw yourself in the deep end with, for example, rock-bottom
        full-bore 20-rep squatting with minimal warmup work when
        you're used to parallel squatting, for 8-rep sets and three
        progressive warmup sets prior to your two work sets. The last
        thing you need is an injury.

T3.4   Remember, one person's meat can be another person's poison.

TRAINING 4
**I've been on a high-intensity abbreviated program
for three months. I gained 25 pounds and am truly
amazed at my results. My bench press has gone up
40 pounds and the same for most of the other
exercises. I recently came across a book on partial
reps training, and it's pretty much the same as high-
intensity abbreviated training: big compound
movements done infrequently while continuing to
pile on weight. But in this case you only lower the
weight 3 or 4 inches. Is it worth trying?**

T4.1   Why change your training when it's working so well? Stick with
        what's working so well.

T4.2   I'm not a fan of partial-rep training. Generally speaking, typical
        trainees are not suited to higher-poundage partial-rep work. It's
        a recipe for injury for many people. Leave this sort of work for
        those who are truly advanced and physically robust enough to
        be able to prosper on it. Partial-rep training can have merits in
        some specific situations, but its merits have been exaggerated by
        some people, and shortcomings played down or even ignored.

TRAINING 5
**You suggest for drug-free hard gainers a goal of 300
pounds on the bench press, 400 pounds on the
squat and 500 pounds on the deadlift (300-400-500).
You also suggest a rep speed of 3 seconds on the
positive movement, and 3 or more seconds on the
negative movement (3/3). Does this mean that the
300-400-500 have to be done at 3/3? Also, how much**

would you advise a trainee to reduce poundages by when the rep speed is reduced to 3/3?

T5.1   In BEYOND BRAWN, perhaps due to putting the rep speed matter in late (in order to give a guideline for bar "control"), and not honing it enough before going to print, I overstated matters when I wrote that the positive stage of a rep should take at least three seconds. In the subsequent printings of the book, this matter has been corrected. Different exercises have different "stroke" lengths. Some exercises can be performed in smooth control a little faster than 3 seconds for the positive. Three or more seconds for the negative is still a good rule of thumb, other than in very short-stroke exercises.

T5.2   I was wary of a seconds specification distracting people from the greater priorities, so I made this qualification in BEYOND BRAWN:

T5.3   "Let rep smoothness and the pause test be your guides for rep performance. It is not necessary to count seconds, or to lock yourself into a specific cadence for each exercise...do not get so locked into a precise number of seconds that you become a slave to time. The focus should be on control, form and progression."

T5.4   But 3/3 is still a good *general* guideline to use (there's also the brief between-reps pause too, in addition to the 3/3 approximation); and yes, the 300-400-500 numbers, or thereabouts (relative to bodyweight), can still be met by most very determined hard gainers (who are not limited by age) while using impeccable form, and controlled smooth cadence. Relative to bodyweight, the 300-400-500 numbers translate, for men, to about 150% bodyweight in the bench press, 200% in the squat, and 250% in the deadlift. These numbers are not ceilings, however. Many determined and dedicated hard gainers can exceed at least one of these three percentage targets.

T5.5   When first moving to smooth (non-explosive) and controlled form with good bar pathways, a reduction in weight is needed; but to what degree depends on what sort of cadence and form was used previously. The poundage will come back over a few months or so, together with better development. Here's the biggest benefit: By training with much less risk of injury, you set your stall out for safe, long-term training free of injuries, which is *precisely* what you need if you're to realize your full potential for muscle and might.

T5.6   Related to the matter of rep speed, I wrote an article in HARDGAINER issue #62 (September-October 1999). Because it's relevant, I'll excerpt from it, with some changes:

T5.7   "I've not said that moving slowly means that training must therefore be safe. Slow reps can hurt people, just like fast ones, if the bar pathway is wrong, or if a hostile exercise is being used. One of the worst injures I've had was when I gave 10/5 cadence training a trial, years ago. I was performing the bench press and the very slow ascent stalled just before lockout. I lost the balance of the barbell, the bar tilted, and I badly injured my left shoulder. (I was training alone, without a spotter.) Very slow training can be dangerous, just like any training in which form breaks down.

T5.8   "Here are two relevant quotes from BEYOND BRAWN:

T5.9   "'Rep form is related to rep cadence and between-rep pauses, but slow cadence does not necessarily mean good form, and fast performance does not necessarily mean the use of poor technique. Slow does not always mean strict, just like fast does not always mean cheating. And heavy low-rep work does not necessarily mean fast reps.'

T5.10 "'A slow rep can still involve terrible exercise form, and some exercises—e.g., snatch, clean and jerk, clean, and other explosive movements—must be done quickly.'

T5.11 "There are several factors involved in training safely. Avoiding harmful exercises, using excellent form (i.e., bar pathways), and having balanced musculature are all big factors. Highly proficient Olympic weightlifters are proof that it's possible to train explosively without getting injured. But I prefer to build a margin of error into training, hence why I don't promote explosive training or exercises that can only be done explosively. I'm not, however, anti Olympic lifting. I'm for Olympic lifting, but the proviso is that expert hands-on coaching is available, and the trainee concerned is suited to that type of lifting.

T5.12 "Generally speaking, my writing is directed at trainees who are not interested in competitive lifting—Olympic or power—and thus have no need to use any explosive training. None of the exercises in my book on technique need to be done explosively, unlike the clean, for example.

T5.13   "Some authors are primarily writing about training performed
          under their eagle eyes. But nearly all readers of HARDGAINER and
          my books train by themselves (or with a training partner), and
          don't have an expert to watch them rep by rep, and correct any
          errors as soon as they slip in. A slight error in form will much
          more likely yield injury if an explosive cadence is used, than if
          non-explosive form is used.

T5.14   "It's one thing to talk about using speed correctly. But very few
          people can do that—just look around almost any gym at almost
          any time. Giving an okay on explosive speed, even a qualified
          one, will be misinterpreted or misapplied by many if not most
          trainees, and have them throwing and dropping the weights in
          their usual travesty of 'controlled' training.

T5.15   "I do believe in a slower rep cadence than some authors and
          coaches do, but not a contrived one. A 3/3 cadence, or
          thereabouts, is not super slow. I don't practice or recommend
          explosive lifting. Neither do I practice or recommend 'tapping'
          the chest in the bench press, for example. One person's 'tap' may
          be another's 'bounce,' just like one person's 'control' may be
          another's 'out of control.'

T5.16   "At the bottom of the bench press I recommend barely touching
          the chest, and pushing up immediately, or pausing for a second
          first (while staying tight). In both cases there would be just
          enough force applied to get the bar moving—not an explosive
          thrust. Keep the bar moving smoothly. Once the bar is moving,
          then it may be an all-out drive to keep the bar moving, albeit
          relatively slowly. On the final rep or few of a set you'll need to
          muster all the force you can to get the rep moving off your chest,
          but even then the bar should move smoothly, and there should
          be no explosive thrusting.

T5.17   "With the right attitude towards safety, and taking the
          appropriate actions, confidence is produced that yields or
          intensifies the passion needed to train hard and productively.
          Being concerned about safety is not negative.

T5.18   "Over the decades, with few exceptions, the safety aspect of
          weight training has been played down or ignored by the training
          world. Form has been given short shrift. Rep cadence and
          control have been given short shrift too. And 'cheating' has even
          been encouraged by many, to get out the final rep of a set. It's no

wonder that weight training has acquired such a reputation for causing injuries, and has produced so much work for chiropractors, medical doctors and physiotherapists.

T5.19 "I may risk a very few trainees overdoing the safety-first mentality, and being so wary of getting hurt that they never train hard enough to gain, in a *misinterpretation* of what I recommend. But better that than have people understate safety concerns and thus most of them end up having to live with injuries and endless frustration, like millions of others already have.

T5.20 "Some men with more training and coaching experience than I and most other writers and authors in the training world—Dick Conner, Ellington Darden and Arthur Jones—also promote the use of non-explosive training, and have seen tremendous results from it. It's not the only way to train, but when properly used I believe it's the safest way for most people to train, and one that can be super productive, especially for hard gainers and anyone who trains alone without a truly competent and alert coach to supervise every rep."

TRAINING 6
What's the big deal about rep speed?

T6.1 Rep speed is one of the most critical aspects of bodybuilding, and one that's usually given cursory if any attention.

T6.2 Banging out reps like most people do, is not the way to go. The "banging out" of reps is at the root of most training-related injuries. *Training will only build the physique you want if you do it consistently enough, progressively enough and for long enough.* You can't train consistently and progressively for a period of years if you keep getting injured. Ask around any gym and you'll find many people who are "carrying" one injury or another, and training around injuries. You'll also find people who can't train hard any longer because of injuries from the past. And you'll find many people who can no longer do the most important exercises such as squats, deadlifts, stiff-legged deadlifts and dips because they have so many weak links in their bodies. *Don't let this happen to you.* It *will* happen to you, however, if you train in the same "banging out" the reps way that most trainees do.

T6.3 Some people don't get injured easily. The genetically highly gifted are physically more robust than most people. This means that they can get away with a degree of training abuse that over 95% of bodybuilders can't. But if you imitate their training volume and rep speed, you'll overtrain *and* get hurt.

T6.4   Watch most people train and you'll see that they take one second (or less) to "lift" a barbell, and no more than about another one second to "lower" (drop) the barbell ready for the next rep. *This is not controlled training.* Sooner or later, and usually sooner rather than later, this speed of training will produce injuries, and repeatedly so.

T6.5   Safe training is largely about three factors:

a. Choosing exercises that are safe and appropriate for you.

b. Using immaculate exercise technique.

c. Using controlled rep speed/cadence.

T6.6   In addition, *appropriate* weight selection is critical so that a trainee can actually use good technique and a controlled cadence. If a trainee uses a heavier weight than he currently has the strength to handle properly, he won't be able to exercise good form. Proper weight selection is that which *just* permits the target rep count but *without* any compromise on good form. Never should good form be compromised for the sake of using a heavier poundage. Too fast a rate of poundage increase on the bar is one of the most common training errors, and leads to form degradation and "cheating." Cheating is foolish, and a route to training ruin.

T6.7   With immaculate exercise technique and a controlled *smooth* rep speed, most exercises are safe for most people. But you must stick primarily with the big building exercises if you want to get big and strong. The "detail" exercises won't make you big. Bodybuilding is not just about safe training, but about *effective* training. If your muscles aren't growing, then something is wrong and needs putting right.

T6.8   If you use an uncontrolled rep speed, even good exercises performed with good biomechanics will hurt you. Even if you use a controlled rep speed, and are using exercises that *on paper* are safe and productive, *if you use sloppy technique you'll get hurt.* You need to get all three elements in order: good exercise selection, immaculate form, *and* a controlled rep speed. Get all three right, every workout, *and* train progressively, and you'll have taken the biggest steps you ever can towards training safely *and* productively, and reaching your goals over the long term.

T6.9   The "right" rep speed varies from exercise to exercise, because different exercises have different "strokes," i.e., they have different ranges of motion. You can't, for example, expect the shrug to take the same time per rep as the chin; and the overhead press has a longer stroke than the supine bench press.

T6.10   As noted in the previous answer, keep your rep speed at 2–3 seconds for the lifting portion, and at least 3 seconds for the lowering portion. Most people use a throwing and dropping style of training, rather than a controlled cadence.

T6.11   All reps of a set don't take the same time period each. The final rep of a set, when you're really giving your absolute all to grinding it out, may take longer—perhaps over 4 seconds for an ascent in the bench press, for example. Especially watch out for going too fast at the start of a set, when you have more strength than you need to perform each rep.

T6.12   At your next workout, consciously time your reps during your warmup work, e.g., "one thousand and one, one thousand and two, one thousand and three." Count like this mentally, but don't speed up as the set progresses. Get the feel for the required rep control during your warmup work. Then move to your work sets. You'll need to cut back your weights to begin with. Cut them back by whatever is needed so that you can perform your target reps while maintaining the controlled rep cadence. Then over the next month or two or three, *gradually* build your weights back *while maintaining* controlled form. The poundages will come back, but this time you'll be forcing your muscles to work more intensively because you'll have taken most of the momentum out of the picture.

T6.13   After a few workouts you'll be able to replicate perfectly controlled rep speed without needing to count mentally. When you're training really intensively you shouldn't be thinking of anything other than getting out your reps in good form. You must not be distracted. To keep rehearsing the controlled rep speed, perform the mental "one thousand and one, one thousand and two," etc., counting on your warmup sets. And have a training partner or assistant check on your rep speed during your work sets, to let you know if you're still in control when it matters most.

T6.14   Once and for all, ignore those who take liberties with rep speed, exercise form or whatever. Train safely and correctly, and then you'll still be training progressively in years to come, when other people in the gym are either treading water in their training, or repeatedly recovering from injuries, and yoyoing from one injury after another, and never actually making any new-ground progress in strength or growth.

T6.15   Explosive training greatly increases the stress on your musculature and connective tissue. It's at the root of training injuries *even when exercise biomechanics are fine*. Avoid explosive training if you're interested in training safety and longevity.

T6.16   Briefly pause for a second or few after each rep. Don't knock out your reps in a continuous fashion. And for those exercises where there's a period of full contraction in the flexed position—e.g., calf raise, pulldown, chin and curl—hold that position for a second or two before lowering the resistance to the starting point for the next rep.

TRAINING 7
Do I really need lots of exercise variety, like the mainstream says I do?

T7.1   No. Consider this illustration, based on accumulated experiences of typical trainees over many years: John stays loyal to the squat for quad development, for five years. He never even thinks of using leg extensions, hack squats, leg presses or Smith machine squats. Over the five years he slowly but relentlessly builds up the squat poundage from a start with 125 pounds for 8 reps. After five years he's able to squat 370 pounds for 20 reps.

T7.2   Ted thinks that variety and diversity is the way to go. He mixes up his exercises, never sticks with any one combination for more than six weeks, and always does at least two exercises for his quads each workout, and always gets a great pump. After five years of this he still can't squat with 250 pounds for 20 reps, and his quads still don't look bigger than those of most professional soccer players.

T7.3   By being able to handle 370 for 20 perfect-form reps, there's no mistaking John's credentials as a bodybuilder, though not an elite-level one. His thighs are built. And all without a single leg extension, leg press, hack squat or Smith machine squat.

T7.4   It's a terrific physique you're after, not the use of a variety of exercises for the sake of it. Keep your training simple and basic. Become terrifically strong in a small pool of big exercises, and then you'll become terrifically well developed. It *is* that simple.

TRAINING 8
Some trainers and writers, even from outside the mainstream, recommend training the full body three times per week. What's the real scoop on training frequency?

T8.1   Training frequency is one of the variables, including rep count, number of sets, exercise selection and training intensity, that can vary considerably across different trainees, accordingly to genetic, age and lifestyle variations, among other factors.

T8.2   What matters is what works for you—what produces steady progress. This doesn't necessarily mean what's *optimal* for you, if optimal is not practical for you week in and week out. Perhaps being trained hands-on by a coach, squatting till you barf every five days, feeding every two hours and sleeping ten hours every night produces your optimal rate of gains, but if you can't sustain that for month after month, it's not practical for you no matter how ideal it may be. Practicality has to be married with what's ideal, to produce something you can stick with over the long haul. If, however, you can get your life organized sufficiently to follow your "ideal" program for 4–6 weeks every once in a while, go for it. But for most of the time, a different approach needs to be used, one that will fit into your usual lifestyle.

T8.3   You need to find the training frequency relative to your intensity level, training volume and satisfaction of recovery factors that produces steady gains for you. If you add two pounds to the bar every squat workout, then of course if you squat three times a week you're going to make much faster progress than if you only squat once a week. But if you can't add two pounds to the bar if you squat more frequently than one time a week (once you're in new poundage territory), then that's the best you can do, and a greater frequency is irrelevant.

T8.4   For hard gainers, to train the full body intensively three times per week will constitute gross overtraining. Even many easy gainers with very responsive physiques can't gain well on that sort of schedule.

TRAINING 9
If someone came up to you and asked "Why is squatting a superior lift?" what would you say?

T9.1   The squat is *potentially* a superior exercise because, in a single movement, it has the potential to work so much musculature in an intensive way. It also activates some sort of "mysterious" growth mechanism that helps produce overall growth. This pair of big benefits combine to explain why the squat has been described as "the growth exercise." *But these terrific benefits only apply if you squat safely, intensively and progressively for a sustained period.*

T9.2   Not everyone can squat safely and intensively, but most people can. Many people fail to derive benefits from the squat because they don't know what good form is, let alone actually practice it. And among those who do exercise good form in the squat, many add poundage too fast, and then the good form degrades into poor form, with injury around the corner.

T9.3   Form is the first thing that needs to be in place. But good form alone isn't good enough—it has to be combined with hard work, progressive poundages, and building up over a period of years to handling impressive weights. Only then will the great benefits accrue, and the potential of the exercise be realized.

TRAINING 10
Why, generally speaking, shouldn't I weight train more often than twice a week?

T10.1   Other than in special cases, weight training more than twice a week causes overtraining for most people. Overtraining won't make your muscles bigger. I know that most gym members weight train more often than twice a week, but most of them are going nowhere. Of those who are making good progress, they are usually genetically gifted and/or drug enhanced.

TRAINING 11
Why can't I build mass and detail at the same time?

T11.1   To build mass and detail simultaneously means you have to
         include many "detail exercises," and train more often than I'm
         advising you to. This increased volume and frequency of
         training means that you would demand more from your
         recovery ability, and spread your effort and focus thinly over
         the larger amount of training. Even if you manage to stimulate
         growth from this increased volume of training, you'll be
         incapable of recovering properly because you don't have the
         outstanding genetics required to tolerate that sort of workload.
         You'd neither develop mass nor detail from such a strategy.

T11.2   Don't complicate body*building*. Build your body by focusing
         on a few big compound exercises, and dedicate several years to
         getting increasingly stronger and stronger still. Leg extensions
         won't build big quads, but squats will. If you squat *and*
         perform leg extensions, then the latter will distract you from
         the former, and rob you of some of your precious recovery
         ability. Not only that, but many leg extension units are set up
         in such a way that your knees could be injured, and then you
         wouldn't be able to squat.

T11.3   If you want to get decent sized muscles, you need to build up to
         being able to squat over 400 pounds for many reps, and bench
         press over 300 pounds for reps, at around 190 pounds
         bodyweight and average height. Then if you want to get *very* big
         muscles, you'll need to be blessed with the genetics that will
         allow you to build up to handling over 550 pounds in the squat,
         and over 400 pounds in the bench press, at around 220 pounds
         bodyweight. And if you want to develop *huge* muscles, you'll
         need the freakish genetics that will permit you to build up to
         handling around 500 pounds in the bench press, and over 650
         pounds in the squat, at 250+ pounds bodyweight.

TRAINING 12
Why can't I build muscular size and definition at the same time?

T12.1   Because each has its own set of requirements, and to mix them
         means you're unlikely to get much from either. Focus on
         developing bigger muscles *without* getting fat, *or* focus on
         attaining increased definition but without losing muscular size.

T12.2   There are, however, four groups of people who can increase
         muscular mass while dropping fat: (a) those who are gifted

genetically, (b) those who are new to training, (c) those who are coming back following a long layoff, and (d) drug users. Few people are highly gifted for bodybuilding, no sane person should be taking bodybuilding drugs, and you're only a beginner once. So the great majority of sane bodybuilders can't build substantial muscular mass and drop fat at the same time.

T12.3   Building bigger muscles is challenging enough without making the job even more demanding by trying to drop fat as well. If you're overweight, then focus for as long as it takes on ridding yourself of excessive fat while holding onto all your muscular mass. Otherwise, focus on developing bigger muscles and keeping yourself in anabolic mode. Don't, however, make the mistake of gaining mass so fast that you gain more fat than muscle. Letting a little fat accumulate while you develop *a lot* of muscle is acceptable, and usually *necessary*, but becoming fat won't make you happy. A policy of slow and steady gains is usually best. Fast gains are usually fat gains.

TRAINING 13
Why shouldn't I use the numerous exercises that I see the champs using?

T13.1   Because you won't benefit from them. Not only will you not benefit from them, they are likely to set you back. The competitive "elite" are at a level you're not, and their needs are different to yours. Don't even think about training akin to them until you already have very big muscles.

T13.2   Build a big muscular body *before* you concern yourself with developing the details. Substance comes before detail.

TRAINING 14
Some people tell me I have to use "shaping exercises," and without them I'm never going to have a good physique. Is this right?

T14.1   The quickest and most effective way of "shaping" your muscles is to develop bigger muscles. Never mind if the inner segment of whatever muscle is not quite in perfect balance with the outer segment of that muscle. What matters is having some substantial muscle in the first place. Without substantial muscle you'll never know what "shape" you have. But "shape" is mostly a genetic thing.

T14.2 Focus on developing good sized muscles. Once you're really big, strong and impressive, *then* you can concern yourself with getting everything in perfect balance. But until that point, the few percent of muscular imbalance is irrelevant. If you try to develop perfect balance while you build your body, you'll end up with neither balance nor size because you'll overtrain on excessive training frequency and volume.

TRAINING 15
All the big guys at the gym tell me I have to train much more than you say I should. Who's right?

T15.1 Those men are able to respond to a greater training volume and frequency than 95+% of people. They are among the last people you should consult for training advice that's relevant to genetically typical trainees.

T15.2 Those men may be the same ones whose solution to training woes is to boost their intake of drugs, or to change the stack of steroids they are using. That's how "scientific" their training is. Only when their health fails will they learn of the stupidity of their strategy.

TRAINING 16
Why shouldn't trainees round their backs when they squat and deadlift?

T16.1 Your backbone is a curved structure. Maintaining your natural curves is critical for keeping your back strong and resistant to injury. If you flatten your lower back—for example, by rounding your upper back—your back will lose its natural strong structure, and will be *far less* resistant to injury. In fact, rounding your back usually makes injury inevitable if you're using weights that are challenging for you. Slouching inevitably flattens the lower back, and is one of the reasons why poor posture causes back problems. To fully grasp the flattening effect on the lower back, stand side on to a mirror without your shirt on. Notice the effect on the curvature of your spine from slouching and moving your hips forward and rearward.

T16.2 When you apply stress to your back through weight training, it's hugely exaggerated on your vertebrae and inter-vertebral discs if you don't maintain your back's natural curves. You'll never fully appreciate the value of a healthy back until you no longer have one. A serious back injury will devastate your training, and can come about from just *a single* incident of rounding your back during a heavy squat or deadlift. *Don't learn this the hard way!* Pay great attention to good posture while you train. Here are three examples:

a. While standing between reps of the squat, keep your shoulders pulled back, and hips pushed firmly to the rear, to hold your lower back in its arched position—but don't *exaggerate* the degree of arch. Then when you descend and ascend, keep your shoulder blades retracted, head up, chest out, and hips pushed rearward.

b. When you deadlift (be it stiff-legged or bent-legged) *never* let your back round. Keep your shoulders pulled back at all times. Should you feel your shoulders starting to "give," dump the weight immediately. In the stiff-legged deadlift in particular, if you use an excessive range of motion, rounding of the back is inevitable. This is just one of the reasons why you shouldn't exaggerate the range of motion in this exercise. Avoid performing it from a platform or bench.

c. When using the standing calf machine, never slouch or hump your shoulders. Maintain the shoulders-back and lower-back-arched position. This applies when using the standing calf machine for calf work *and* for shrugs.

T16.3   The terms "rounding" and "arching" of the back are opposites. When the back is rounded, the shoulders slump forward and the lower back is flattened (and the arch is lost). When the lower back is arched, the shoulders are naturally pulled to the rear and the back is no longer rounded. By the same token, when the shoulders are pulled back, the lower back should be arched.

TRAINING 17
Why shouldn't I arch my back when I bench press?

T17.1   Arching your back in an exaggerated way during the bench press applies greatly increased stress to the back—in an opposite way to rounding the back in some other exercises. The exaggerated arch in the bench press has produced many back injuries, and is one of the most common mistakes trainees make while performing this exercise. It's characterized in its most exaggerated state by trainees lifting their heels off the floor as much as they possibly can, and raising their hips as much as possible too. This is dreadful form, and undisciplined training.

T17.2   When you bench press, a small degree of lower back arch is normal, and safe. But never exaggerate it. Keep your feet flat on the floor, and never lift your hips off the bench. You may need to raise your feet on a platform in order to minimize the degree of arch in your lower back. Have someone watch you from the side as you bench press. If your arch is very obvious, and especially if you have short legs (or are using a bench taller than standard), put something stable under each foot in order to raise your feet several inches.

TRAINING 18
How long should I rest between sets?

T18.1   As a general rule, I recommend you rest long enough so that you can do justice to each set without having to reduce weight in order to maintain your rep count. If you move quickly between sets, by taking a minute or less, you'll make woefully incomplete recovery. Consider an illustration of a trainee who can just squeeze out 8 good reps with 250 pounds in the bench press. If he was to take just one minute between sets, his second and third sets of bench presses (assuming he was performing three work sets) would drop in reps to perhaps 5 and 3 respectively, if not fewer, because he'd be making such incomplete recovery. To keep your reps up (when training hard), you'll probably need to rest 3–4 minutes between sets of the bench press. Smaller exercises don't need so long. For the really big exercises—the squat and deadlift—you may need *another* minute or so of rest in order to do full justice to any second or third work set(s).

T18.2   If you'd be content performing a decreasing rep count for each repeat set (assuming you're doing multiple work sets per exercise), you could reduce your rest interval. This is an individual matter. What matters is more iron on the bar in good form over time, and making progress. If you can achieve this with short rests between sets, do it. But if your poundages get stuck, then so will your progress, and a change is needed.

T18.3   Generally, I recommend you leave the fast-paced training for bodybuilders who are already big and strong, and who are focusing on refining and honing their well-developed physiques. This may include *you*, eventually, if you train well in the interim.

TRAINING 19
People tell me I'm not performing enough sets to grow on. What do you say?

T19.1   The bottom line is not how many sets you perform, but the results you get from the sets you do. The bottom line, for getting bigger muscles, is getting stronger, and then stronger still, and always in impeccable form. Providing you're adding a little weight on a very regular basis to each exercise you perform, you're bang on track. That's what counts, not the number of sets per se.

T19.2   If you did just one work set of squats each week, but added 2 pounds a week for two straight years, you'd add 200 pounds to your squat. That would make you grow, greatly. But if you did three work sets twice a week, and struggled to add a couple of pounds to the bar once a month, you'd only add 50 pounds over the course of the two years. Which alternative would produce the most muscle? Weight on the bar, in good form, is the bottom line, not the number of sets.

TRAINING 20
Where I train, everyone seems to be changing their routines every few weeks. Why do people keep changing their training routines?

T20.1   Chopping and changing training programs is one of the most common mistakes bodybuilders and strength trainees make. Once you're so big that size is no longer a concern, then you can chop and change your program if you wish. But to get really big and strong in the first place requires a different approach.

T20.2   Why do people change their programs so often? It's usually because the programs they try don't work. So they keep trying new programs in the hope that one of them will deliver the goods. But the programs they try are nearly always the same type—excessive in training volume and frequency. Changing from one interpretation of overtraining to another won't make any difference. You need to move to a program that's not built on overtraining—i.e., move to abbreviated training.

T20.3   If you've been following abbreviated training, and it's not been working satisfactorily, ask yourself if you've really been delivering *all* the required components. The success of a training program is a lot more than a list of exercises, reps and sets. As

I've pointed out repeatedly, if you're cutting corners with your nutrition, rest and sleep, you'll impair if not kill your progress. And if you're not training hard, you won't stimulate any growth.

T20.4   There's no "magic" drug-free program that will build you up any faster than what I describe in my books. The "magic" is in the unrelenting application of consistent effort and progression in the gym, and the rigorous attention *outside of the gym* to ensuring adequate nutritional intake, rest and sleep *every* day.

T20.5   Be truthful with yourself. Are you really delivering, *daily*, the requisite dedication, nutrition, rest and sleep? And when you train, are you really working hard, and with impeccable exercise form? If you've not been delivering on *all* of these critical components, you've been your own worst enemy. Trying another program, set of exercises, and a different rep and set scheme won't make a difference if *all* the requirements for a productive program are not in good order. And trying to substitute food supplements for proper food won't work, and neither will throwing in a few supplements on top of an inadequate general diet. Try food supplements if you want to, but only *after* you have your knife and fork, and milk/blender diet in perfect order.

TRAINING 21
Why do I feel weaker on my work sets if I skip on my warmup sets? I'd have thought that by saving on energy by doing very little warmup work I'd have had more energy for the main sets.

T21.1   The work sets are the ones that stimulate strength increases and hence growth. To be able to do your best at them, you need to perform enough warmup work. Too little warmup work is bad for two reasons. First, you fail to "lubricate" your joints and get your muscles, tendons and ligaments physically ready for rigorous work. Second, your body won't be able to harness its full strength. For many people, at least for the *big* exercises, a quite demanding final warmup set (of 90% or so of your work set weight) is necessary in order that progress can be made on the work set. For a high-rep work set you don't need the same high reps for your warmup sets. In the 20-rep squat, for example, half a dozen perfectly executed and controlled reps with 90% of your work set weight should do the job for your *final* warmup set. For medium-rep work, such as 6-rep bench pressing, a final warmup set of 4 reps with 90% or so of your work set weight should be adequate. You'll probably not need to go as high as 90% for the final warmup set of a *small* exercise.

T21.2   You may even find that the first few reps of your final warmup set (with 90% or so of your work set weight) will feel *heavier* than the first few reps of the actual work set.

T21.3   For many people, a too-light final warmup set will lead to a *reduced* work set performance relative to if the final warmup set had been heavier. Trying to "save" energy by skimping on warmup work can *diminish* work set performance because muscle fiber recruitment isn't triggered enough by skimpy warmup work. To what degree this applies is an individual matter, but it's better to do too much warmup work than not enough. Be sure, however, to rest for a few minutes before your first work set, so you're not tired from the final warmup set.

TRAINING 22
I've been training for some years and when my bench press reached a max of 140 kilos (311 pounds), and I could also do 7 reps with 120 kilos, I was working out three times a week in a periodized way. As I read about high-intensity training (HIT) I began to bench press once a week. Although my body mass increased, I nowadays can barely do 5 reps with 116 kilos, warming up with 50 kilos (10 reps), 70 kilos (5 reps) and 90 kilos (1 rep). Then 116 kilos (5 reps). It seems that I can't increase my reps at this point. Some people say not to do any warmups whatsoever. Is that right? What kind of warmup should be done for the bench press?

T22.1   There are so many variables at play that I may not be able to put my finger on a particular problem without being able to watch the questioner train, and learn about how well or otherwise he's satisfying recovery factors outside of the gym. One person's interpretation of HIT can be very different to another's.

T22.2   One work set to failure per exercise may not be suited to you. Perhaps you're stale from training in general. Perhaps you haven't been eating or sleeping well. Perhaps you have major stress in your life that's messing up your training. Or perhaps you're simply not warming up adequately—more on that later.

T22.3   If you were more comfortable with multiple work sets to not-quite failure, then do that. Don't lock yourself tightly into a single way of training. Always allow yourself a degree of latitude to fine-tune a program to suit you. What matters most of all is progress. If it's happening, albeit slowly, you're on track. If it's not happening, then make changes until it *is* happening. But the first things you need to change may not be in the gym. Assuming that you're using an abbreviated program, and really are training hard, consistently and with good form, it may be out-of-the-gym recovery factors that are seriously amiss. But if everything outside of the gym is in good order, then look to making changes in the gym.

T22.4   Anyone who advises skipping warmups for the bench press is way off base. Some HIT aficionados minimize the degree of warming up, and this is a risky and even foolish strategy for many people. For sure you must warm up well, and it's much better to err on the side of too much rather than not enough. In fact, if you've reduced your warming up recently, *that alone* could be responsible for your bench pressing decline.

T22.5   Immediately prior to your work set of 116 kilos (255 pounds) for 5 reps you're currently doing 90 kilos (198 pounds) for a single. That's *far too little* preparatory work. To "prime" your musculature so that it's fully ready for a work set (including triggering lots of muscle fiber recruitment), most people need more than a single rep with 78% of a 5-rep work-set weight. As noted in the previous answer, I recommend up to 90% or so of your work set weight for your final warmup set. A 90% weight in this example, would be 104 kilos (228 pounds). That's a 30-pound difference relative to what you've been doing, *and* I'd have you do at least 3 reps, *not* a mere single. These changes will produce a big difference in the "priming" of the musculature relative to what you've been doing recently. The final warmup set should be taxing, not a dawdle, otherwise it won't "prime" you for your work set(s).

T22.6   Based on what you've told me it's unlikely that you need less warming up than what I've outlined here. *And perhaps you need more—experiment to see.* Not doing a final warmup set that's demanding may knock *at least* several reps or 10–20 pounds off your work set performance of a major exercise. Move to a more thorough warmup, take a few minutes rest after the final warmup set, and then perform your work set(s). Be sure to keep yourself warm and well covered during the between-sets rest periods.

TRAINING 23
It seems there's a consensus that trainees do not require a lifting belt. Would you advise that I jump straight into a new routine without a belt, or do I need some form of preparation? Should I make a special effort to strengthen my lower back first?

T23.1   Just start the new routine with poundages below your best—say 85% or so—and take a few weeks to build back to your current best weights. That six weeks or so (or longer if need be) should provide the time for your body to adapt to the rigors of training without a belt, and for your natural "corset" to build up in strength and conditioning.

TRAINING 24
I'm trying to abbreviate my workouts more. I plan to include weighted chins. I figure that will be enough biceps work, but will that work my back enough? The point is to *abbreviate*. This exercise would be my only biceps and back work (other than the deadlift). Is this enough back work? Will chins be as productive as pullups, or should I add something like dumbbell rows?

T24.1   The deadlift and chin, if worked intensively, should provide enough work for the back, at least for most people. The most important factor with chins and pullups is not whether a supinated or pronated grip is "better," but which one is most suited *to you*. Some people find the supinated grip uncomfortable, even after having tried different widths of grip spacing, so the pronated pullup is the only choice. The bottom line for successful training is finding a few exercises that you can do well and safely, and then sticking with them for a long time while building up poundage relentlessly. If you build up to chinning in good form for 8 reps with 50% of your bodyweight strapped to your belt, you'll have excellent back and biceps development, regardless of which grip you use. If you row as well as chin, in the same program, you risk too much of a good thing (depending on the individual), and as a consequence may stagnate or only produce minimal gains.

TRAINING 25
Is a row needed for back thickness if I do stiff-legged deadlifts and curl-grip chins in my routine?

T25.1　Maybe, maybe not. Some people do really well on chins, whereas others say they do better on some form of rowing. Try the stiff-legged deadlift and curl-grip (supinated) chin for a cycle, then try the stiff-legged deadlift along with a row for a cycle, and see if there's a difference in the thickness of your back.

TRAINING 26
After completion of a ten-week (or any other time frame) cycle, would 5% over my top work sets' weights be a reasonable goal for my next cycle? Is it too much or too little? Do the goals differ for beginning, intermediate and advanced lifters?

T26.1　A 5% target for exercise poundages is a good one for the short term, but whether you'll need one or more cycles to get there depends on the length of cycle, how well you train, and your stage of training. Go for the target, but don't put a fixed time frame on the cycle. Keep the cycle going and going. As long as you're adding a tad of iron on a regular basis to each of the big exercises, you're doing fine and shouldn't change a successful formula.

TRAINING 27
I work two jobs (45+ hours a week) and go to summer school in order to graduate from college. So, I'm busy! I've been doing the 20-rep squat program for seven weeks (routine done twice a week) and most of the time find myself dragging my feet in spite of how I train or how much I sleep. I've thought about going to a more abbreviated schedule. What are your thoughts?

T27.1　You need to adjust the routine to accommodate your recuperative abilities. Try dividing the routine into two parts, and alternating the two separate routines. Each exercise will then be trained once a week, instead of two times. You'll still be training twice a week, but your training volume per workout will be halved. That should make a substantial difference, and greatly aid recovery. Combine this with more nutritious food, and as much rest and sleep as you can get, and gains should start happening.

TRAINING 28
I do 5 sets of 8 reps for every exercise. I do 4–5 exercises for each muscle group. I train six days a week using a three-day split. Yes you would

probably say that I'm overworking my muscles, but I still continue to grow. So why change? The thing I would like to stress is, everyone is built differently; not everyone responds alike. So my advice to everyone is to try different things. One piece of advice might work for one guy but might not work for you. In my case I'm naturally lucky.

T28.1 There's a wide range of individual variation, but you're in the very small minority. Hardly anyone can grow on this Schwarzenegger-style program. Millions of trainees over the years have proved that Schwarzenegger-style training doesn't work for the huge majority of bodybuilders.

T28.2 Easy gainers have more training options than do hard gainers. Easy gainers have plenty of room for manoeuvre, hard gainers don't. Easy gainers are very fortunate, but can never fully understand how blessed they are because they have never experienced legitimate hard gaining. I reckon you'd make the same or *even better* gains on less than half your current training volume. Then you would have time for other things in your life, without compromising on your bodybuilding progress. So I would say that even someone as gifted as you should still experiment with reducing training volume.

TRAINING 29
Since muscular shape is genetically predetermined, it appears meaningless to perform any isolation exercises at any time other than the accessory ones (e.g., crunch, L-fly, calf raise, neck and grip work). I'd like to know your opinion on the subject since you've pointed out the need for isolation exercises at the "advanced" stage.

T29.1 Most of the training of muscles from "different angles," using isolation exercises, is conventional bodybuilding bull that produces overtraining, and often the use of harmful exercises that exaggerate stress around certain joints. But where the "different angles" approach can have value is in applying stress in a different way so that exercises can be found that better suit the individual. For example, the bench press and parallel bar dip work similar musculature, but apply stress sufficiently differently for some people to be able to train much more productively on one than the other.

T29.2   Similar things can be said for other pairings of exercises that work comparable (but not necessarily identical) musculature— e.g., the barbell press and the dumbbell press. But these are compound exercises. Minimize the use of isolation exercises, and focus where you really need to in order to build substantial size and strength—on the compound exercises. But from the variety of compound exercises, choose the ones that best suit you and which you especially enjoy. Then become really good at them.

T29.3   Sometimes a different but comparable big exercise is substituted to give a specific joint a "break" for recovery purposes but *without* ceasing demanding muscular work. The change of "angle" can sustain hard work but while stressing the joint concerned in a sufficiently different way that it gets a "breather."

T29.4   The "need for isolation exercises at the 'advanced' stage" comes when you're truly big and strong and discover that you've some "imbalances" which can be evened out, at least to a degree, by isolation exercises—e.g., perhaps your rear deltoid is lagging a tad, or the lateral head. But such concerns are only for a minority of trainees who are big and strong enough overall to be worried about such minor issues. For everyone else, to try to attend to such matters of "balance" will distract from the building process and/or produce overtraining that will negate gains in size and strength.

TRAINING 30
What's your opinion on the idea that in order to maximize muscle growth, higher volume is required? Do you think a lifter may benefit from increasing his training volume as a part of a cycle?

T30.1   Depends on what you mean by "higher volume." If you mean 10, 15 or 20 sets per bodypart, like in much of the mainstream, that's training suicide for hard gainers. But if you mean trying 3–4 work sets per major exercise, instead of just a couple, that might be a good idea, and is worth trying for a month or few in an exercise or two per workout. To a degree, a bit of extra volume can compensate for a slight reduction in intensity. Not only that, but some people may find, for example, three not-quite-to-failure (but still hard) work sets per exercise more productive for adding poundage to the bar over the long term, than a single set to failure.

T30.2   The bottom line is adding poundage to the bar consistently, not training intensity per se. Intensity is just one of the variables involved in producing poundage gain, *albeit a very important one.* Training volume is one of the areas where you need to experiment to see what you like most, and what does the best job for you. You may need to vary things somewhat from cycle to cycle, for best results; but don't change anything that's working well. Keep the range of experimentation sensible. Forget about the sort of volume training that appears ad nauseam in the glossy muscle magazines.

TRAINING 31
I've read that the incline bench press is a superior exercise to the regular bench press. Would it be acceptable to substitute the incline press?

T31.1   Yes it would be, but keep the incline on the low side. The higher the degree of incline, the less the stress on the chest. If you want the exercise to target your pecs heavily as well as your shoulders and triceps, don't turn it into a seated almost-overhead press.

T31.2   The parallel bar dip is a fine substitute for the bench press. The key thing is to find the exercise that works best for you and which you can keep adding weight to. Some people can handle most good exercises safely and well. But some people have limitations or particular structural factors that make some exercises more productive and safer than other movements. Some sensible trial and error is needed.

TRAINING 32
It seems to me that mixing it up with sessions of higher reps then lower reps, added with high intensity then lower intensity alternately, is a sensible way to train. What's your view on this?

T32.1   The trouble with mixing things up is that it can lead to lack of consistency. For example, if sometimes you squat 20 reps for one work set, other times do 3 x 8, and sometimes 5 x 5, you're going to have trouble maintaining progression on each scheme. Hard gainers are usually best off sticking with one format for a decent period, so that they know exactly what they need to do next time in order to progress. If you're moving from one thing to another, and not repeating a given format until a few weeks later, you're going to be all over the place and trying to handle a variety of things instead of focusing on one. It's best not to complicate things. Choose one set/rep format for each exercise, and one that you like, and then stick with it and become really good at it. Perhaps change the format from cycle to cycle, but not from week to week or even month to month.

T32.2   Some people argue that the variety is good, to keep your body in a state of flux. That "instinctive" training has been at the root of much training failure. It might work for "elite" performers with great genetics and drug assistance, but it's training suicide for drug-free, typical trainees.

TRAINING 33
Do you think it's possible to improve recovery ability? If I train the squat once a week, after a while couldn't I move up to once every five days, to accelerate gains?

T33.1   If you've been cutting corners on the various aspects of recovery, you can easily improve your recovery ability—rest more, sleep more, and eat much better. But if you're near the limits of your recovery ability because you already rest a lot each day, sleep nine hours every night, and eat very well with a caloric and nutritional surplus, you may not be able to increase your recovery ability significantly through those components. If you're overtraining, then cut back on volume in the gym and you'll increase your speed of recovery between workouts.

T33.2   Get all the components of recovery in excellent order, and don't overtrain. *Then* you can experiment with different squatting frequencies. If you're able to add a couple of pounds every week to your squat (while squatting once a week), and are consistently going into new poundage territory, things are going very well. Keep it up for a year, and you'll add 100 pounds to your squat. Keep it up for two years and you'll add 200 pounds. Wouldn't that satisfy you?

T33.3   Maybe you could get there faster. For a few weeks, try squatting every fifth day. If you're *still* able to add a couple of pounds each squat workout, and do it consistently, then that's even better progress than from squatting once a week. But if you find that progress is harder to make, and you're dragging your feet and not recovering properly, you're squatting too frequently and should return to once every seven days.

TRAINING 34
I've started a new program where I'm just working the squat, deadlift and bench press once a week. Is this sufficient to produce a well-rounded physique, or should I add direct shoulder and upper-back work?

T34.1   For the short term, this would be okay; but over the long term it would produce strength and development imbalances. If you want to stick with a super-abbreviated program, you need to vary the exercises you use, from cycle to cycle, to produce more balanced development. I'd say you'd be better off adding a few exercises to your program, and dividing them up in such a way that you avoid overtraining.

T34.2   For just a three-exercise program, the squat, parallel bar dip and pullup/chin is probably more "balanced" than the big three only. Then if, for example, you add an overhead press, stiff-legged deadlift, calf work and the L-fly, you'll have a far more balanced program. Perform four exercises on one day each week, and the other three on another day. That's still a very abbreviated program, but one that will produce a more balanced physique in terms of both development and strength.

TRAINING 35
Instead of progressing on a different small number of key exercises in different cycles, would it be possible for some people to make good progress in more exercises in the same program if training is kept brief and made more infrequent for some exercises? Consider two programs of two routines each running concurrently, with program A being alternated week to week with program B:

MONDAY (A): squat, calf raise, crunch, side bend

FRIDAY (A):   dip, row, shoulder press, "breathing" pullover, L-fly, grip work

MONDAY (B): leg press, calf raise, crunch, side bend

FRIDAY (B):   deadlift, bench press, pullup, "breathing" pullover, L-fly, grip work

Repeat Mon (A), etc.

Could this offer benefits like more balanced development, progression in more exercises, little overlap, low volume and less risk of overtraining? Is there a significant danger of some people being unable to progress in certain exercises when training them only once every two weeks?

T35.1　I think the strategy of increased exercises spread over more (but still brief) workouts could work well for some people. It falls into the basic format of abbreviated training focusing on the big exercises. What matters most, however, is what works *for you*. Give it a try, and see. Some people may find that training some exercises only once every two weeks may not yield progress on one or more of those movements, but you'd have to try for yourself and see. If your poundages keep moving into new ground in the big exercises by a tad of iron every time or two you train them, then things are looking good, and you should continue. But if you find progress is not as good as it was on a program of fewer exercises, then revert to the simpler strategy.

TRAINING 36
Is the lunge a "big" movement? I'm lunging with 90% of my bodyweight. I step forward with one foot, lunge, step back, repeat with other leg. I hold the bar across my back as in the squat. I feel my shoulders, upper/lower back, quads, butt and hamstrings. I incorporated the lunge on my second workout day. I perform 15-rep squats and stiff-legged deadlifts on my first workout day. Have I split my exercises properly? Should I limit upper-body work? I'm splitting up dips, shoulder presses, chins and curls.

T36.1　The lunge certainly can involve a lot of musculature, and from that point of view it could be called a "big" exercise. But it can put a great deal of unnecessary stress on the knee, and if balance is lost could lead to a nasty accident. The lunge is an unnecessarily risky exercise. And in your case, on top of the squat and stiff-legged deadlift, lunges could produce overtraining.

T36.2　Four exercises for your upper body shouldn't be excessive, providing you don't overdo training frequency or volume, and providing you attend fully to the factors of recuperation. The bottom line is progress. If it's happening, fine. If it's not, then make changes until progress *is* happening.

TRAINING 37
What rep range and effort level is ideal for retaining muscle mass while dieting?

T37.1   There's no ideal rep range for everyone. In a nutshell, what you need is hard work on whatever rep range (or specific number) best suits you for maintaining your existing strength. The specific count may vary from exercise to exercise. To retain muscle mass while dieting, you need to maintain your strength. To do that you need to avoid overtraining. The usual training fare while dieting is to overtrain, which can lead to a loss of as much muscle tissue as fat.

TRAINING 38
What percentage of your max (for a given rep count) should you stay at when you're maintaining muscle mass and shedding fat?

T38.1   I don't think you should be concerned with a percentage of your max. Just train hard on a rep range/count for a given exercise that has proven successful for you in the past—the percentage would probably vary from exercise to exercise. Do your absolute best to hold your strength as you trim the bodyfat off.

TRAINING 39
I'm an 18-year old male who's been training for four years. I would classify myself as a moderate hard gainer. I'm 5-11, 190 pounds with about 8-10% bodyfat. I currently have few responsibilities and a lot of time to devote to weight training (including recovery and diet). What kind of program would you recommend for someone in my situation—an intermediate level trainee entering his peak years for bodybuilding success, who doesn't have much stress or responsibility to distract him from weight training? Most of what you've written seems aimed at people who are significantly older than me, with many more demands on their time, which would interfere with their training. How would you alter one of your standard programs to fit me?

T39.1   To alter a standard abbreviated program would almost certainly mean increasing training volume and/or frequency. You may have the recovery capacity at present to be able to cope with such increased demands, and still make some progress. But why push your recovery ability to the limits? I'd say you should still follow a standard abbreviated program and reap a faster rate of progress than an older and perhaps overworked and stressed out trainee would. Make the most of your current optimum recovery circumstances—they won't last long-term. Then you can really pack on the gains over the next year or two, and make the finest progress of your life. If you expand on a standard abbreviated routine, and "unabbreviate" it, you may still make gains, but not as good as you would on the former strategy. Then you would miss your chance to experience the very best gains possible. Don't try to find the most training you can still make some progress on. Instead, stick with a standard abbreviated program, train very hard, maximize your recuperative ability, and see how fast you can progress.

TRAINING 40
I'm currently squatting 220 x 20 and have been making nice progress. The problem is the length of time it takes for my legs to recover (2–3 days). I like to run for cardio but don't want to risk an injury on sore legs. I want to be able to run almost every other day. I squat twice a week. Any suggestions?

T40.1　Recovery time of 2–3 days for the squat is quick. Most people need more recovery time than that, when squatting very intensively. Of course, recovery is quicker from a reduced degree of intensity. A lot of running will, eventually, put a brake on your squatting progress. You're also risking overtraining that may mar both your running and squatting. You'll have to decide what you want as your exercise priority—running, or squatting and muscle building—or perhaps you want the best you can manage of each but without getting the most of either. For cardio health, three times a week is tops. Anything more than that is training for reasons other than cardio health.

T40.2　If you run two or three times per week, and squat hard just once a week, you'd substantially reduce the chance of overtraining, and should be able to take your squatting further over the long term, while still keeping your running in. I'd urge you to take safety measures with your running, to reduce the chance of wear and tear injuries—run in very good shoes, run on a giving surface (not concrete or pavements), and don't overtrain.

TRAINING 41
Considering aerobic work as well as weight training, what kind of cardio work should I do, and how much is enough? Also, what about "hard" aerobics?

T41.1   This varies, depending on individual conditioning/fitness, age, recuperative abilities, overall lifestyle demands, fitness goals, motivation, nutritional intake, sleeping habits, and more. What can be too much for some people may not be enough for others.

T41.2   For example, if you're new to training, or coming back after a long layoff, and if you're over 40 years old, you're going to have a different exercise tolerance than someone of the same age who has been training consistently for 25 years. Just two gentle 45-minute weight-training workouts and 15 minutes twice a week of moderate aerobic work will be enough to wipe out most 45-year-old novices. But start such novices off very gently, both on the weights and aerobics fronts, and slowly pick up the workload and effort levels over time, then six months later those novices can prosper on two intensive 60-minute weight-training workouts, and two relatively vigorous 30–40 minute aerobic workouts each week. The human body is wonderfully accommodating, and can adapt to great increases in workload and intensity, *but only if the increases in load and effort are gradual and over time.*

T41.3   What some people interpret as overtraining is really only a lack of conditioning/fitness. Had the workload been introduced from an easier start, and increased *progressively* over time, "overtraining" wouldn't have occurred. Doing too much too soon is the classic error of all types of training. Not only does it produce a negative physical reaction, but in most cases a negative mental reaction too—"This is too much for me. I can't continue this." You need both physical *and* mental adaptation from a gradual and progressive increase in workload.

T41.4   A basic template of two abbreviated weight-training workouts per week (usually two different sets of exercises), along with two or at most three aerobic sessions each week, will work for most trainees *providing all the components of recovery are satisfied, and as long as the program is built up to from a gentle start.* Naturally, if you cut corners on the sleep and nutrition fronts, you'll be unable to recover fully from your training as a whole, and "overtraining" will result.

T41.5　As far as aerobic training goes, you don't have to become a professional or semi-professional athlete to improve your cardiovascular fitness substantially. Two or three sessions of 30 minutes or so of aerobic work that keeps you slightly breathless— but you could still hold a conversation, albeit haltingly—is enough to produce great benefit and is not physically tough to do. Anything much more than that, duration and frequency wise, is training for reasons other than pure cardiovascular fitness, and would probably seriously compete with your weight training and risk compromising your progress in strength and physique.

T41.6　The foregoing is in essence the approach promoted in BEYOND BRAWN. It's a simplified approach. There's a lot more to aerobic training, however, than the simplified approach. For most people most of the time, the simplified approach is a fine option and will do a good job. This *isn't* to say it's the *optimal* approach. The most important factor in aerobic training is *consistency*. No matter how "optimal" an aerobic program may be, if it's not being done week in and week out it's not going to do you much good over the long term. So whichever approach you choose, it should be one you enjoy so that you keep it up indefinitely.

T41.7　Most weight trainees are not interested in very high levels of aerobic conditioning. Very high levels of aerobic conditioning aren't, however, necessarily synonymous with good health. Additionally, the training involved in developing a very high level of conditioning will almost certainly compromise your strength and physique progress. "Moderate" aerobic conditioning yields lots of health benefits.

T41.8　For healthy trainees who are mentally and physically up to the task, there's the alternative of shorter but more intensive aerobic work—"hard" aerobics. This is good news for trainees who find lower-intensity longer-duration aerobic work so unchallenging that motivation is hard to sustain. Another bonus is that the hard aerobics require a reduced time investment relative to the less-stressful but longer-duration approach. But generally speaking, if you can't dedicate to the simplified approach promoted in BEYOND BRAWN, I think you're unlikely to be able to dedicate to the tougher but probably more efficient approach. It's better that you adopt relatively gentle aerobic work for half an hour twice a week for the rest of your life than take on something tougher, albeit probably superior, but give it up after a month or few because it's too rigorous, and then do no aerobic work whatsoever.

T41.9 Short but hard aerobic work produces benefits out of proportion to the limited duration of the work, due to the increased aerobic capacity it produces. Improved aerobic capacity appears to be *the key* to substantial cardiovascular health benefits. Aerobic capacity increase is far more dependent on intensity of work than duration. *If the cardio work is not of sufficient intensity to cause adaptive changes in the cardiorespiratory system, an increase in aerobic capacity will not be produced.* For a heavily referenced and peer-reviewed scholarly paper on this approach to cardio work, reviewed by some leading exercise scientists and epidemiologists, see "Examining the Validity of Exercise Guidelines for the Prevention of Morbidity and All-Cause Mortality," by Richard A. Winett, Ph.D., and Ralph N. Carpinelli, Ed.D., in the journal ANNALS OF BEHAVIORAL MEDICINE, reference 2000; 22:159–178.

T41.10 For hard aerobics, after warming up, you need to push yourself hard (at up to 85% of one's maximum heart rate) for only 4 minutes or so to produce the appropriate stimulus. This could be continuous work, or interval training—say alternating 20 seconds of very hard work with 10 seconds of rest, i.e., 8 "sets" of each. With a warmup of about 5 minutes, and a cooling down period of a similar duration, the *whole* session could be a mere 14 minutes.

T41.11 Most people will likely find that interval-training complicates matters and makes it tricky to stay at the required heart rate. If you want to try the interval method, I'd urge you first to have a couple of months of experience of the steady approach.

T41.12 Progressively work into the hard aerobics. Start at 70% and pick up the intensity gradually over several weeks to 80%, performing the aerobic work twice a week. After a few weeks at 80%, go up to 85%. But you must be free of any risk factors such as hypertension. If you're a novice at exercising, and/or in poor cardiovascular shape, invest in at least a month of two of lower-intensity longer-duration aerobics, to condition your body for something more rigorous. *But get the consent of your physician before doing any hard aerobics*, just in case you have risk factors you're not aware of that would preclude such a stressful way of exercising.

T41.13 For increasing aerobic fitness, as Dr. Winett of the Center for Research in Health Behavior at Virginia Tech, Blacksburg, USA told me, "...there doesn't seem to be any relationship between duration of training and increasing fitness. Rather, intensity as defined by percent of oxygen consumption—more easily conveyed as a percentage of maximum heart rate—seems more important. So, there's really no reason to start with longer duration easier stuff *unless* you're a novice and/or in very poor aerobic condition."

T41.14 The commonly used age-adjusted maximum heart rate (220 minus your age) *may not be accurate in your case.* If you *over*estimate your maximum heart rate, the 85% exercise level of it (for hard aerobics) could end up working you too hard, which might be dangerous. On the other hand, if you *under*estimate your maximum heart rate, you're unlikely to train intensively enough to produce big benefits from brief bouts of aerobic work. Take the guesswork out of your calculations and actually discover your maximum heart rate *with the expert help* of a cardiologist or other trained medical professional. *Don't try to discover this yourself!*

T41.15 Since working at a specific heart rate is *critical*, a reliable heart rate monitor is *essential* so you know *precisely* and *immediately* what rate your heart is beating at. It's vital that you know right away if you're working too hard or not hard enough, and respond accordingly *pronto*. You can get a basic heart rate monitor for about $50.00. When you consider this as an investment in your health that you'll use for many years, it's a very small cost. You don't need a sophisticated monitor with many features; a bare-bones model will do the basic job you want.

T41.16 With lower-level longer-duration aerobic work, immediate recognition of your heart rate isn't essential. To find out your heart rate, just stop what you're doing, count your heart rate for 15 seconds and then multiply that number by 4.

T41.17 Like with weight training, beyond a certain level of work *at a sufficient intensity*, more aerobic training is not better (for health benefits) and may even be counterproductive. In addition, the volume of work required to stimulate substantial improvement appears to be *a lot* less than we're commonly led to believe by the exercise world. Especially with hard aerobics, two stints per week may be quite sufficient to do a terrific job of producing plenty of health benefits. Three sessions could be overkill. If you want a third session, make it the lower-intensity longer-duration style.

T41.18 Importantly, as your conditioning/fitness improves, you'll need to gradually increase your pace of work (or resistance) in order to produce a given percentage of your maximum heart rate. For example, after a couple of months or so of adaptation, the pace/workload that *used to* produce the 85% rate will become just a transition during your warmup on the way to the higher level of work that's now needed to produce the 85% rate.

T41.19 You may want to adopt the approach recommended by Dr. Winett, and make hard aerobics twice a week your actual aerobic "training"—i.e., graded warmup of about 5 minutes, the *prescriptive* 4 minutes at 85% of maximum heart rate, and a graded cooldown of at least 4 minutes. Then other types of aerobic "work," because they are at such a lower intensity, come into the category of "recreation" rather than "training."

T41.20 To quote Dr. Winett: "Separate out this kind of very prescriptive cardiovascular training [the "hard" aerobics] from leisure pursuits and recreation for fun and burning calories. Easy walking, hiking and swimming, yard work, sports, etc., fill that bill and have a lot of physical and psychological benefits.

T41.21 "Alternatively, a person could combine them. For example, somewhere within a 45-minute walk, systematically do a graded warmup for several minutes and then walk stairs or a hill at the designated/prescriptive heart rate for several minutes; then do a cooldown and continue the walk.

T41.22 "I think for a person who's resistance training, it's a huge mistake to use cardiovascular training for caloric expenditure and fat loss. That really requires long duration and the data on fat loss is this: without prolonged higher intensity training there really isn't much evidence for fat loss from cardiovascular training—and that kind of training will surely compromise strength. A better prescription is weight training for muscle mass, brief cardiovascular training for fitness, modest caloric reduction [through diet], and more caloric expenditure through recreation.

T41.23 "If a person wants to get a higher level of fitness, it won't be in the frequency or duration part; it will depend upon their responsiveness to cardiovascular training (which has huge individual differences), how hard they want to push themselves, and if they start prioritizing cardiovascular work over weights.

T41.24 "Doing some decent cardiovascular training shouldn't be optional but *part* of the exercise equation. The notion that it will compromise strength and muscular development really only applies to long duration, very frequent and fairly intensive training."

T41.25 Specifically what type of aerobic work you do will be influenced by how demanding you want the work to be, how much aerobic fitness you want, whether you want to burn a lot of calories, and what condition you're in at the time. Accurately assess your current condition, determine your goals, and then take it from there.

T41.26 While you shouldn't underestimate your body's ability to adapt to training, don't expect the impossible. You won't be able to adapt to and prosper on six two-hour weight-training sessions a week along with an hour of aerobics daily, unless you're a genetic marvel. There's a limit, and for most hard gainers the basic template of two abbreviated weight-training sessions, and two or at most three aerobic sessions each week is a good rule of thumb. Progress to that level over time, if you're a novice, and fine-tune the weight training and aerobic work to suit you.

T41.27 Even if you've been training with weights for years, but haven't been doing any aerobic work, still work the aerobics into your schedule progressively, or otherwise you'll suffer from "overtraining." Don't go jumping straight to 40 minutes of moderate-intensity aerobic work three times a week. Instead, for example, start with no more than 10 minutes twice a week, and build up at a minute or so each week until you're at 30 minutes twice a week. Haste usually makes waste, so don't rush. Then once at the level of 30 minutes twice a week, perhaps choose between whether to progress to 40 minutes twice a week, or add a third session and work to 3 x 30 minutes per week, or make one session a week a shorter but much harder aerobic session, or turn both sessions into hard aerobic work.

T41.28 Whether you perform aerobic work after your gym weights work, to minimize your number of training days, or perform it on "off" days, is an individual matter. Try it both ways, and see which works best for you—results wise, and convenience wise. If you perform the cardio work after your weight training, I recommend you don't do them back-to-back, but wait at least 20 minutes or so. This will help you to do justice to the aerobic work.

T41.29 Prior to each aerobic session *always* take a few minutes to warm up, to enable your body to adjust to the exercise. To do this, start your chosen aerobic activity at a very gentle pace and slowly pick up the effort so that after 5 minutes or so you're right at the level of effort you've planned for that session—i.e., moderate intensity (that keeps you only slightly breathless) for 30 minutes or so, or much higher intensity for just 4 minutes.

T41.30 Especially after a stint of hard aerobics, be sure to perform a graded cooldown. Take as long as is needed to wind down gradually from the high heart rate to a point where your breathing has returned to normal, *prior* to actually ceasing the exercise. During the cooldown you *continue* to exercise, but at a diminishing intensity over 4 or more minutes.

TRAINING 42
Do you believe that someone can productively do conventional deadlifts on the first training day and trap bar/shrug bar deadlifts on the second day?

T42.1 Yes, but there's a risk of overtraining. As with many things, however, you need to experiment to find what works best *for you*. That's what works *best* for you, not just what works to some degree. The trap bar/shrug bar deadlift is more of a squat than a deadlift for most people, so the overlap between the deadlift and the trap bar/shrug bar deadlift may not be very great, depending on the individual, so you may be able to prosper on doing the two exercises on different days.

T42.2 Experiment with, say, doing the two exercises on different days each week, and see how you go for 6–8 weeks. Then, keeping intensity and volume the same, and while satisfying the factors of recovery in the same way, put the two exercises in the same workout for the next 6–8 weeks, and see if poundage progression continues as before, stalls, or accelerates. Then drop one of the two movements for the next few weeks, and see if poundage gain on the remaining exercise improves. Then you would have some feedback to base future program design on. But for the experiment to be fair, you'd need to keep other variables constant—training and non training. If you go changing your diet and sleeping habits, or adding exercises, that will invalidate the experiment.

TRAINING 43
I can't figure out why my squatting performance varies so much. I try for 20 and don't stop until I'm stuck on the pins. For example, a few weeks ago I got 21 at 265, and upped the weight to 275 for the subsequent sessions. The last three workouts I only

got 17, 16 and 11! I do legs once every four days. I'm going to give it one more try at 275, and if unsuccessful I'll drop the weight until I can do 20 again. What do you think?

T43.1 Squatting 265 x 21 wasn't a base for moving to 275 for 20 reps. A 10-pound increment was way too much. Big poundage increases are one of the biggest mistakes in weight training. You should have moved to 267 the following week, and you'd have made all 20 reps. Then you should have moved to 269 for 20, and so on. In this way it would take you five weeks to get to 275, but you'd get there, make all 20 reps each time *with room to spare*, and create the gaining momentum that would permit further progress *providing that* you attend fully and consistently to all the components of recovery.

T43.2 So drop back to 265, and squat just once a week. Get all 20 reps, and then next week take on 267 x 20, get it and then the next week tackle 269 x 20, etc. Later on you may need to add just a single pound to the bar each week.

T43.3 Crank up your diet, and rest and sleep more. Then you can realistically target 300 x 20 after 4–6 months. Do it in the incremental, slow and steady fashion, and then when you get to 300 x 20 you'll have laid the base for even further progress.

TRAINING 44
When is it best to do the L-fly in relationship with overhead presses, dips and other upper-body work?

T44.1 Not before major shoulder work, as that would tire your assistance musculature. I'd recommend you perform the L-fly at the end of a workout, or at least after your upper-body pressing work in a given workout. If, however, you perform the L-fly immediately after your pressing or upper-back work, that would likely mar your performance in the L-fly. So it would be better to perform the L-fly later on in that workout, or in another workout that may not include any pressing or upper-back work.

TRAINING 45
I just put abbreviated training to work about a week ago. I was wondering if you think extra triceps work is needed because none of the workouts list any exercises for triceps.

T45.1   Extra work for the triceps is not needed—the bench press or dip, along with the overhead press in many cases, provides plenty of work for the triceps. More than that will likely be overkill.

TRAINING 46
Why do most abbreviated training routines almost never have assistance work like the close-grip bench press, but almost always have the curl included? The triceps is larger than the biceps.

T46.1   Most abbreviated programs don't have close-grip benches included because they already include the regular bench press or parallel bar dip, and an overhead press. That's two exercises which work the triceps hard. Many programs include the curl for two reasons—one is that many people are just emotionally attached to direct work for the biceps, and the second, and more important, is that the biceps often don't get the same degree of work that the triceps do, from the big exercises. If you perform chins, the biceps will get lots of work, but if you row and not chin, the biceps involvement is reduced.

T46.2   If you want to add a set of close-grip benches to your program, that would probably be okay unless you're close to the edge of overtraining. If you trim a work set off either the regular bench or overhead press (assuming you're doing more than one work set of each), you'll produce the "room" for the close-grips.

TRAINING 47
I like to start my training with pullups, bodyweight first and then weighted, but I'm not sure how to warm up on this exercise. Should I be doing another exercise first to warm up the area, or is it safe to use bodyweight pullups as a warmup?

T47.1   If you're capable of performing pullups (or chins) with a lot of additional resistance, a warmup set with no additional resistance may be all you need. But if you can only handle a few pounds of additional resistance, the bodyweight pullup is going to be too near your work set weight to be a warmup. I suggest you do pulldowns for a warmup. Even when you can perform pullups with a lot of additional resistance, you may still want to perform a set of pulldowns as your first warmup set, followed by a second warmup set of bodyweight-only pullups. If you're very strong, you may need an additional warmup set of pullups, with half the additional resistance you're going to use for your work set(s). If or when you're that strong, you may not need the initial warmup set of pulldowns. But it's always better to err on the side of too much warmup work rather than too little.

TRAINING 48
As a beginning trainee of one year, I've started to work with the Rader chest pull. I'm in my late thirties and am wondering about the best strategy for this exercise. I currently do 10 reps after each exercise in my routine. Would it be better to do a few sets each day of the week, or only on workout days, and what would be the best rep range? How long should someone my age train this exercise for best results, and will I regress if I quit training it?

T48.1   The fastest benefit from the Rader chest pull is usually experienced by trainees in their teens or early twenties. Performing 10 reps of the Rader chest pull after each exercise in your program sounds like a good strategy, as long as you built up to that load gradually, to avoid excessive discomfort in your rib cage. Because the Rader chest pull is not a systemically demanding exercise, and its purpose is not to increase muscular growth, you can also perform a set or few on your non-workout days. I'd say that at least 10 reps per set, and as many as 20, are fine for this exercise. But when doing the movement as often as you are, 10 reps may be enough.

T48.2   I suggest you take a very accurate measurement of your chest now, and make a note of *precisely* how you took the measurement, so that you can replicate it at future recording times. Take the measurement once a month, and track your progress. If you're seeing progress every couple of months or so, keep doing what you're doing. If you're not seeing any progress, try a different training strategy, and compare results.

T48.3   An increase in overall chest girth is not, however, an indication that rib cage increase was necessarily involved. The girth increase could be a result of increases in back and/or pec musculature. You'd need to distinguish between increases in pec and back musculature, and those in rib cage depth and width. Probably many people have attributed chest girth increases mostly to rib cage enlargement when in reality their back and pec size increases were bigger contributors. Measurements alone can be misleading, so I suggest that you use measurements *and* photographs (especially from the side view) to track possible changes in rib cage size.

T48.4 Whether or not you'd lose any rib cage enlargement produced by the Rader chest pull, only you can determine through experience. I'd speculate that someone who developed an increased rib cage along with increased musculature would likely keep most of the former but while losing most of the latter, following a *sustained* layoff from all weight training (and Rader chest pulls). So that would be a test for detecting actual rib cage enlargement, assuming you have some measurements and photographs from *before* you started using the Rader chest pull, to use for comparison purposes. This is not, however, a test many trainees would willingly want to do.

TRAINING 49
I've just started a new cycle and I decided to put in the stiff-legged deadlift. I'm almost 16 years old, and weigh 135 pounds. I started by using 20-kilo plates on each side. Do you think I'm working with too heavy weights? Do you think I should wait and just work on the squat until I can squat about 200 pounds, and gain a bit of weight? Also, I feel like the stiff-legged deadlift is stretching the back of my thighs too much, though I feel that I'm flexible. Is this normal?

T49.1 Because I can't observe you training, I'm at a huge disadvantage. Using 20-kilo plates together (presumably) with an Olympic bar, adds up to 60 kilos or about 135 pounds. That means you started out with bodyweight for resistance. That's way too much to learn proper form, especially for someone aged just 15. No responsible coach would have allowed you to do that. (Even if you use an exercise bar, you'd still be using too much weight for introducing the stiff-legged deadlift into your program.)

T49.2 Reduce the resistance for the stiff-legged deadlift to 50 pounds total, but while *not* increasing the range of motion. Using smaller diameter plates will increase your range of motion if you do the exercise from the floor. Get in a power rack, if you have one available, and set the pins so that the bar is positioned where it would be if you had 20-kilo plates on it Alternatively, you could elevate the bar (loaded with small plates) on blocks of the appropriate height. The power rack alternative is the simpler option. As another alternative, some specialist suppliers of weightlifting gear sell plates with the diameter of 20-kilo ones, but with a fraction of their weight. Then add just a few pounds to the bar each week *so long as you made your target rep count the previous week*. Don't add large increments. Little and often is the best way.

T49.3   If you can't stiff-legged deadlift as I've outlined, forget the exercise for the time being. Just stick with the squat. Regardless of whether or not you stiff-legged deadlift at the moment, *don't* perform low reps in the squat. You're too young for low reps. Stick with at least 10, and *be sure you really do use good form.*

T49.4   If the stiff-legged deadlift, or squat, seems to be stretching your hamstrings (rear thighs) greatly, you're likely to be needing increased flexibility there. Test your hamstring flexibility. Sit on the floor with your legs straight and together. Now, while bending *only* at your hips—i.e., *no* rounding of your upper back or neck—see how far you can hold down your legs. Do this alongside a mirror, so that you can see whether or not you're cheating by rounding your upper back and neck. If you can't hold your ankles (while keeping your legs straight), then your hamstrings are inflexible and need progressive and careful stretching over a few weeks to loosen them up.

TRAINING 50
Experience has shown that I've sufficient recovery ability to train most exercises, and certainly the main exercises, only once a week. Is there any good reason why grip work is likely to be an exception? Do you think it likely that my (somewhat lagging) forearm development could be accelerated through being trained twice a week instead of once?

T50.1   What matters most to you is what works for you. Sensible experimentation is what you should try. Give twice-a-week grip training a try for 2–3 months, and see how it goes. I suggest you perform a different type of grip work at each of the two weekly sessions—e.g., crushing and/or holding work at one workout, and wrist rolling at the other.

T50.2   Include some finger *extension* work at least once a week. For example, put your fingers *inside* a thick elastic band, and open your fingers against the resistance of the band. Add bands according to need. Alternatively (and this a tip I got from John Christy), you could put your hand in a bucket of dry rice and open your fingers against the resistance of the rice. This method permits a greater range of motion that the other method, and is easier to control.

T50.3 You need this extension work to balance out the strength of the *gripping* muscles and the finger *extension* muscles. This is important in helping to avoid the elbow problems that can occur when there's a serious strength imbalance between the opposing muscles in the forearms and hands.

T50.4 If the increased frequency of grip work produces an accelerated rate of strength increase in all grip work, stick with it; and *perhaps* later on even try a third grip session per week, e.g., pinch-grip work. But if it doesn't help, revert to the lesser frequency. As with all training experiments, you need to ensure that form and effort are in place, and recovery factors are in perfect order—nutrition, rest and sleep. A training experiment will have little value if form and/or effort are lacking or inconsistent, and if corners are being cut in recovery factors.

TRAINING 51
My chest is too developed in relation to my lats and shoulders. Is there a way to work towards getting myself in better proportion? I'm in very good shape with a naturally low percentage of bodyfat. It's just that my chest muscles are too big in relation to the rest of me.

T51.1 I suggest you do minimal work for your chest—incline presses only, once a week, or perhaps only once every other week. Channel the "saved" energy, *without* overtraining, into your shoulder and back work. If your pecs continue to grow, then drop the incline presses for a while—until pec atrophy is sufficient to even out your upper-body musculature. Then add just sufficient pec work to *maintain* that level of development. If or when your shoulders and back development get ahead of your pecs, step up the intensity or frequency of chest work to bring up the lagging pecs. Better to keep your pecs slightly behind—because you'll find it relatively easy to bring them up to par—rather than have them ahead and try to play catch up with your apparently less responsive shoulders and upper-back development.

T51.2   Chest and triceps work are usually interrelated. The two best compound movements for the triceps are the bench press, especially with a shoulder-width grip, and the parallel bar dip. You can't work your triceps with either of those if you're letting your pecs atrophy, or at least you can't work your triceps intensively on them if you're keeping chest work low key (because of the heavy pec involvement). Overhead presses may be enough to give your triceps enough work, without much pec involvement. If not, add pushdowns to your program.

T51.3   Perhaps, you've been training your pecs more efficiently than your shoulders and lats. Find out what has worked so well for your pecs and compare it with what has not worked so well for your shoulders and lats. If you find that you've simply done a better job with your pecs—better form, greater effort on progression, greater enjoyment of chest exercises, etc.—then apply to your shoulder and lat work the principles that worked well on your pecs. Undoubtedly, many people have a bodypart or two that is/are more responsive to training than other bodyparts. Many people, however, simply train some bodyparts better than others, and that may offer the main explanation for the greater responsiveness of the former.

TRAINING 52
When I train I sometimes get so excited that I feel like adding more weight than I know I should, and breaking my form a tad to get out an extra rep. Is this really so bad if I don't make it a habit?

T52.1   You may get away with it for a while, especially if you're very young, but sooner rather than later you'll rue the time you let your heart get ahead of your head. If you take a liberty in a big exercise, you could pay a heavy price—one that could keep you out of intensive training for a long time, and possibly plague you for the rest of your life. Millions of trainees have tried something which, on hindsight, they knew they had no business doing, and regretted it afterwards. *Be disciplined at all times.*

T52.2   I reported an example of my own, of getting caught up in the heat of a workout, and then regretting it, in HARDGAINER issue #57 (November-December 1998):

T52.3   "A few weeks ago I was performing warmup sets on my Tru-Squat®. I was using my usual stance, with 19-1/2 inches between the insides of my heels, and toes well flared. I have this stance marked on the platform, for consistency of reproduction. Because this is quite a wide stance for someone of my height (5-9), and it means that my feet are bang on the perimetral frame of the machine's platform, I got this notion that I should narrow my stance a little. Caught up in the excitement of a workout, I acted. I brought my heels in, narrowing my stance by about three inches. This placed my feet inside the frame of the platform. The 20 reps went perfectly, and felt a tad less demanding than the previous week's. I even had half a kilo more iron on the weight carriage. My knees felt fine, and I was delighted.

T52.4   "The next day my knees started aching, and my satisfaction from the previous day turned into annoyance at my having changed a stance that was working well. I suffered several days of pronounced discomfort.

T52.5   "It wasn't until ten days later that my knees felt back to normal. I usually squat once every seventh day. This time I waited sixteen days. Then I returned to my usual stance, with a further half kilo on the bar. The set went well and I suffered no delayed-onset soreness. Seven days later I squatted again, with a further half kilo of added weight, and again it went well with no delayed-onset soreness.

T52.6   "On hindsight, to adjust one's squat stance by three inches and continue to use one's best working poundage, is foolish even if there's no history of knee problems. But for someone with my knee track record, such a substantial adjustment was madness. In the heat of the workout while gearing up for the 20-rep squat, I was oblivious to the foolishness. And I'm normally so careful when I train.

T52.7   "Whenever you make adjustments to your form, no matter how minor they may appear, do it in an incremental and progressive way, and never while using your current best working weights. The more of a history of physical problems and injuries you have, the more careful you need to be. I paid the price with a period of discomfort, and one missed squatting session. I could have paid a much heavier price.

T52.8   "I could still try a closer stance, and do it progressively, but I'm not going to bother. What I'm doing is working well, so why tinker with it? The greed for 'the more' is ever present; so watch out for it in your own training! Slow and steady progress is the target. If that's happening, stick with it for a period of a year or two, and then you'll see substantial progress. Try to hasten the progress, and though you might succeed, the more likely result will be that you disrupt the slow but steady progress. The greed to speed things up too often ends in killing progress, and producing injury. Especially watch out for training too often, adding weight too quickly, including unnecessary exercises, and adding bodyweight too fast. But the irony is that the 'slow and steady' approach is the fast way over the long term. It's sure, safe and practical. And that's what sensible training is all about."

TRAINING 53
I'm training for a triathlon but still want to improve my basic strength. I'm not a hard gainer in that I can train for five out of seven days and not suffer too much from overtraining. Any ideas for a general strength routine? I'm 5-8 and 204 pounds.

T53.1　You should still use abbreviated training even though you may be able to make some (but not as much) progress on a more conventional but time-consuming approach. You want maximum return per hour of training investment. You're already on an extensive overall workload, while training for a triathlon. Even though you're not a hard gainer you could still quickly go over the threshold into serious overtraining by weight training more than you need to, and thus stymie *all* your training.

T53.2　I'd recommend just two brief weight-training sessions a week of two major exercises each, or one workout a week of four exercises. (Perform warmup sets plus just two work sets per exercise.) Train hard on those four exercises, keep adding weight, stick with it for a long period, and you're going to get a lot stronger. If you find you start dragging your feet in general, and your overall performances drop, reduce the weight-training frequency to once every five days for the program of two different workouts, or once every ten days for the single workout program, and see how that goes. But *very importantly*, don't drop into high-intensity weight training from the very first workout. Start out easily, and take 6–8 weeks to *gradually* pick up the intensity *before* you're pushing hard. That period of *gradual* adaptation should enable your body to marshall its resources to cope with the increase in load.

T53.3 As far as the four exercises go, make them *all* big ones that you can perform safely, e.g., squat, stiff-legged deadlift *or* Romanian deadlift, bench press *or* dip, and chin *or* a supported row.

TRAINING 54
Do you think the 20-rep breathing method will work on all exercises, or just the squat?

T54.1 The great tradition for 20-rep, "breathing," rest-pause work is on the squat, though it's used successfully in some limited quarters for the deadlift, too.

T54.2 Don't get overly concerned with rep counts. There isn't a "magic" number for a given exercise that will yield terrific results while other rep counts will yield nothing, all other variables being constant. Though many people can get good results from different rep counts for the same exercise (during different cycles), some people do find progress easier to make from one rep count than others. If you have what it takes to train well, and deliver on the recovery front too, you'll be able to make gains on more than one rep count, for any given exercise. Conversely, if you can't make any gains on 5-rep work, then chances are you won't be able to make gains on 8, 10, 12, 15 or 20 reps.

T54.3 The ingredients for success with any rep count are the same— excellent form, hard work, satisfying recovery needs, and poundage progression on each exercise. To deliver the necessary poundage progression you have to deliver fully on the recovery fronts. Even if your training is excellent, if you cut corners on the recovery front, you'll compromise if not kill your progress.

T54.4 Choose a rep count per exercise you feel comfortable with, and enjoy—and it may vary among exercises—and stick with it. Much more important than rep count, is effort and form, and delivering the recovery goods when out of the gym, in order to produce the poundage gains in the gym that will produce stronger and bigger muscles.

TRAINING 55
Many lifters speak about split routines where they work the basic exercises once a week, and claim each muscle group is only worked once a week. But if a person trains twice a week on a split routine, no matter how abbreviated or how the exercises are

split, they are actually working many of the muscle groups twice a week. So wouldn't the ideal routine for a hard gainer be a full-body workout—e.g., squat, dip and chin—that allows a full 5–7 days of rest for all the muscles between sessions? Or do I have the theory wrong?

T55.1   If you train using more than one routine, then at least some degree of overlap will occur *if* you're using major exercises. It would be possible to use isolation exercises and arrange workouts so there's no overlap to speak of. But without the big exercises you're not going to have a productive training program, at least not for hard gainers; so that's not an option.

T55.2   With the big core exercises, if say you're training twice a week and alternating two routines, how you spread the exercises over the week can greatly affect the degree of overlap between sessions. If you're using a program of squat, deadlift, dip and chin as your core exercises, supplemented by L-fly, and ab and calf work, that gives you seven exercises. If you were to squat and deadlift on separate days, you'd get great overlap, and would in effect work the involved musculature twice a week; but put both exercises on the same day, and you would eliminate that overlap. With the squat, deadlift and L-fly on one day, and the other four exercises on the second day, there would still be a small degree of overlap, but nothing substantial.

T55.3   Just three exercises in your total weight-training program, *as a long-term strategy*, is going to produce imbalances, and neglect important secondary exercises such as the L-fly, and ab and calf work. The important secondary exercises need to be included, at least in some cycles. When you have six or seven exercises in your total program, you may prefer to divide your program into two parts, rather than do it all at a single workout.

T55.4   How much training you do per workout will influence your overall recovery time and ability. You may have no problem recovering from and progressing on three different exercises at each of two weekly workouts (as long as the exercises are divided *with minimum overlap*), but put all six in one workout, and you may struggle to progress. On the other hand, perhaps the opposite will apply to you. Individual variation can be considerable—you need to do some trial and error, and see what works best for you.

T55.5   If you can make the *same* poundage gain per squat workout on
the two illustrative options (single program, and the divided
program), that would mean you'd be adding weight once every
five days on the former, and once every seven days on the latter.
If you can do this over the *long term*, you're going to make faster
progress on the every-five-days program because you'll
accumulate weight increases quicker. But perhaps you can't
make full recovery with only five days between squat sessions,
and need seven. What you want is the greatest training
frequency that permits you to add weight as often as possible.
In practice, however, this means infrequent training—but
obviously, the more poundage increments you can make, the
better. The bottom line for building muscle and might is
progress in terms of weight on the bar in consistently good form.

T55.6   Now to return to the specific question. A good very abbreviated
program may be the squat, chin and dip every 5–7 days. But at
least some of the time, I'd prefer the inclusion of a few additional
exercises (deadlift, overhead press, L-fly, and calf and ab work),
though not necessarily all of them in the same program. To do
6–8 exercises in a single routine is overkill for many if not most
hard gainers—hence where the divided program of two different
routines comes in, providing overlap is minimized.

TRAINING 56
**I've been an athlete for 20 years, training and
competing at college and national levels. The
problem is that my calves are non-existent! I've run
the track, sprinted, and "plyometric-ed" myself
silly! Does this mean that to stimulate growth in
my calves I have to destroy them in the gym more
often than the next guy? It seems to me that they
resist adaptation to their normally heavy loads.**

T56.1   Sounds like you've been grossly overtraining your calves.
Increased overtraining isn't going to help. How's the rest of your
physique? If you're small everywhere, your calves are going to
be in line. If your thighs are 21 inches, then you can't expect to
have 17-inch calves. If you're only 150 pounds bodyweight, at an
average height, you can't hope to have big calves. But if you're
very well built everywhere else—200 pounds or so at an average
height, and no more than about 12% bodyfat—and have applied
yourself as seriously to calf work as to other bodyparts, *then* you
have a problem. Few people, however, are in that category.

T56.2   If you're small everywhere, you need to get everything growing. For every 10–15 pounds of muscle over your whole physique, you can expect to have half an inch or so more on your calves. Something similar can be said for the upper arms. For hard gainers, bodypart specialization is usually a waste of time. It's overall "specialization" through abbreviated training—and getting the whole body growing as a single unit—that's the key to getting the individual bits and pieces in good order.

T56.3   It's not uncommon to have a bodypart that's much less responsive than the rest of your physique. From that point of view, you may need to be smarter about training the lagging part. But the basic approach of training the body as a whole, to produce growth overall, is still your best ally. Once you're big and strong everywhere, *then* you can try localized specialization programs to bring up a lagging part. But don't try to bring up a lagging bodypart when your problem is really a lagging physique in general.

TRAINING 57
I've started doing trap bar deadlifts on one training day and trap bar shrugs on the other. Other work consists of presses, rows, curls, grip, calves and abs, all one work set each. I'm still a few pounds shy of doing bodyweight in the 20-rep squat. I'm concerned that maybe I should do stiff-legged trap bar deadlifts and save the trap bar deadlift until I'm advanced enough where I'll squat once a week and trap bar deadlift the other. Do you think it's okay to continue the twice-weekly squat and weekly trap bar deadlift, or would I be better off with the stiff-legged version? Or is this a marginal concern?

T57.1   *What matters most of all is more iron on the bar in consistently good form, and not getting injured. Many variations of abbreviated training can produce this end result.*

T57.2   There's a great deal of overlap between the trap bar/shrug bar deadlift (with bent legs), and the squat. To squat twice a week, and trap bar/shrug bar deadlift once a week, is in effect three bouts of squatting. I'd say that you're going to burn out on that, sooner rather than later. I recommend you anticipate this, and take action now to prevent slowed (or negated) progress.

T57.3   I suggest you stick with the squat and stiff-legged deadlift (using a straight bar or trap bar/shrug bar, though I prefer the straight bar), and leave the trap bar/shrug bar *bent-legged* deadlift till later. If you can squat well and productively, *then squat on!* Stiff-legged deadlift just once a week. If you can progress on the twice-weekly squatting, keep it going. But if or when you're dragging your feet, I'd recommend dropping to just once a week, or at least reducing to once only every five days or so.

T57.4   The trap bar/shrug bar is a fine training tool, especially for the deadlift and shrug, but even too many good exercises will wear you down and produce stagnation. So be prudent in how many exercises you have in your program, and keep fine-tuning things so that you can consistently add more iron to the bar. But the training alone is only part of the overall picture responsible for making gains. Excellent attention to out-of-the-gym factors—rest, sleep and nutrition—is essential.

TRAINING 58
I'm 18 and throw the shot put and discus. My coach set me up on a strength-building program where I lift heavy 2 or 3 times a week and light 1 or 2 times per week. This is in addition to throwing twice a week and sprinting once a week. The lifting is based around the powerlifts, military press and pullup, along with assistance work. This routine is a whole lot. I asked my coach about overtraining and he told me to rest a lot, eat a lot, eat healthy, and that without any outside stresses I should be fine. I feel drained on my off days, but the next day my energy is back. Do you feel that a young hard gainer, under ideal conditions, can thrive on this program? My lifting sessions are between 45 and 75 minutes, not including warmups.

T58.1   This workload is far too much for gifted athletes, let alone typical hard gainers, even young ones. With time you'll be dragging your feet and merely going through the motions in the gym. Progress would stop, and if you continued to push hard you'd develop a severe case of overtraining, along with sickness and injuries.

T58.2   You'll make better progress if you reduce your weight-training frequency to just twice a week. Even that, on top of two throwing sessions each week, along with running, is a heavy load. If or when your strength progress stagnates, you may need to modify your program, while still weight training twice a week, so that each exercise, especially the powerlifts, is only performed once a week—for warmups plus one or at most two work sets each.

TRAINING 59
Even though my strength is increasing, my size is not. I thought that if your strength increases it's inevitable that your size will increase. Am I wrong?

T59.1 If you're not eating a caloric and protein surplus, you'll put the brakes on your development. While you may be able to build more strength without increasing your overall size, there's a limit, and sooner or later you'll reach it. While the *general* rule of "get a lot stronger and you must get bigger muscles" stands, the correlation between size and strength can vary substantially from person to person. A bigger muscle isn't necessarily a stronger muscle; and a stronger muscle isn't necessarily a bigger muscle.

T59.2 Assuming that you're not training on very low reps, partial reps or low-rep rest-pause reps—where you can get a lot stronger without getting much if any bigger—I suggest you try increasing your caloric and protein intake. You may also benefit from increasing your training frequency or volume *a little*—for details on this, see Chapter 21 of the *revised* edition of BEYOND BRAWN.

TRAINING 60
I tried the squat but it bothered my knees even after stretching and warming up, and applying the form corrections suggested in your technique book. Can I get the same results from doing 2 x 12 with the trap bar as opposed to 1 x 20 in the squat?

T60.1 If you stretched before you were well warmed up, that may have produced problems for your knees. Stretching should occur *after* warming up. I'd prefer it to be done between sets or at the end of a workout, rather than before the workout proper. The exception to this rule is when some gentle and progressive stretching is needed to loosen up an obviously tight muscle.

T60.2 The trap bar/shrug bar deadlift can be a fine substitute for the barbell squat. For some people it's a *more* productive exercise.

Trainees who find the squat hard to progress on—assuming that they really have learned and applied good form, tweaked for their own individuality—should give the trap bar/shrug bar deadlift a good try. And 2 x 12 work sets can produce good results, just like a single 1 x 20 work set can. If you feel in better control with 2 x 12 rather than 1 x 20, fine. The rep count per se is not the important issue. What matters is more iron on the bar each workout or two, in consistently good form, for a few years. That will add a lot of muscle.

TRAINING 61
Would this program produce overtraining: trap bar deadlift 2 x 12, press 2 x 10, bent-over row 2 x 10, curl 1 set to failure, stiff-legged deadlift (straight bar) 1 x 15, twice a week? I'm 16 years of age. And should I up my protein intake for best results?

T61.1   If you're adding iron to the bar every week or two, to each exercise, and you keep doing it for month after month, your program is working and you're not overtraining. But if your progress in the gym slows, or halts, and assuming that you're training hard, *and* eating and sleeping well, you probably would be overtraining. Then you would benefit from reducing the training frequency of the same workout, or dividing your exercises up over two different workouts, and training each exercise just once a week.

T61.2   If you're already consuming 1.5 grams of protein per pound of bodyweight, you'd probably be taking in more than you need. If you're consuming under a gram per pound, you'd almost certainly benefit from a protein hike. But whatever protein intake you're on, it's worth an experiment for a couple of months (during a period of intensive training, and new poundage territory) to see if a protein boost accelerates your progress.

TRAINING 62
What's your opinion on Super Slow™? I read about it in BRAWN but couldn't find any reference to it in BEYOND BRAWN. I'm also curious how Super Slow fits in with the slow-twitch/fast-twitch "theory" of muscle tissue and muscular development.

T62.1   In my experience, and generally speaking, training with a very slow rep cadence, for most people for most of the time, is too contrived a way of training to be done long enough to deliver results. But some people have obtained good results from it. I want people to train safely and productively over the long term. If Super Slow or any other interpretation of very slow cadence training can deliver that for you, then go with it.

T62.2   For every person who has let me know that he got good results from using a very slow rep cadence, I've had many complain that the training was so boring and artificial that they couldn't use it for long enough to yield gains, and that their enthusiasm for training quickly waned. Enthusiasm has to be high if you're to train hard and consistently. This doesn't mean that the actual training must be fun per se. Hard training is not "fun," but the satisfaction of training hard, and producing good results, is "fun." Once the initial period of adaptation to a very slow cadence has been achieved, poundage gain is usually so slow that motivation suffers. With reduced motivation for training, you can't train hard and consistently for a long period, and thus you aren't going to experience good results.

T62.3   Super Slow also almost demands expert supervision, and there are hardly any people around qualified to give such supervision. Few people can train super slowly without supervision to ensure that everything is in order and consistent from workout to workout. It may also be that there's a certain type of mindset or personality that's suited to very slow training, and most trainees don't have it. Also, at least for some exercises, high-quality machines are desirable for very slow training, but these not available to 99+% of trainees. Very slow rep training is very difficult to do in busy commercial gyms, because they are so full of distractions and competition for equipment.

T62.4   I'm insistent on the need for perfect form and a controlled rep cadence. I've no time for any macho mentality that puts weight before form. Using controlled form is one thing, and I'm all for excellent form and a controlled cadence, but you don't have to move to such extremes as Super Slow in order to achieve a controlled cadence. This is not, however, to say that just because a very slow cadence is used, form is necessarily good or safe. It's possible to use lousy form but a very slow cadence. Don't think that very slow training is automatically safe. Some of the train-very-slowly folk make an exaggerated claim for the safety of slow reps. I sustained one of the most frustrating and nagging injuries I've ever had while training in a very slow cadence.

T62.5 While lousy form can be performed with any cadence, by slowing down their rep cadence people are usually made more form conscious. I'm all for people being more form conscious. Most trainees move the bar too quickly, and neither use good technique *nor* a controlled rep cadence. But you don't have to reduce to a 10/5, 8/4 or another very slow cadence in order to have excellent control over the resistance. Reducing form cadence to three seconds for the negative portion, and 2–3 seconds for the positive phase, is enough of a slow down to produce the required bar control. You can go slower if you wish—and even into the "artificial/contrived" range—but it's not a necessity for good control.

T62.6 I'm very safety conscious. In fact, few writers have hammered away at safety factors like I have over recent years. I'm relentless in promoting good form *and* effort *and* progression. The use of progressive poundages is a recipe for disaster if it's at the expense of impeccable form. So consistently good form comes first, and then comes the intensity of effort needed to produce the increase in strength that yields the extra tad of iron on the bar next time around. So progressive resistance is what bodybuilding and strength training are about, but the critical caveat is that form has to be good and consistent.

T62.7 Most trainees don't have the temperament or tenacity to adhere to the very slow rep cadence protocol, month after month, year after year. It's a very grueling way of approaching progressive resistance. Some people falsely believe that very slow cadence work is not "real" training, and for wimps only. Such people have never been through a proper Super Slow workout. Very slow cadence training is brutal, and because of the accompanying reduction in exercises poundages, is a huge dampener on the egos of most people.

T62.8 To train with the consistency needed to produce good results over the long term, you have to be "up" for training at nearly every workout. If, as is the case with many people, slow cadence training produces boredom and a sense of drudgery, the zeal needed in order to keep training hard week in and week out, will wane. Of course, "many people" isn't everyone. That's why you need to do some trial and error, and see what works best for you.

T62.9 To repeat what I wrote earlier, I'm not against performing very slow reps, providing they are delivering the goods for you. What matters is what works *for you.* If very slow reps work for you, train that way—but I'd say you're one of the exceptions. *Some people, however, are forced to train using very slow reps due to serious joint limitations (see page 288). Very slow reps may be a godsend to enable these people to train hard and safely on big exercises involving the "limited" joints; but "very slow" need not mean extremely slow—6/6 or so, for example, should be slow enough even for major joint limitations.*

T62.10   As far as "how Super Slow fits in with the slow-twitch/fast-twitch 'theory' of muscle tissue and muscular development" goes, I don't know of any such theory. Fiber typing and its role in rep cadence is highly complicated, and incomplete. You're *much* better off focusing on the things that really count—hard work on the big exercises in consistently good form with ever-increasing poundages. Applying that credo will build bigger and stronger muscles without a single thought ever being given to fiber types. Don't complicate matters and lose sight of the priority issues that should command 99% of your training attention.

TRAINING 63
I've used a two-days-a-week program (splitting the body into two workouts), but recently used a four-day split that works every bodypart once a week. Isn't this the same as the two-days-a-week program, with the same amount of recovery time?

T63.1   Even a two-days-a-week split or divided program, when major compound exercises are used, will produce some overlap between workouts, though this can be minimized by, for example, putting squats and deadlifts on the same day. The greater the degree of overlap, the more likely that at least some bodyparts get two major hits per week, which is overkill for many people.

T63.2   When you divide your exercises over four separate workouts, there'll be some degree of overlap in at least some of the workouts. You may end up working some bodyparts more than twice per week. By dividing your overall program over four parts, most people will end up performing more exercises and work per week than they would if only training twice a week.

T63.3   Further, you have four workouts per week, which means that you have only three non-weight-training days per week. That's more "on" days than "off" ones, which is almost a guarantee of overtraining for the vast majority of trainees.

T63.4 All in all, moving to four days will increase the demands on your body, and greatly increase the chance of your moving beyond what your recovery "machinery" can cope with. The only people I've known who could respond well on that sort of regime were either genetically gifted, drug enhanced, or genetically gifted *and* drug-fed. While you might be genetically gifted to a sufficient degree, the chances are you're not; and I'd hope that you're intelligent enough not to mess with drugs.

T63.5 You'd be giving yourself a much better chance of making good gains if you returned to a two-days-a-week program, and worked on fine-tuning that and your out-of-gym factors, rather than consider something drastic and likely harmful such as four-days-per-week training. Not only are you likely to get better gains, but you'll have more time for a life outside of the gym and your work. Abbreviated training is a winner all round.

TRAINING 64
I've been told I should use a full-body routine twice a week. Isn't this more than you generally recommend?

T64.1 Maybe you would prosper on training the same full-body routine twice a week, at least *for a while*. I would put most beginners on such a schedule; but later on I'd likely move them onto another schedule while, in most cases, still weight training twice a week.

T64.2 Generally speaking I don't believe that training the same full-body routine twice a week is the best way to go once a trainee is beyond the beginner's stage. For most non-novices most of the time I think it's too frequent a schedule for working the *same* big exercises *very hard*. A better way is to train very hard on the same full-body routine less often than twice a week, to provide more recovery time between hits on the same exercises. Alternatively, train twice a week but use a different set of exercises at each of the two workouts so that each movement is trained no more frequently than once a week. Or, divide the body into two parts with minimal overlap, and alternate the two workouts over *three* training days each week. Then each bodypart gets trained three times every *two* weeks—i.e., once every four or five days.

T64.3 Experience affects training frequency. Beginners usually need to train each exercise more often than experienced trainees, so they can learn the skills of the exercises quickly, and because they are not yet training very hard.

T64.4   Intensity affects training frequency. For experienced trainees
         who really train "balls to the wall," some will need to allow for
         more recovery time. But at a lesser intensity, though still "hard,"
         a greater frequency of training may be required. If, however, the
         intensity is anything less than "hard," you're unlikely to
         stimulate growth no matter how frequently you train.

T64.5   Nutrition affects training frequency. If you cut corners on the
         nutrition front—calories and/or nutrients—you'll compromise
         your recovery and extend the time you need to recover fully
         between workouts. But eat really well and you'll recover quicker,
         and thus be able to get back into the gym sooner for another
         productive workout, i.e., a progress-yielding one. But overdo caloric
         intake and you'll get fat. You need to strike the right balance.

T64.6   Sleep affects training frequency. Even if your training and
         nutrition are perfect, if you're shortchanging yourself in the
         sleep department, you'll delay recovery and thus stretch out
         your productive training frequency.

T64.7   Productive bodybuilding and strength training are the result of a
         package of factors. To maximize your rate of progress you need
         to get many components in good order. You may still be able to
         progress while cutting a small corner or two, but you won't
         make your optimum progress that way. Cut more than just the
         odd corner and you'll kill your progress.

T64.8   The bottom line is progress. If your training is working well even
         if you're not training fully in line with the general guidelines I
         believe are best for most trainees, that's fine. But if your training
         isn't working, you need to make changes. While it may not be
         your gym work that's primarily at fault—because the problems
         could be mostly in the nutrition and sleep departments—for most
         trainees the gym component leaves a lot to be desired.

T64.9   Because I can't see you train or observe your eating and
         sleeping habits, I can't put my finger on specific shortcomings
         that apply to your individual case. Even if I watch a video
         recording of a workout, what I'd get is unlikely to be a typical
         workout. The fact that a recording is being made would
         probably produce important changes in the training—harder
         work and perhaps tighter form. Figuratively speaking, I'd need
         to be a fly on the wall for a few workouts while you train, to
         see precisely what you do. A mere list of what you eat isn't

enough either. I'd need to see what you eat on a regular daily basis, rather than hear what you get on a good day, which is what I usually get when someone tells me about their nutrition.

T64.10 Many coaches teach people to train the way they have found to be successful for them (the coaches). In doing this they forget to consider that most other people don't share the coaches' recovery abilities, tolerance of exercise-induced discomfort, genetic inheritance, lifestyles, etc. I can think of a number of coaches I've known over the years who have lifestyles and genetic inheritance very different to those of typical trainees. So when the latter apply the training methods used with success by the former, they find them not only unproductive but harmful in some cases. While this isn't as bad as the "follow the champions to become a champion" mentality promoted by those who pander to drug-assisted genetic phenomena, it's the same sort of thing.

T64.11 You have to train yourself. You need to learn enough about training so that you really know what you're doing. You also have to know enough about yourself to be able to fine-tune general guidelines to find a productive overall formula that works well for you. You need to do some sensible trial and error experimentation. Further, you need to evaluate how well or otherwise you satisfy all the components of recovery—be very demanding, discover the shortcomings, and then put them right. *Become your own expert trainer.*

TRAINING 65
I read in an article that you wrote, that extreme variety in training could be destructive for a hard gainer. Does this mean that I should stick with the same exercises, exercise order, reps, sets, etc., for months? How long should someone continue to use the same exact routine?

T65.1 You should stick with the same routine for as long as it keeps working. If you design and implement a good routine you can make consistent gains from it for over a year, without any changes other than putting more iron on the bar on a regular basis. *Gains are what matter, not how many different routines you clock up in your training career.*

T65.2 Chopping and changing routines is usually symptomatic of serious errors in program design, effort level, progression scheme, rest and sleep schedules, and nutrition. Chopping and changing routines can also be a sign of lack of faith in good training methods—even good methods need to be married with patience in order to yield good results.

T65.3 Playing around with numbers of sets and reps, exercise order, between-sets rest periods, etc., while not addressing the major faults (such as in exercise selection, effort, form, sleep and nutrition), will never make an unproductive program productive.

T65.4 If you're training with genuine effort and good form, focusing on a few big compound exercises *that suit you*, resting well between workouts, sleeping at least eight hours a night, and consuming six meals/feeds a day that keep you in caloric and protein surplus, you're doing what's needed. The precise order of exercises, and numbers of sets and reps, for example, are secondary. Many abbreviated programs will do the job. Choose one, fine-tune it to suit you, and then hammer away at it for a long period. With effort, good form and a big-exercises focus, and rest, sleep and nutrition all in good order, progress will happen *if you're patient*. Just keep adding iron to the bar, and you'll grow.

TRAINING 66
Since I've started training in the abbreviated style, with no isolation work for my arms, I've noticed that my entire body grows and changes for the better, but my arms don't. Just tell me that it's possible to get respectable arm development from an abbreviated program.

T66.1 If you build up to dipping with bodyweight around your waist, and chinning with about half of your bodyweight around your waist, you'll have decent biceps and triceps without any isolation work for your arms. But "decent" doesn't have to mean 18+ inches. If you've been rowing for your back, and bench pressing for your chest, then perhaps you've been getting a lot less biceps and triceps work than you would from chinning and dipping. The precise core exercises you choose can have a big impact on how well your arms are trained and developed.

T66.2 Maybe your lagging arm development is a genetic thing, maybe your specific selection of exercises is not good, or maybe you need some specific arm work. In case it's the latter, I suggest you add some specific arm work no more than twice a week, and see if that makes a difference. Take accurate measurements, work hard and briefly, and see how things go for a few months. If the extra work helps your arms, keep it in. If not, drop it.

T66.3   Many hard gainers find special trouble developing their arms— it's often a characteristic of "hardgainingness," primarily due to below-average muscle belly length in the arms. Leg and back development comes with much less struggle, though still requiring much hard work and consistent dedication. Anyone who develops very big muscular arms has above-average length muscle bellies in his arms, and was never a hard gainer, at least not in the arms. But people who have long muscle bellies in their arms usually have them most elsewhere too.

T66.4   This doesn't mean that trainees with very big muscular arms didn't have to train hard, and be dedicated, but that the genetic potential and responsiveness was there for big arms. Anyone with an arm of 18+ inches, was never a hard gainer. In fact, 17 inches (with a tight waist) is beyond what bona fide hard gainers can realistically build.

T66.5   Recognizing their superior responsiveness to training, relative to that of a genuine hard gainer, is a hard pill for most easy gainers to swallow. Few people like to acknowledge that progress came *relatively* easy for them. Some easy gainers even poke fun at people of a lesser strength and size, claiming that genetics have nothing to do with it. There are people around who've trained with just as much effort and dedication as those who built 18-inch arms—or even with *more* effort and dedication—yet remain with arms a couple of inches smaller than the big-arm crowd. There's more to big muscles than just effort and dedication, though of course without effort and dedication even a terrific potential for big muscles will come to nothing.

TRAINING 67
Why is there some instruction in HARDGAINER and other forums of abbreviated training that are at odds with what I read in BEYOND BRAWN?

T67.1   I covered this in my editorial in HARDGAINER issue #56 (September-October 1998):

T67.2   "HARDGAINER is not an expression of just my opinions, but a forum for a variety of views on abbreviated basics-first training. So inevitably some advice is published that I disagree with.

T67.3   "I would personally never recommend that anyone trains in an explosive way (unless he's a skilled Olympic-style weightlifter), or uses high-risk exercises, or goes to muscular failure at the expense of good form.

T67.4   "I am, however, experienced enough to know that some people train in that very risky manner on a regular basis, and do so relatively safely. But they are the exceptions. More important is the fact that most people who persist with explosive training, high-risk movements, and form liberties are racked with injuries.

T67.5   "I would never touch the odd-object lifting that some people encourage. And neither would I ever consider doing any explosive lifting even with barbells or dumbbells. My body has limitations due to my having used explosive lifting and loose form in the past. I'm living proof of what happens if you abuse exercise. Had I not abused exercise so much in the past I'd be able to use a wider range of exercises now than I actually can, but even then I'd still not use high-risk exercises.

T67.6   "There are exceptions to every rule, but those exceptions should not be presented as role models for the rest of us. I tried to copy such role models, and paid a heavy price.

T67.7   "I'm not keen on singles or very low reps, and never use them myself, but I know they can be safe for some people providing immaculate form is used, and limit weights are not used very often.

T67.8   "Not performing presses behind neck, barbell rows, rock-bottom squats, stiff-legged deadlifts from an elevated surface, cleans, jerks, snatches, odd-object lifts, or any type of explosive exercise, doesn't mean that the individual concerned is less of a training devotee than someone who can do those exercises. And not being willing to go to muscular failure at the expense of safe exercise form does not indicate a wimpish character.

T67.9   "The most sensible approach is to train safely for the long term. And for nearly everyone that means avoidance of all explosive lifting, sloppy form and high-risk exercises. The conservative way is the best way. So modify accordingly any abbreviated training program you want to use.

T67.10 "Many coaches are naturally more robust than are typical trainees, because those coaches are not typical hard gainers. Because they can get way with various liberties they usually apply the same approach to their charges. But I am a typical hard gainer, so I know the score for hard gainers.

T67.11 "A surprising number of coaches give excellent advice in their writings and lectures regarding the use of controlled exercise form and the avoidance of explosive movements, but then in practice they allow great liberties with form and rep cadence. I've witnessed this glaring contradiction both in person and on video recordings, and have been shocked. Watch out for this contradiction, and be sure to follow the recommendations for controlled exercise form and rep cadence.

T67.12 "Some coaches, however, suffer from serious injuries as the result of their years of training bravado, and are now shadows of their former selves. They have learned the hard way of the perils of taking training liberties. Don't learn by the same route!"

TRAINING 68
When microloading from week to week, which work set do you increase the poundage on? Is it the first work set, your last, or in between (if you're doing three work sets)? Is it the same for all the core exercises? What about secondary exercises?

T68.1 There are different possible ways of handling this, but I suggest you go for simplicity and consistency. The microloading goes on for all the work sets of a given exercise at a given workout. Assuming you make your target reps at each of the work sets for a given exercise, add another microload for all work sets next time, etc. So if you're doing 3 x 5 work sets in the bench press, for example, and last week you got all 5 reps in each set with 265 pounds, then make it 266 for all 3 sets this week. If you get all 3 x 5, then move to 267 next time. But if you only made 5, 5 and 4, as an illustration, then stick with the 266 for another workout or few until you get all 3 x 5.

T68.2 The same idea applies to all of the core exercises, though the increment you use will vary. For the overhead press, for example, when in the tough stage of a cycle—and in new poundage ground—a pound increment, when expressed in terms of a percentage, is going to be over twice as much as a pound on your deadlift. So while you may be able to add a pound a week to your deadlift and squat for ages, make it half a pound in the overhead press, and perhaps alternate weeks some of the time. Find your own way.

T68.3   Keep in mind that The Golden Fleece is to train hard and add a tad of iron every week or two *without any perceived increase in effort needed.* Then you know you're building the strength to cope with the increased load. If from week to week there's a perceived increase in effort needed—and I'm *not* talking about the early stage of a cycle here—then you're going to stall very soon. Rather than persist with this and then stall, make changes in your recovery and/or training so that you build strength between workouts and can thus add a tad of iron, again and again and again, without perceiving any increase in difficulty.

T68.4   For secondary exercises, because they use far less weight than the core ones, adjust the weight increments accordingly—a smaller increment and put it on less frequently.

T68.5   As your work sets increase in load, adjust your warmup weights accordingly. There's no need to increase your warmup sets' weights in perfect line with your work sets. Simplify things, for easier loading of bars. But for every 10-pound gain on a given exercise's work sets, bump up all your warmup sets by 10 pounds. As you get substantially stronger, you may need to add an additional warmup set, because you'll have a far greater "distance" to cover to build up to your working weight.

TRAINING 69
I'm coming back after a minor back injury. My chiropractor and I have decided that I should start squatting with extremely reduced poundages to ensure proper form. I'm in the eighth week of my cycle and it's clear that my progress in the bench press, press and bench-supported T-bar row will halt long before my squat. Should I continue on my squatting progression and max out on my other exercises, or continue squatting and reduce my other exercises to about 85% and insert a "mini-cycle," to try to keep progressing?

T69.1 I'd suggest you slow down your rate of poundage increase on the exercises other than the squat, to get more "mileage" out of the gaining momentum. When you feel you've reached the current limit, and have applied all the cycle-extending suggestions in Chapter 15 of BEYOND BRAWN, start a new cycle with reduced poundages and/or some exercise changes, but keep the momentum going on the squat. If you've cut your squatting poundages back severely, and you're not rushing the progression there, it will likely be quite a while (a year or longer) before all your exercises are moving along at comparable intensity levels.

T69.2 Don't rush your return to high-intensity squatting. When coming back from an injury, the most common mistake is rushing, which often leads to a relapse, and starting over again. Get it right first time—slowly, steadily, safely, surely and successfully.

TRAINING 70
I've been doing chins using continuous reps, and can now do 10 from a dead hang. I've been thinking about experimenting with rest-pause chins. Most people, however, would probably consider it cheating if they saw someone doing rest-pause chins. Do you think that rest-pause is a productive way to do chins? If so, what's your advice on how to go about doing them?

T70.1 Rest-pause chins are an option, but I think you should get much more mileage out of chinning the way you have been. For chins, many people find 10 reps on the high side for adding weight to, so I suggest you drop to say 6. Adding weight to sets of 6 reps will probably be significantly easier than to sets of 10. I suggest you get a dipping belt, and start by adding a pound a week to your chins, performing a couple of work sets. As long as you get your 2 x 6 (and the second set will be harder than the first, so the second set is your "barometer" one), add a pound next time. When progression becomes tough, perhaps after 2–3 of months or so, slow the progression to half a pound a week, or even alternate weeks. Initially set a target of 10 pounds around your waist, for 2 x 6. Get that, and then work to 20 pounds. Get that, and then work to 30 pounds, and so on.

T70.2 Later on, after you can chin with a decent weight—at least 50 pounds—you can consider doing something else, such as rest-pause, but I think bodyweight plus 50 pounds is the minimum "qualification" for such "advanced" stuff.

T70.3   As far as rest-pause reps go, you need consistency if your record keeping is to have any meaning. Choose your between-reps pause period—e.g., 10 or 15 seconds—and then stick with it. Chin while facing a clock, keep your hands on the bar between reps (loosely, to spare your grip), and as soon as the signal from the clock comes that your pause period is up, perform your next rep pronto—no extra few seconds. You need to be able to take your grip on the overhead bar easily. If you can't reach the bar easily, stand on something of the right height so you can keep your hands in position throughout the set, but without actually having to support your weight between reps.

TRAINING 71
In the dip and chin, even if I reduce the weight a lot I can still barely perform more than 5 reps. Is 2 x 5, with 5 minutes rest between sets enough for growth? I can dip with 70 pounds and chin with 40.

T71.1   Just keeping adding weight. If you add enough poundage, your muscles will grow. But just a few pounds won't make any noticeable difference. Using impeccable form, build up to 150 pounds around your waist for the dip, for 2 x 5, and 75 pounds in the chin for 2 x 5, and then the involved musculature *must* be significantly bigger. But it will take time to build up that sort of increase—probably at least eighteen months. And consider that bodyweight increases will accompany the strength gain, so that's additional resistance you need to lift, which will likely delay the time needed to make the targets of 150 and 75 pounds.

TRAINING 72
I have trouble getting psyched up to train hard. Please give me some suggestions to help me get charged up for my training.

T72.1   I'll quote from my editorial in HARDGAINER issue #64 (January-February 2000), and add a caveat at the end:

T72.2   "Recall your early months of training, or a few workouts that were memorable because you trained with someone who really pushed you to your limit. Compare them with your workouts of this week. Are you bristling with the same enthusiasm? Are you fired up? Are you training like there's no tomorrow? Are you full of passion, but while training in a disciplined way?

T72.3　"If you're a sports fan, you probably get highly charged up when you're rooting for one side during a big game. Maybe you play along as an imaginary team member. If you do, I'll wager you play with a super level of enthusiasm, and probably achievement too—perhaps scoring the winning goal, home run or touch-down, for example. That's the degree of enthusiasm, energy and commitment you need in your workouts.

T72.4　"Especially if you've been training for a few years, it's easy to get in a rut. Even very serious trainees, at least some of the time, go through the motions to some degree, and fail to make the most of each never-to-be-had-again opportunity to make progress. You can't turn back the clock to put a poor workout right. Challenge yourself to give of your best every single workout—not just passion per se, but disciplined passion. Passion with no discipline is a recipe for ruin. Bravado that leads to taking liberties with form, exposes you to a high risk of injury, and is reckless. You can't progress if you're injured.

T72.5　"Create imaginary scenarios to help charge you up for your work sets. Perhaps create life-or-death scenarios where you must deliver superb workouts in order to survive. Or put yourself in imaginary sporting situations that take you to new heights of enthusiasm. Bring the situations to vivid life in your head. Feel the extreme level of passion that someone must feel when making a winning score in the Rugby World Cup, American Super Bowl, or English F. A. Cup, for example. Hold that passion and energy for each work set.

T72.6　"Create a multitude of different scenarios, and play one of them for a given work set. Different scenarios will be more suited to certain exercises than others. Play whatever mental games you need, to crank up your effort and commitment levels, and make each work set count. Even if you don't think you've been going through the motions in your training, if you were to compare your current level of effort to what you would do under extreme passion and urgency, you'd find that you're a rep or few short in every work set.

T72.7　"Training is too wonderful an activity, and life is too short, to be able to afford any 'going through the motions' workouts. From

your very next training session, train as if each workout will be
your last. Train as if you're a condemned man waiting for the
gallows, but knowing that a great workout will give you a
further few days of grace; and then produce a great workout
again and again and again. A few months of this and you'll
experience some of the best gains of your life. And that will
psyche you up even more—nothing succeeds like success."

T72.8　　Now for the caveat: Cranking up training intensity needs to
be accompanied by a cranking up of the components of
recovery. If you don't provide rest, sleep and nutrition in very
good supply, the intensified training may actually cause
regression. Intensive training is merely the stimulus for
strength increase and growth. To produce strength increase
and growth, you must supply enough calories and nutrients,
along with sufficient rest, sleep and recovery days to *permit*
growth to occur. Eating, resting and sleeping should be the
easy components, relative to the demands of training
intensively; so be sure to get the easy stuff in especially good
order whenever you really deliver on the gym floor.

TRAINING 73
I know I shouldn't hold my breath while I train, but I find it so difficult not to hold my breath on the hard reps of a set. Do you have a tip to help me?

T73.1　　Yes, don't close your mouth. Keeping your mouth open—and it
only needs to be slightly open—will prevent you from forcefully
holding your breath. It's when the lips are jammed shut that
problems with breath holding occur, with resulting headaches,
dizziness and, at the extreme, even blackouts.

TRAINING 74
Some people say that after 96 hours of resting a muscle from training, it starts to atrophy and lose strength. On Monday I do upper body in one session (bench press, behind-neck press, chin and curl). The other session (situp, bent-legged deadlift, squat and donkey calf raise) would be on Friday. Am I correct in letting every bodypart rest a whole week?

T74.1　　The 96-hour myth has been one of most harmful notions in the
training world. It has led to many people training more often than
they need—producing overtraining, stagnation and frustration.

T74.2   You can answer your question yourself. Use the program you describe for a few months. Train hard and seriously, and be sure to *fully* satisfy all the factors of recovery. Eat well including a caloric and protein surplus, sleep at least eight hours each night, and don't run yourself ragged with out-of-the-gym activities. If you do all those things, you'll not lose strength. In fact, you should steadily gain strength, just as thousands of others have on a similar sort of strategy. Just as they proved "muscle atrophies after 96 hours of rest" is a load of bunk, so will you.

T74.3   Two additional comments on your program: By using the front press or the dumbbell press (rather than the behind-neck press), you'll reduce the chance of injury to your shoulders and rotator cuff. Second, I recommend you squat before you bent-legged deadlift, not the other way around (so that you don't squat with a fatigued lower back), and perform another exercise in between, so you can do full justice to the bent-legged deadlift.

TRAINING 75
I've now reached a point where I'm not increasing my weight on the bench press and shoulder press. I do two sets each of these a week, and was planning on reducing my weight and building it back to see if I can beat my best. Would you recommend this, or do you have a better idea as to what I could do?

T75.1   A number of reasons could explain why you've stalled on these two exercises. Cutting back and building up again—and using microloads once you're *almost* (but not quite) back at your best weights, and then nudging into new ground—may do the trick. *But*, if there's something serious amiss in your training program, or components of recovery, and they are not fixed, you'd likely stall at the same point again.

T75.2   If you've been trying to increase your poundages by 5 pounds at a shot, then stagnation is no surprise. Move to an increment of a pound per shot on the bench press, and half that on the overhead press, but only add the increment providing that in the previous week you made your full target of reps.

T75.3   If you've not been training very hard, crank up your effort level. If you've been overdoing things on the intensity front—forced reps, pre-exhaustion, drop sets or negative reps—then drop all the overkill stuff, and return to straight sets.

T75.4   If you've been cutting corners on the sleep front, start getting eight hours sleep minimum every night. If you've been skipping the odd feed/meal, and not getting your full quota of calories, protein and quality food each day, then you need to put all that right. If you've been running yourself ragged on your non-training days, put that right and get rested. *If you've been compromising on the recovery front, then you'll also have been compromising on the training front.*

T75.5   When you've made corrections in any of the aforementioned areas, and if you *still* can't progress in the bench press and press, there's another strategy to try: If you've been bench pressing and overhead pressing at the same workout each week, try dividing them over the two workouts—to spread the load. If, however, you've been doing them at separate workouts, try doing them at the same workout, to give you a full week for your pressing structure to recover between sessions.

TRAINING 76
I'm losing my grip on the deadlift even though the rest of my body wants to carry on. Any ideas on how to solve this?

T76.1   First, make sure you're using a bar with deep and sharp knurling. If the bar you use has no knurling, or barely any knurling (as is often the case), then it has no use for heavy deadlifting. You may need to use a different bar. Second, if the knurling is fine, make sure that you clean the bar regularly so that the knurling is not clogged with chalk or dirt. Use a hard brush to remove clogging. Third, use lots of lifter's chalk (magnesium carbonate). You can buy this from many exercise equipment or outdoor pursuits stores. Fourth, use a reverse or mixed grip for the deadlift—one hand supinated, the other pronated. Alternate which way around you have your hands from set to set. Fifth, hold the bar in your hands, not your fingers. Really get your hands wrapped around the bar.

T76.2   Getting all these five factors in good order can make an instant world of difference to your grip. But the sixth action to take doesn't yield its benefits immediately. Grip work needs time and effort before it pays dividends. Add grip work once or twice a week to your program—timed holds, preferably with a thick bar, is excellent grip work. That should be perhaps your first-choice grip strengthening exercise. Do it at the end of one

workout, and choose something else for the other session—
wrist roller using a thick handle, for example.

T76.3   Put all these points into practice, and you'll have a much
stronger grip. Finally, when deadlifting and going into new
poundage territory, use *small* increments from week to week.
When your grip is near its limit, you should still be able to hang
on next time for the duration of the set *if* you've just added a
pound to the bar. But if you've added 5 or 10 pounds to the bar,
grip failure is almost inevitable. Apply the increased demands
on your grip *gradually*.

TRAINING 77
**I've come across high-intensity training (HIT) and
am wondering if it lives up to its claims. Reading
HIT literature, the general message is that we all
could gain much better using a HIT protocol. Even
further, I see claims that if one doesn't work to
failure, one won't grow. I'm truly confused. I use
two work sets, both of which are to 1 or 2 reps
short of failure. I try to add a couple of pounds
each workout. I feel I'm progressing, yet I'm drawn
towards changing my workout.**

T77.1   A number of training methods work, HIT being one of them.
But HIT comes in several different forms. Some of the training
options described in BEYOND BRAWN belong in the HIT camp.

T77.2   Some strands in the HIT camp have very strident if not bigoted
and arrogant spokespeople. Rather than focus on offering the
training masses a variety of alternatives to the mess of
conventional instruction, a number of people seem more
interested in name calling (even *inside* the HIT camp), almost
obsessively theoretical positions (especially on rep speed, and the
merits of some machines), and making exaggerated claims that
are just not credible for drug-free typical people. At least some of
the time, the "in-fighting" seems to focus on the 5–10% the
combatants disagree on, and forgets the 90–95% they agree on.
The in-fighting also seems to have forgotten that it's conventional
training and its proponents which should be receiving flak, not
fellow members of an alternative though diverse approach.

T77.3   As well as giving HIT a bad name, and causing lots of conflict,
this leads to some people thinking they have all the answers,

and to hell with anyone who thinks anything different—"my way or the highway!" This produces conflict rather than useful discussion, and fragments the non-mainstream training culture. Such internecine struggle is common in most if not almost all "counter" movements, thus weakening their influence, and helping to maintain the power of the establishment.

T77.4   The claim that you *must* train to failure in order to progress in strength and size is false. *There are some very strong and well developed trainees who've never trained to total failure.* Some people believe that you can't train too hard. The notion that you can't train too hard has been at the root of much frustration and failure.

T77.5   In my youth I was a real believer in "you can't train too hard." It seemed so logical, like its leading proponents appeared to be. I "lived" it for a period of years, yet made no progress despite genuinely being the hardest trainer at the gyms where I worked out. The factors of recovery were not given enough importance by the "you can't train too hard" school, training days were too frequent, volume was too high, and intensity enhancing techniques were abused. I wasn't in a minority of one in getting nowhere on this sort of training. Countless others suffered in exactly the same way.

T77.6   Proponents of the "you can't train too hard" philosophy, or at least their leading examples of its "correctness," were drug-fed genetic standouts. So we were still at square one, with training methods for drug-fed genetically blessed people being promoted as appropriate for the typical masses. While the methods were radically different to those of Schwarzenegger's, and a step in the right direction, the actual result was little or no improvement for the training masses.

T77.7   A number of interpretations of abbreviated training work. No single one is "best." Some are better and more practical for some people than others. Some are of higher risk than others. But all can work at least for some people for some of the time. You don't have to have the "very best" training method in order to make good gains. The search for the "very best" method usually leads to a lot of wasted training time. Find something that works for you, is safe, and that you can stick with, and then keep at it for a good few years. Then you'll realize your potential for muscle and might.

T77.8   The bottom line isn't the "camp" you're in, or how well you can quote actual or pseudo science, *but whether or not you're progressing*. If you're getting stronger on a regular basis while using consistently good form, your training is working, and there's no need to make changes. *Progress is the name of the game.*

T77.9   Very importantly, and as I've pointed out many times, keep in mind that if you're not progressing, it may not be your training that's at fault, but insufficient attention to all the components of recovery. No changes to your training—including jumping to another "camp" or strand—are going to make much if any difference if you're cutting corners with your dietary, resting or sleeping habits. If your recovery "machinery" is out of whack, your training will be out of whack too, no matter which or whose interpretation of training you use. Most people too quickly assume that lack of progress is due to their training being at fault.

T77.10   If you're training hard on an abbreviated program dominated by the big exercises, working out no more than twice a week while hitting most exercises only once a week each, and are using consistently good form, then your training should be adequate to deliver at least some progress (poundage on the bar) on a regular basis *providing you deliver on the recovery front* (and assuming you want to get bigger and stronger). It may not be the best progress you can make, because your training program probably could be improved, but your program should still produce some progress.

T77.11   *However, if you know you're slacking in the effort department, give more importance to the little exercises than the big ones, never strive to add poundage to the bar, take liberties with exercise form, or treat the gym as more of a social club than a place of serious work, then you're seriously missing the boat in the gym, and no degree of attention to the elements of recovery will make that pseudo training work. Be totally honest with yourself, and ask searching questions about your performance in the gym.*

T77.12   Even if you've a perfectly designed training program, and have fully attended to all the recovery factors, if you don't have the ferocious passion to train hard in a disciplined way—using consistently perfect form—then all the "perfect" program design and satisfaction of the components of recovery will be wasted. Successful bodybuilding and strength training is the result of getting the *whole* package in good order.

T77.13   Finally, a note on the concept of training one or two reps short of failure. I've referred to this concept in BEYOND BRAWN, as one of the intensity options. There's a big risk, however, in recommending training one or two reps short of failure because some people may think they are training to failure when they are actually already stopping one or two reps short. If they cut another rep or two off, they will be several short of failure. No way will that stimulate growth. Be honest with yourself. One or two reps short of failure means just that, not three, four or five reps short, which would make a mockery of hard training.

TRAINING 78
I think I know what to do in order to realize my bodybuilding potential, but doing it is something else. I'm so busy at work, and then my family are so demanding when I'm at home. So delivering consistently on the training and related factors is so very difficult. Do you have any tips to help?

T78.1   When my passion for training was at its most rabid—in my youth—I had the time and leisure on my hands to deliver fully on the rest and sleep fronts, and never skipped any scheduled feeds. But because I didn't know how to channel my training zest and commitment, all the dedication and discipline out of the gym, and the misdirected effort in it, amounted to little.

T78.2   Later in life, once I had the knowledge of how to train, I was so overworked by the rigors of publishing HARDGAINER, running CS Publishing and writing books, along with the demands of being a family man with two young children, that I wasn't able to deliver consistently on the recovery front. That during this latter stage I would go long periods with little or no progress is purely a result of my not delivering on the recovery front consistently enough, because I was training well enough.

T78.3   The same applies uncompromisingly to all hard gainers—if you don't deliver both in *and* out of the gym, you'll get little or nothing from your training. This reality doesn't apply as severely to easy gainers, because the latter can take liberties in and out of the gym, and yet still make some progress though not their fastest. Relative to easy gainers, hard gainers have far less leeway for corner cutting on the rules of training and recovery.

T78.4   Life can be very demanding. During our most responsive and youthful training years we rarely have the know-how to make the most of youth. Just like when we're young, we usually don't have the money or sense to make the most of youth. Then when later in life we have the money and sense, we may no longer have the body or spirit to make the most of the money and sense. Youth is wasted on the young!

T78.5   Whenever you think that delivering on *the package* for bodybuilding and strength training is tough going—which it certainly is if you're very busy, and have major family commitments too—remind yourself that having the good fortune to be able to dedicate yourself to training, and everything that should go with it, *is a privilege*. Eventually you won't be able to train hard, or dedicate yourself to anything, so make the most of the going while it's good—no slacking, no corner cutting, and no excuses. Get to work and make the most of your wonderful but not infinite opportunity to train and achieve physical improvement.

T78.6   There's no easy way to build a terrific physique. It demands know-how together with the extraordinary discipline to put the know-how into concerted, diligent and consistent practice. The more demanding your life, the more determined you need to be to find the time to train, and the time to attend to all the related components of recovery. One of the biggest advantages of abbreviated training is that it's a practical way to train for busy people, because its time demands are so much less than those of conventional training.

T78.7   In your case I'd urge you to super abbreviate your training program—two or *at most* three exercises per workout (big movements, of course). Alternate two different workouts, training at most only twice a week and probably better only once every five days or so. And regardless of your lifestyle, if you want to progress in muscle and might, you still have to deliver on the eating and sleeping fronts.

TRAINING 79
Do you think that the regular bent-legged deadlift is superior to the stiff-legged deadlift?

T79.1   Depends on which bent-legged deadlift you're referring to, whether or not you're squatting, and you as an individual.

T79.2   If you're squatting, the regular deadlift with a straight bar is, in some ways, redundant, because of the heavy degree of overlap. (The trap bar or shrug bar deadlift has even greater overlap.) The stiff-legged deadlift provides more work for the hamstrings than does the regular deadlift, and perhaps more lower back work too, but while still working the upper back and traps hard. So the stiff-legged deadlift may make a better complementary exercise for the squat than the regular deadlift. If, however, you find the regular deadlift safer, then that's sufficient reason to use that movement rather than the stiff-legged deadlift. However, if you reduced the range of motion of the stiff-legged deadlift by a few inches, and converted to more of a Romanian deadlift (with no pauses at the bottom of the movement), you may find the stiff-legged deadlift to be safer.

T79.3   If you trap bar or shrug bar deadlift, you're actually doing more of a "squatlift" than a deadlift, and increasing the stress on your lower body and taking some of it off your back. If you're trap bar or shrug bar deadlifting, the squat is largely redundant, and a better compliment would be the stiff-legged deadlift *or* straight bar deadlift, in order to fully work the back musculature too.

TRAINING 80
Please give us some guidelines on using negative chins and dips as part of an abbreviated training routine. I've been using negative chins. They seem to have helped my regular chins considerably. Is there a limit to using them?

T80.1   The bottom line, as always, is progress. If you're making progress, and are not taking any form liberties or pushing your luck, then keep at what you're doing. Negatives are very demanding, and it's easy to overtrain on them. And in some movements, it's easy to lose control of the exercise and get hurt. Dips are likely to have a greater potential for loss of control than chins. An alert spotter is recommended to "catch" you if you lose control. Set the exercise up in such as way that you have depth predetermined (like described in my book on form), so you can't go too deep even if you lose control. To play safe, end a set of negatives as soon as a negative takes less than 3–4 seconds to perform.

T80.2   One set of negative dips and chins, once every 2 or 3 weeks, or for several consecutive weeks and then have an "off" period, may be a good general way to proceed, but you need to juggle with the variables yourself. If what you're doing isn't working, then you have to change something. But what you're doing in the gym may be fine. If, as I've noted many times, you're cutting corners with your nutrition, rest, sleep and recovery "machinery," then that will kill any progress from even a "perfect" training program.

TRAINING 81
I don't perform the bench press with a barbell because of shoulder issues. I use dumbbells instead. What dumbbell weight would be equivalent to a 300-pound bench press with a barbell?

T81.1   A 240–255 pounds total for the pair of dumbbells is an approximation for a 300-pound barbell bench press. Here's the relevant quote from BEYOND BRAWN:

T81.2   "The combined weight of two dumbbells is usually less than can be used in the same movement done with a barbell. The total used in bench pressing or overhead pressing with dumbbells will, typically, be about 80–85% of what can be moved in a barbell in those two exercises. This assumes familiarity with using the dumbbells. Until you're familiar with the tricky balance of using a pair of dumbbells, it's unlikely you'll be able to handle 80% of your barbell weight. This dumbbells-versus-barbell comparison applies to exercises where two dumbbells are used simultaneously. It does not apply to exercises where one side is done at a time, e.g., dumbbell row."

TRAINING 82
How radical do I need to be when designing my training program?

T82.1   As radical as you need to get the job done. Some hard gainers need to be more radical than others. Set about finding what *you* need, in a logical way. Start by getting all the components of recovery in *100% perfect order.* Only *then* should you tinker with your training. For example, start with eight exercises divided over two routines, alternating the two schedules over two weekly workouts. If that doesn't produce steady gains, prune back to just two or three exercises (big ones) per workout. If that doesn't start gains moving, decrease training frequency—move to alternating the two different workouts on a Monday, Friday, Wednesday, Monday...rota.

T82.2   Unless you're truly an extraordinary case, you're going to
        start making good gains somewhere along that progression,
        assuming you really are sleeping well every night, really are
        consuming a caloric and nutrient surplus every day, and really are
        training hard on just a few of the biggest and best exercises. You
        may want to experiment with a once-a-week *single* workout
        of only three or four big exercises. Not only that, but *perhaps*
        you may need *even less frequent* training, which takes me to
        the next question...

TRAINING 83
What about people who train each exercise only once every two weeks, or even less frequently?

T83.1   A few people have reported improved gains from training each
        exercise only once every two or three weeks. This is very radical
        thinking other than in the deadlift where once-a-fortnight
        training is not heretical. Individual variation can be considerable.

T83.2   That very few people have reported improved or at least not
        reduced gains from reducing their training frequency so
        radically, can have at least two explanations. First, few people
        have the interest or "courage" to try such a radical approach,
        and thus very few people will ever know whether or not this can
        help them. Second, perhaps out of the few who've tried it, most
        didn't get improved gains. But that may not necessarily be a
        reflection on the actual training frequency per se, but the degree
        of commitment put into the training. At least some of those who
        try such a radical approach may not really have their hearts into
        hard training, so are never going to make much if any progress
        on any type of program. Most people who have real training
        zeal will want to train more often, and thus are highly unlikely
        to try something very radical.

T83.3   There's a danger in suggesting the possibility of benefits from
        very infrequent training. It could encourage such a laid back
        attitude that the commitment to training and the components
        of recovery, and progressive poundages, are not delivered upon.

T83.4   I always assume I'm reaching really determined and committed
        trainees. If I suggest trying really radical approaches, that *doesn't*
        mean I'm encouraging a casual approach. *Far from it.* I'm into
        results. If you have to use a very radical training frequency in
        order to achieve results, or *improved* results, do it.

T83.5 If you're not gaining much if at all from the "standard" radical approaches of abbreviated training, then try the super radical. You've nothing to lose from an experiment for two or three months. Train each big exercise in your program just once every two weeks, and see if that enables you to add more poundage to the bar than you would from your usual frequency. If it does, you've found something *to help you.*

T83.6 If, for example, you can only add your usual pound to the squat bar every two weeks as against once a week, you're going to progress faster on the more frequent squatting schedule. If you find it harder to add a pound to the bar every two weeks than once a week, you're better off on the latter. If you can add a couple of pounds every two weeks, you'd be making the same progress as you would at a pound a week, but with less training. If you can add more than a couple of pounds to the squat bar every two weeks, then you're going to make faster progress on the less frequent squatting. But what might be good for your deadlift and squat, for example, may be bad for your dip, chin and press.

T83.7 That a given frequency of training is good for one trainee doesn't mean that it will be good for another. Individual variation is considerable in terms of how the factors of recovery are met, the level of effort in the gym, and individual tolerance of exercise, etc. What matters is how *you* respond to a given protocol.

T83.8 *At least some if not most of those who've benefited from a super radical training frequency would have progressed on a more frequent schedule had they paid much greater attention to their nutrition, ate more, and got more rest and sleep each day.*

TRAINING 84
Is changing rep ranges necessary for continued gains in size and strength, or do you recommend changing them every cycle purely for sake of preventing boredom?

T84.1 Changing rep ranges is not necessary; but from cycle to cycle, rep range changes can be a good idea for many people, to help provide the variety that helps maintain enthusiasm. But be sure you change to a rep count that works for you, or otherwise it would be a wasted change. The variety should help your progress, not just provide a change for the sake of change. If you prosper much better on one rep range than others, for a given exercise, it wouldn't make much sense to change at all. Successful training is the best antidote to boredom in the gym. Even if you always do sets of 5 reps in the bench press, for example, if you keep getting stronger, that's what really matters. I doubt you'd be bored if, over the next year or two, you were able to steadily but relentlessly build up to bench pressing an additional 100 pounds, while never deviating from sets of 5 reps.

TRAINING 85
Recently the parallel bar dip increased my stalled bench press by 10 pounds. I got frustrated at my bench not increasing (stalled for a month) that I switched to dips. I did five weeks of dips building up to the point I was at maximum effort. Then, through impulse one workout, I decided to bench. I did 10 pounds over my personal best with some to spare. This was without benching for five weeks.

In your opinion can one achieve better results by alternating cycles of dips and benches than doing cycle after cycle of benches?

T85.1   You took quite a risk to go for a personal best in your bench press after having not benched for five weeks. That's the sort of thing that often causes injury.

T85.2   Try alternating cycles of benches and dips, and see whether that works well for you. Both the bench press and dip are very good exercises, if performed with good form. Both can produce terrific results. You may find one is more suited to you than the other. If so, it would make sense to exploit the advantage you have.

TRAINING 86
I read somewhere that Bob Peoples used to alternate squats and deadlifts. When he used to get stale in one he switched to the other. Does this mean that for people for whom alternating works well for progression, they should go for it?

T86.1   Bob Peoples was a stupendous deadlifter, though his humped-back style is totally off limits for regular mortals. Peoples deadlifted 725 pounds at a bodyweight of just 189 pounds, in 1949.

T86.2 I'm all for doing what works for you. If you're going to alternate the squat and deadlift, the latter needs heavy thigh involvement or otherwise your leg strength may back track significantly while you focus on the deadlift. If you deadlift with either the trap bar or shrug bar, you'll get lots of thigh involvement, and will be alternating similar exercises, as the trap bar or shrug bar deadlift is far more similar to the squat than is the straight bar deadlift.

TRAINING 87
Why are seated or standing overhead dumbbell or barbell presses in the "big movement" grouping with squats, deadlifts, dips, etc? I don't see how working such a small grouping of muscles would stimulate the same growth as squatting.

T87.1 Any overhead press can't compare with intensive squatting when comparing total muscular involvement and growth potential. But behind the really big exercises—e.g., squat and bent-legged deadlift—comes the next tier of major exercises, which includes overhead press variations, along with the dip, bench press and chin, as examples. The overhead press is included in the big movement grouping to distinguish it from the isolation movement grouping—laterals, for example.

TRAINING 88
Is progression without training to failure good, and can I keep it that way? When I train I usually progress with about 0.25–0.5 kilo on the bar. But I'm worried that I'm not training hard enough. I never take a set to failure, but maybe one rep before. My progression is still going fine, but is going to failure needed to grow? If I push myself harder and raise the intensity, would progress come easier or greater? Would that be beneficial in the long run?

T88.1 That you're making progress without training to failure is proof that going to failure isn't necessary for progress. However, perhaps going to failure may enable you to progress at a *faster* rate. Or, perhaps pushing it harder may not increase progress. Or, perhaps pushing harder may slow progress. I don't know. These are matters only *you* can discover *for your particular case.*

T88.2 What you describe as one rep short of failure may actually be as hard as what some people describe as going all the way. Or perhaps what you describe as one rep short of failure is actually 2 or 3 reps of real failure. I don't know because I can't witness your training.

T88.3   You need to try different things, within reason, one at a time. If something helps, keep it. If something hinders progress, drop it. But don't worry if you're actually making progress. Start worrying when you're *not* making progress, and then take action to make changes so that you get progressing again.

TRAINING 89
I help a female trainee, 33 years old, who's extremely lean. She has been training in my home gym for the past three months. She works the complete body with ten exercises, three times a week, one set and 8–10 reps. She would like to have defined muscle with no increase in her present size. What protocol would you suggest?

T89.1   If she's extremely lean, she shouldn't try to get leaner still, as there could be health implications. As she's very lean, she should already have defined muscle, assuming there's enough there to see. If there's very little muscle, she needs to build some muscle. But if she doesn't want to increase her present size, then she's stuck—because she doesn't have any bodyfat to lose to allow for muscular growth without overall size increase.

T89.2   I'd suggest you convince her that 8–10 pounds of muscle evenly spread over her body, at her current bodyfat percentage, would enhance her appearance—giving her fuller muscles at the same degree of definition.

T89.3   To get that extra size, I'd urge her to train less. Training her whole body three times a week is going to keep her stuck where she is. Drop to just twice a week and see how that goes. If she starts growing, stick with it. If she's still stuck, spread the ten exercises over two workouts, and alternate workouts while still training twice a week, thus hitting each exercise just once a week. She'll need to increase her caloric and protein intake a tad in order to provide the raw materials for growth.

TRAINING 90
I prefer to do one set of the flat bench to failure and one set of the incline to failure. Also, I prefer to

do one set of chins to failure and one set of rows to failure. Is it better to do two sets of flat bench and two sets of chins to failure, and forget the inclines and rows? If so, why?

T90.1   It's good to use all four exercises, but not necessarily in the same program, in order to produce more balanced musculature. The issue is how best to use the four different exercises. The only way to really know is to try the options, and compare the results. After a cycle of rows *and* chins, and benches *and* inclines, perform a cycle with just one of each of the pairings. If you find that your poundages move upward better on the latter, then you're probably better off with just one of each pairing each cycle. You could then alternate which you use at successive cycles.

T90.2   But if you find you can progress simultaneously in both of each pair as well as you can when they are done separately (in different cycles), then keep them all in at the same time, as you're doing now.

TRAINING 91
You advocate cycling your workouts: starting at a lower intensity and slowly building the intensity to maximum; then maintaining that high intensity workout for as long as gains keep coming. When gains stop, you recommend taking a short layoff and then starting another cycle similar to the previous one (except possibly for slight variations in rep schemes or exercises).

Why not just increase your breaks between workouts as gains begin to slow down? Why cycle at all? If you stop gaining it means that you're not giving your muscles enough time to recover, so why not simply increase the recovery time between workouts to keep the gains coming? By following this scheme you might go from lifting once every 3 days to once every 4 days, every 5 days, etc. Since you're getting more time to recover, it seems as though gains shouldn't stop (unless one's diet or sleeping habits are unsound), and you would need to work out less, which would be more efficient. And you would never have to halt your gains by starting

a new cycle. If desired, new exercises could be substituted from time to time in your workout, but you would never end your cycle (if you could even call it a cycle at this point).

Just curious what your thoughts are.

T91.1   In BRAWN I advocated structured cycles. One of the changes to my views on training over the years since writing BRAWN—which I reflect on in the second edition of BRAWN, and go into great detail on in BEYOND BRAWN—is that generally speaking I no longer advocate such structured programs and layoffs. This is *not*, however, to say that that approach doesn't work any longer. It's just that I now prefer to recommend cycles with no predetermined end points.

T91.2   I'm all for adjusting training frequency and the components of recovery in order to extend gains for very long periods—to milk the cycle dry. "Natural" cycling of intensity still occurs, however. Due to the ups and downs and changes of life there are times when you have to ease back or change exercises. Then you need to take it relatively easily for a few weeks while you increase the weights and intensity, before pushing into new poundage territory again.

T91.3   Some of my earlier views on training are outlined in your first paragraph. My later views—explained in BEYOND BRAWN—are reflected in your second paragraph.

TRAINING 92
What advice could you give someone who wants to lose fat and trim down? I work a full-time job, and I'm also a full-time student, with a small child at home to boot. Most nights I only manage five hours of sleep. I know the importance of rest in an exercise program, so that leaves me Saturday and Sunday to train, with maybe Monday morning since I know I can get a good rest on Sunday night. In nine months I've gained 20 pounds of fat! I've trained on and off for over 15 years (I'm 42). I suspect a two-day split is where you'll steer me. I own a good treadmill, so walking is a definite possibility. It's just the rest and recovery issue that has me frustrated. Any ideas?

T92.1 A major mistake most people make when starting or restarting an exercise program is doing too much too soon. This especially applies to very busy people. In your case I suggest you weight train just once a week, and walk on your treadmill twice a week. Get that embedded in your weekly routine, and working, and *then* (later on) you could consider doing a bit more. But do too much—either now or later on—and you'll quickly give up.

T92.2 Cut back your diet so that you're in a *slight* caloric deficit, and be patient to accept a *slow* but gradual weight loss. Fast weight loss involves muscle loss as well as fat loss. A slow loss is far more likely to be fat only. I'd suggest you weight train on Sunday, with just three big movements (e.g., squat, bench press and deadlift, or squat, dip and chin) and two small movements—calf raise and ab work. Do warmups plus two work sets per exercise, use impeccable form, and add a little weight every week to the big exercises.

T92.3 Get on your treadmill on Tuesdays and Fridays. Start with just 10 minutes, and add a minute a week. Build to 30–40 minutes twice a week, at an intensity that keeps you *slightly* breathless. Over time you should be able to *gradually* pick up the effort level while maintaining the *same* perceived level of work. Once you're at the 30–40 minutes twice-a-week mark, I suggest you move to harder but shorter aerobics workouts as described in T64, to take your cardiovascular fitness to a higher level. At that stage, maintain some recreational walking two or three times each week for burning calories, to enable you to consume more calories without getting fat.

T92.4 If you stick to this very abbreviated program for a year, with unrelenting consistency, you'd greatly increase your strength, trim fat, and substantially improve your cardiovascular conditioning *despite* your recovery "machinery" being deficient. You'll need to get more sleep in order to keep progressing, but at your current near-novice stage you can probably go a fair way even as you are, though your rate of progress is going to be impaired by deficient recovery "machinery."

T92.5 It's not just your training and physique progress that are compromised when you shortchange yourself of sleep. Your health is harmed too, along with your working and studying efficiency. The sooner you take corrective measures, the better.

TRAINING 93
I know you generally advocate that hard gainers train only twice a week. But it's hard for me to train all of my body in only two workouts a week without really wearing myself out. Right now I'm lifting three days a week as follows: bench press, shoulder press and dip one workout; lat pulldown, barbell curl and ab crunches another workout; and squat, stiff-legged deadlift and standing calf raise another workout. Given that program, is the three-days-a-week frequency still too much?

T93.1   Whether or not it's too much for you will be shown in the results. If you're progressing steadily, you're doing fine. If you're stuck, all is not well. I'm assuming, however, that all is very well on the critically important recovery front. If you're cutting corners with your sleep and diet, and/or running yourself ragged during the day, you'll reduce if not kill your progress. But if all *is* very well on the recovery front, your progress (or otherwise) will be all down to your training.

T93.2   If dividing your nine exercises up over two workouts slows your progress relative to dividing them up over three workouts, you should stick with the latter. Results are what count most. Generally speaking, two abbreviated weight-training workouts a week and five off days produce better recovery for typical trainees than three abbreviated weights workouts and four off days. But I can't argue against good results. So if three abbreviated sessions work better for you than two slightly longer (but still abbreviated) workouts, go with the former. But perhaps two different workouts per week of just three exercises each might work even better.

TRAINING 94
My left arm is naturally smaller and weaker than my right. And my pecs differ greatly, my left being larger. What do I do?

T94.1   I suggest you use dumbbells for your chest, shoulder, arm and back work, but your weights should be determined by your weaker side. So, for example, if you can only use say a 50-pound dumbbell in your left hand in the dumbbell bench press, but could handle 65 pounds in your right hand, you must only use a 50-pound dumbbell in both hands, and perform that same rep and set count for each side. Your stronger side will go along for the ride, so to speak, to begin with. You should stick with this until your weaker side has caught up with your stronger side. Then both sides can move into new poundage territory, though you'll likely always find that your naturally stronger side will progress more easily than the other side. It could take a year or longer to even out the strength imbalance.

TRAINING 95
I've been using an abbreviated training routine twice a week for three months. My chest is 2 inches larger, my thighs 1 inch larger and my abs 2 inches smaller. I'm generally stronger than before, but my calves have shrunk an inch. Am I doing something wrong so that my calves are shrinking? Do I need to do complementary exercises just for the calves?

T95.1   Other than perhaps short-term use for special cases, calf work should always be part of an abbreviated training program; otherwise most people will end up with lagging calf development. Experiment with training your calves once a week and twice a week—say two months of each, comparing the same volume and intensity of work per session—and see which works best for you.

TRAINING 96
I love conventional deadlifts (not stiff-legged deadlifts), and I love squats. Would it be harmful or overtraining to do them both at the same workout?

T96.1   The bottom line is what works for you. If you steadily and relentlessly increase your poundages on both movements, you're not overtraining. If you get "stuck" on one or both, something is amiss and you may be overtraining. Assuming you're really eating, resting and sleeping well (and *not* cutting any corners whatsoever), you'd need to make adjustments to what you're doing in the gym, to get progress happening again. Then you should experiment with volume and frequency of training, and how you divide your exercises over the two workouts, to find what works best for you.

T96.2   As a general recommendation I'd advise squatting and deadlifting on the same day as there's a lot of overlap between the two movements. If they are trained on different days each week, your lower back in particular may not get enough rest, and perhaps your knees and quads too.

TRAINING 97
I'm 34 years old and have trained with weights for approximately 10 years. I've spent the majority of my workouts doing upper body exercises and now look disproportionate. Additionally, I've historically had a hard time gaining mass on my lower body. I'm looking to put substantial inches on my legs and glutes. What would you recommend?

T97.1 Even if you have a natural greater responsiveness to upper-body work, by neglecting your lower body you're not giving yourself even a half decent chance to build good legs. Not only that, but by neglecting your lower body you're also limiting your upper-body development. Especially for hard gainers, lower-body work (of the right sort) is a "driver" that puts an increased gaining momentum into upper-body work.

T97.2 What would I suggest? Squats and stiff-legged deadlifts, or trap bar/shrug bar deadlifts (which are really squats with the bar in your hands) and stiff-legged deadlifts. Whether you use squats or trap bar/shrug bar deadlifts should be determined by your structure. While most people can squat well enough to gain well from it, there's a substantial proportion of people who will do much better from trap bar/shrug bar deadlifts.

T97.3 Either way, you must use impeccable form. These are major exercises, and form is no simple matter. I've covered the form of these major exercises in extensive detail in my technique book.

T97.4 I'd suggest you squat or trap bar/shrug bar deadlift once a week, and stiff-legged deadlift once a week too. I suggest you do them at the same workout, to give your lower back a full week of rest between "hits." But while you're "breaking into" the exercises, assuming that you're new to them, you may train them twice a week each. Once you've built up the poundages sufficiently so that the weights no longer feel light, then you may move to once-a-week training on them.

T97.5 *Very importantly*, you must not add weight in too large increments. Start out with a weight you could perform more than twice your target reps with, if you really pushed, and add just 5 pounds a week. When the weight becomes challenging, and you could do no more than 3 or 4 extra reps above your target count if you pushed *very hard*, drop the weight increment to a pound a week, and then keep adding that pound a week for a couple of years. Then you'll have greatly improved legs and glutes.

T97.6   I'd suggest you perform warmups plus two work sets for each exercise, of about 8 reps for the stiff-legged deadlift, and 10–12 for the squat. But you choose the rep count that best suits you. After at least six months of adapting to the squat you may want to move to the 20-rep variety.

T97.7   Include calf work too. Perform a warmup set plus 2 or 3 work sets twice a week for a few months, then later on experiment with just once a week, and then three times every *two* weeks— i.e., once every four or five days—and see which helps the most to build size and strength on your calves.

TRAINING 98
What would you recommend for an individual who hasn't weight trained for about eighteen months? A two-days-per-week full-body routine working each exercise twice weekly, or a two-days-per-week routine that works each exercise once weekly?

T98.1   I'd suggest the former, for three months or so. As long as you increase your poundages gradually from a very comfortable start (which is the safest and best way to go), three months or so of training should take you to the point at which you start moving weights that are very challenging though not your current *very* best. *Then* move to the two-days-a-week program, but divide your exercises over the two workouts so that each movement is trained only once a week. See how that goes for at least three months.

T98.2   More important than this particular concern are learning and applying perfect form, selecting exercises that are best for you, not getting injured, and using a poundage progression scheme that will keep a steady gaining momentum going for at least a couple of years. To do all of this you need to apply sensible training methods that have been fine-tuned to your individual situation, be disciplined to do what's right at every workout, eat right every day, and sleep well every night too. Successful training arises from a package of factors, with what you do in the gym only a part of that package, albeit a very important part.

TRAINING 99
I currently squat 1 x 20 and follow this with 1 x 10 of stiff-legged deadlift in my first workout, and then deadlift 2 x 8 at my second workout. Would you suggest I drop the deadlift to once every other week?

T99.1 What matters most is what works best for you. If you can gain well on what you're doing, by all means stick with it. But you may make the same gains with a lesser frequency of deadlifting, so an experiment may be worthwhile.

T99.2 Stiff-legged deadlifting *and* deadlifting, every week, is a rigorous schedule assuming you're training hard on each of them. If you find gains tough, are starting to drag your feet and lose your zest for training, and your lower back aches on several days a week, you're overtraining, and a back injury along with training stagnation are around the corner. In such a case I'd suggest you stiff-legged deadlift one week and deadlift the next. Alternate them, with only one form of deadlifting being done in any given week.

TRAINING 100
My training was going real well, perhaps the best ever. Then I developed an elbow problem that forced me to stop chinning. I haven't had an accident, and the only change to my training was the addition of wrist curls a few weeks ago. What did I do wrong?

T100.1 Based on the little information you've given me, there's a good chance that the wrist curls irritated your elbows in some way, which in turn messed up your chinning ability. If so, it's a real shame that a minor if not insignificant exercise "killed" your progress in a major one. Now you'll have to recover, which might take a few weeks; then you'll need a while to rebuild your chinning poundage and regain your gaining momentum.

T100.2 Isolation arm work can easily irritate elbows or wrists, and then one or more of your major exercises will get messed up. If you're going to add isolation arm work to your program, at least do it in a conservative way. Start very light, make sure the exercise(s) and form are suited to you, and at the earliest sign that progress in a major exercise is being compromised, modify or drop the isolation work pronto *before* it ruins your progress elsewhere.

T100.3 *When something is going well, tinker with it at your peril!*

TRAINING 101
After heavy 20-rep squatting, my heart rate is very high. Does this have the same effect on my cardio system that hard aerobic work would?

T101.1 No. The high heart rate from heavy weight training doesn't produce the oxygen consumption that the same heart rate would if produced by cardio work. Heart rate alone isn't the key. The way in which it's produced is critical. A big fright will produce a high heart rate, but that's not going to improve your cardio system.

In a nutshell...

If you design and implement a good program you can make consistent gains from it for over a year, without any changes other than putting more iron on the bar on a regular basis. *Gains are what matter, not how many different routines you clock up in your training career.*

Chopping and changing routines is usually symptomatic of serious errors in program design, effort level, progression scheme, rest and sleep schedules, and/or nutrition. Chopping and changing routines can also be a sign of lack of faith in good training methods—even good methods need to be married with patience in order to yield good results.

Playing around with sets and reps, exercise order, between-sets rest periods, etc., while not addressing the major faults (such as in exercise selection, effort, form, sleep and nutrition), will never make an unproductive program productive.

If you're training with genuine effort and good form, focusing on a few big compound exercises *that suit you*, resting well between workouts, sleeping at least eight hours a night, and consuming six meals/feeds a day that keep you in caloric and protein surplus, *you're doing what's needed.*

The precise order of exercises, and numbers of sets and reps, for example, are secondary. Many abbreviated programs work. Choose one, fine-tune it to suit you, and then hammer away at it for a long time. With effort, good form and a big-exercises focus, and rest, sleep and nutrition in good order, progress will happen *if you're patient*. Keep adding iron to the bar, and you'll grow.

It's usually necessary to get A LOT stronger in order to build MUCH bigger muscles. Generally speaking, you need around a 25% increase in strength (while maintaining impeccable form) for a noticeable boost in muscular mass, and a 50% or so increase in strength for a substantial boost in mass. If you're a beginner, a 25% increase may not make much difference to your size. To make substantial gains in muscular size, beginners may need to DOUBLE their strength AS A MINIMUM, with a trebling of strength being more of a benchmark for something special.

These percentages are generalized and relative to your current level of development; but they clearly show you the way to go—GET STRONGER. Some people need to get a lot stronger than others, to produce the same degree of muscular development.

Exercise Form and Selection

EXERCISE FORM AND SELECTION 1
I've seen some very well-developed bodybuilders performing a few of the exercises and specific techniques you say I shouldn't. Don't you think you might be overdoing your cautions?

FS1.1   Please remember that the really well-developed bodybuilders are not typical people. They have super responsive bodies, most of them (today) are drug enhanced, and they have joints much tougher than most people's. So they can tolerate a level of abuse that you and I can't. Don't imitate such people. But if you do, you'll suffer like many people have over the years, including me, and injuries and possibly long-term joint problems will be your reward.

FS1.2   The mainstream of the training world has been negligent in playing down if not ignoring the potential harm that arises for many people from using high-risk exercises and specific techniques. In years long gone by, largely because of the lack of caution and caveats provided by the mainstream press, I didn't give anywhere near enough attention to the use of minimum-risk exercises, perfect form and a controlled rep cadence. As a result I paid a heavy price, just as millions of other trainees have.

FS1.3   But you don't read much if anything about dissatisfied trainees in the mainstream muscle magazines. There's a great deal that the mainstream neglects to report on in an accurate way, and as a result it portrays a very distorted view of the reality of the training world.

FS1.4   I strongly urge you not to repeat the mistakes I've made, and millions of others, in the hope that *perhaps* you're sufficiently tough and resistant to injury that you'll not pay the same price.

EXERCISE FORM AND SELECTION 2
Some people urge me to squat with my heels on a board or plate, bench press with a very wide grip, and curl with a close grip. Why shouldn't I heed their advice?

FS2.1   Those three specific techniques (and many other high-risk ones) are part and parcel of bodybuilding folklore. While a minority of bodybuilders can use those three techniques without apparent harm, most trainees can't. Most people suffer knee, shoulder and elbow problems respectively—and sooner rather than later.

FS2.2   Don't take any liberties with exercise form. Always use conservative form, and avoid extremes. Extremes push your body to or beyond its limit. *"Very wide," "very close"* and *"fullest possible range of motion" are dangerous dictums.*

EXERCISE FORM AND SELECTION 3
I've noticed that even the big guys usually have lots of aches and pains, are always complaining about one thing or another, and use liniment, wraps and belts. And they keep telling me that there's no gain without pain. Is this correct?

FS3.1   The "no pain, no gain" lie is at the root of much training misery and frustration. If you suffer pain, something is seriously amiss. Keep pushing through pain and you'll end your days of hard training.

FS3.2   There's a great deal of macho bravado in the bodybuilding and lifting worlds. Intelligent bodybuilding and lifting are about long-term training. To train successfully over the long-term, you have to train safely. This means avoiding pain. Of course you have to be able to withstand the healthy discomfort of training, and push out reps when your muscles are screaming for you to stop. That's not the same as pushing through pain. Battling through discomfort from tired and congested muscles is good and desirable. Pushing through aches and pains is madness.

EXERCISE FORM AND SELECTION 4
How long do you hold your breath for during the Rader chest pull? I don't recall it being covered in your previous books.

FS4.1   Hold your breath for as long as comfortable, and throughout the entire time you should be able to feel the "pull" and slight discomfort in your sternum. If you don't feel this, you're not doing the exercise properly. Don't, however, hold your breath until you're almost ready to burst, because you need to be able to perform up to 20 reps or so for a single set. How long you can comfortably hold your breath for will depend on the state of your breathing prior to performing the chest pull (primarily whether or not you squatted prior to the chest pulls), and your general conditioning. With practice, over time, you'll be able to hold each pull for a longer time, for a comparable level of discomfort. I'd say that somewhere in the range of 4–8 seconds per pull will be fine.

FS4.2   As I noted in my exercise technique book, go easy to begin with, especially if you're not performing the Rader chest pull while winded from a heavy leg exercise. The forced and exaggerated breathing will probably make you feel dizzy unless you work into it over a period of a few weeks. Your chest may get excessively sore, too, if you don't work into the movement gradually.

FS4.3   To finish on a very encouraging note, in his article on the "Rader chest expander" in IRON MAN November-December 1951, Peary Rader had this to say: "Our enthusiasm prompts us to say that it is the best chest exercise yet discovered..."

EXERCISE FORM AND SELECTION 5
I've been told I need to do hack squats to develop my quads immediately above my knees. Is the hack squat safe?

FS5.1   Hack squats throw exaggerated stress on the knees, and can produce a lot of soreness in the lower thighs. This has made many people believe that this is good, because they think it will build up the lower thigh without adding size to the upper thigh. Putting exaggerated stress on any joint is *very bad*. Even if the hack squat did develop the lower quads without adding size to the upper thigh (which it can't, actually), there's a heavy price to pay sooner or later—knee problems. Once you have knee problems you won't be able to do any heavy work for your quads; so whatever size you have there, you're going to start losing it once you have knee problems. The priority is training your quads *without* damaging your knees. The hack squat is a hostile exercise. Don't use it.

FS5.2   Some extraordinary hardy bodybuilders perform the hack squat with their heels elevated. And some do it up on their toes, to get their knees as far forward as possible in the bottom position. That variation is a 100% guaranteed knee wrecker for most people. But even the usual hack machine squat is guaranteed to harm the knees of most people, *eventually*. Don't push your luck. Avoid high-risk exercises such as the hack squat.

EXERCISE FORM AND SELECTION 6
I've been told that Smith machine squats are much safer than regular barbell squats. Are they?

FS6.1   Smith machine squats give an *illusion* of safety relative to the barbell squat. With the Smith machine the bar is locked into a fixed pathway so you don't have to be concerned with balance; and you don't have to take a barbell from stands, step back to perform your set, and step forward at the end of a set in order to return the bar to the stands. But when you look further into the Smith machine squat, there are hidden perils.

FS6.2   The Smith machine forces you to follow the bar path dictated by the machine, *but the path of the bar should be dictated by the body.*

FS6.3   If you put your feet forward a bit, in order to prevent your knees travelling in front of your feet at the bottom of the movement, you put your lower back at risk. When your feet are forward, you lose the natural arch in your lower back, and your hips come forward far too much. At the bottom, your hips may even move in front of your shoulders. While you may think you're sparing your knees of a lot of stress, you're loading up stress on your back, and a back injury is around the corner.

FS6.4   *But*, putting your feet forward *does not* really spare your knees. As you descend with your feet forward, there's *exaggerated* friction between your feet and the floor (to stop your feet slipping forward). This produces a shearing force in your knees that, internally, is trying to wrench open your knees.

FS6.5   If you bring your feet back so that they are directly beneath your shoulders, all looks well until you go down in the squat. Then your knees will travel forward in front of your feet, and the stress on your knees is greatly exaggerated.

FS6.6   The Smith machine is a much overrated machine. Don't squat in it, don't bench press in it, and don't overhead press in it. It's only safe to use the Smith machine for short-range movements such as the calf raise and the overhead lockout. It's also good to use for pullups/chins. But that's about it.

EXERCISE FORM AND SELECTION 7
When I perform dips I get very sore in the middle of my chest, between my pecs. Perhaps I'm going too low. What do you think? It doesn't hurt when I'm doing them, but the day after, *ouch!*

FS7.1   You may be going a little too deep, or humping your shoulders, or using too wide a hand spacing, or pressing on a deflated chest. Descend on a fully *inflated* pair of lungs, and don't exhale until you've finished the ascent, or at least have nearly finished. Keep your shoulders pulled back—don't let them slump or round. And avoid an excessive spacing between your hands. About 22 inches between the centers of the handles/bars is about right for most men—but fine-tune (if possible) to find what feels safest and strongest for you. Never use a "reverse" grip that has your knuckles facing inward.

FS7.2   If you follow the above, then for most people—providing excessive depth is not used, and a controlled rep cadence is employed—the dip is a safe and highly productive movement. The safe maximum depth for most people is the point where the triceps reaches parallel to the floor, or *slightly* breaks parallel.

EXERCISE FORM AND SELECTION 8
Supposedly, bodybuilders should squat with a medium or closer stance, to better target their quads. But I can't use this sort of stance without knee discomfort. What am I to do?

FS8.1   Bodybuilding folklore would also want you to elevate your heels on a board (or pair of plates) in order to put greater stress on your lower quads. What bodybuilding folklore doesn't tell you is that this sort of advice has damaged hundreds of thousands if not millions of pairs of knees. Most training magazines and books don't tell you about the downside of their advice for the majority of trainees, but instead focus on the success of a few.

FS8.2   The priority here is that you're able to squat safely and consistently for the *long term.* You must not take chances with high-risk form distortions. Once you have problematic knees you won't be able to do any type of intensive squatting.

FS8.3   Find the squatting stance and setup that's safe for you over the long term. For most people, this means a medium or slightly wider stance, with toes well turned out. Then focus on getting really good and strong at the exercise.

FS8.4   The stance *you* have to adopt may not be the "ideal" for producing maximum quad development, but if the "ideal" hurts your knees, it's not going to do you any good. *What may be "best" according to bodybuilding "theory" may be ruinous for you.*

EXERCISE FORM AND SELECTION 9
Please describe proper form for the hip belt squat.

FS9.1   The conventional barbell squat loads all the body whereas the hip belt squat only loads the body from the hips down. The hip belt squat doesn't have the overall potential of the barbell squat (assuming both can be performed without limitations), but can still be useful, perhaps on a par with the leg press.

FS9.2   The setup position is the key here. *Don't* elevate your heels on a board, as is often recommended for this exercise. The heel elevation is said to be necessary for many people because otherwise they have problems with balance, even if the same people can barbell squat successfully *without* any heel elevation.

FS9.3   Perform the hip belt squat in a power rack, or using some other setup whereby you can hold secure uprights. Start by standing so that the front edges of your shoes are about two inches *beyond* an imaginary line drawn left-to-right between the furthermost edges of the uprights you're holding (with *bent* arms). Fine-tune your setup from there, according to what works best for you.

FS9.4   Holding the uprights will enable you to keep an erect torso and maintain your balance without elevating your heels. Additionally, you need to minimize the forward travel of your knees—i.e., *keep the forward slope of your shin bones to the minimum.* Of course, you should hold the uprights just sufficiently to keep your balance and minimize the forward travel of your knees. Don't abuse the setup and yank on the uprights in order to move more poundage than you can handle properly. Find the minimum involvement of holding on the uprights to do the job, and be consistent with it as you gradually build up the poundage.

FS9.5 Push through the rear of your feet (and *never* through the front of your feet), in order to reduce the stress on your knee joints, help with balance and minimize the forward tilt of your torso.

FS9.6 Resistance can be applied using a barbell, but then there are problems with balance *and* a tipping bar. A better alternative is to stand on two sturdy boxes so that you can suspend plates on a vertical loading pin attached to your belt by a sturdy chain. The elevation enables the plates to travel below your feet.

FS9.7 When suspending the resistance, don't strap it tightly around your waist. Instead, let the belt rest around your hips, where there is a greater mass for natural cushioning. As the weight builds up you may want to put a folded thick towel between the belt and your hips, for additional padding.

FS9.8 My personal experience with the hip belt squat was a miserable one, years ago. I didn't use the conservative setup described above, but the totally freestanding one, using a barbell for resistance, with my heels elevated on a 2 x 4-inch piece of wood. Keeping the barbell from tipping was tricky, but that turned out to be the least of my concerns. Overall balance was difficult to maintain even with my heels elevated. Without heel elevation the exercise was impossible. (I was, however, able to barbell squat at that time without raising my heels on a board.) The heel elevation increased my leg flexion, made my knees travel far too far forward, and my knees complained right from the start.

FS9.9 Having swallowed the "no pain, no gain" foolish macho maxim of the exercise world, I soldiered on, thinking that I was just suffering some "teething" problems. I reckoned I'd adjust to the exercise. A few weeks later, while just hip belt squatting once a week, I had to abandon the exercise due to knee pain.

FS9.10 It took me years before I recovered from this abuse, and to this day I feel there's lasting weakness in my knees as the result of squatting with my heels elevated. Back in my teens, many years before I ever hip belt squatted, I consistently squatted with my heels elevated on a board having a height a tad more than an inch. I didn't know what I was doing, and never had anyone to advise me of the potential dangers for most people of raising the heels while squatting. Many people have suffered as a result of elevating their heels on a board (or plates) while squatting. My experiences are not unique. Please heed the lesson.

FS9.11   I consider the barbell squat and trap bar/shrug bar deadlift to be superior to the hip belt squat, for maximum productivity. A handle squat/modified straddle lift, ball squat and leg press are other alternatives to the barbell squat and trap bar/shrug bar deadlift, and are described in THE INSIDER'S TELL-ALL HANDBOOK ON WEIGHT-TRAINING TECHNIQUE. The step-up is an alternative, too. See elsewhere in this book of questions and answers for how-to instruction on the step-up.

EXERCISE FORM AND SELECTION 10
I'm restricted to flat benching on a Smith machine, and close-grip benching with a free bar, as my right shoulder has a rotator cuff problem. I want to build my upper chest but my right shoulder gets sore and weak quickly using an incline press (45 degrees). My question is which exercise is best, and where do I lower the bar to, i.e., upper, mid or low on the pecs?

FS10.1   No exercise is best for the area concerned if you're injured. Trying to train around an injury is not the way to go. You need to get to the root of the problem, and take the necessary rehab/corrective measures. What you're describing is the development of a potentially very serious problem. If it worsens, you'll eventually be unable to do any chest or shoulder work, and you may even be unable to hold the bar for squatting. Not only are you risking serious damage to your shoulder by training on, but you may produce a problem elsewhere, as your body tries to shift stress off the injured shoulder and place it elsewhere.

FS10.2   Please visit a chiropractor or other physical therapist who has training in and experience of shoulder problems. An orthopedic sports medicine doctor may be able to help you too. Though you may think you have a rotator cuff problem, you may have another type of problem. You must seek professional help. The right professional attention may reduce recovery time to a couple of weeks or so, whereas without the right attention the injury would literally drag on *for years*. Of course, I'm talking about *expert* professional help. As with all therapists, or professionals in general, there's a considerable range of individual competence. You may need to try more than one therapist before finding one who can really help you.

FS10.3   Trigger point therapy may be an invaluable treatment. It has literally been a godsend for toe, knee, lower back, upper back, neck and shoulder problems I've had in the past. It helped me so much that I devoted an entire chapter to it in BEYOND BRAWN. Many readers of that chapter have let me know that they too experienced tremendous benefits when they used the therapy. I suggest you investigate this therapy too. Even if it can't correct your shoulder problem, I can almost guarantee that it will help you in other areas, and sooner rather than later.

FS10.4   Once the shoulder problem has been sorted out, you need to clean up your training so that the possible causes of the problem are removed; otherwise you'll return to square one if the irritants and causes remain in your training. You need to become an exercise form perfectionist, use a controlled rep cadence, and only use exercises that are suited to you. Adding the L-fly to your routine will strengthen your shoulder external rotators, to help reduce strength imbalance in your shoulders. This is an important part of a shoulder injury prevention program.

FS10.5   The Smith machine bench press and press are bad news for the shoulders because the fixed vertical bar pathway forces your joints to work in an unnatural way. Over time, joint or other problems usually surface. Some people have very robust shoulders and can tolerate the Smith machine for a while, but eventually even they can get worn down.

EXERCISE FORM AND SELECTION 11
After switching my squatting form to the one recommended in your technique book, my knees seemed to feel a bit "loose" with a slight twinge. The pain is not intense and doesn't really bother me. But I don't want it to turn into something more severe that will cause me to stop lifting.

FS11.1   You shouldn't be experiencing any knee discomfort. Perhaps you widened your heels too much. Perhaps you flared your feet too much. Perhaps your knees are coming in on the ascent. Perhaps you're not pushing through your heels. Perhaps you increased your squatting depth, and that's the problem due to excessive forward travel of your knees. There's a lot of room for individual tweaking of the basic squatting style in order to find what's best for you. Fine-tune your foot positioning and flare, and even depth of descent if you changed that, so that you don't experience the problem you describe.

FS11.2   Maybe, however, you made a lot of changes in one go, and didn't cut back your poundage enough to allow your body to adjust to the form changes *before* imposing intensive demands on it. You need to give your body the couple of months or so it will need to adjust to substantial form changes *before* you start pushing your current best weights. So cut back the weights, fine-tune the form so that you don't experience any knee twinges, and only *then* build the weights back *gradually* and *steadily*. If you have the form right, and are using a controlled rep speed, you shouldn't experience any knee discomfort whatsoever. With patience you'll build back to bigger weights than you used with your old form, and with an increased potential for strength and growth.

EXERCISE FORM AND SELECTION 12
In HARDGAINER issue #61 (July-August 1999), in your article "Ten Years Wiser," you state "And today I'd never recommend the barbell bent-over row." My question is, "Why?" Please explain.

FS12.1   The barbell bent-over row is a higher risk exercise than the others I recommend for the lats and upper back. It exposes the lower back to unnecessary stress, and has injured countless lower backs over the years. Though the danger is reduced by keeping the knees bent a little, the bar pathway near to the legs, and the back flat or (preferably) slightly arched, the risk factor is still greater in this exercise than in the alternative movements. Why take unnecessary risks when there are safer but yet very productive alternatives?

FS12.2   It's not that the barbell bent-over row *will* hurt you for sure, it's just that a small loss of form—slight yank rather than a controlled pull, letting the bar drift to the front, and slight loss of correct lower back positioning—makes the movement high risk. A slight loss of form in the alternative exercises won't expose you to the same high risk of injury. I recommend playing safe and sticking with lower-risk exercises that come with a margin for error. If there was only the barbell bent-over row for the lats and upper back, that would be another thing. But there are several very good lat and upper-back exercises that carry a much lower risk, assuming they are performed correctly—one-arm dumbbell row, chin/pullup, prone row, seated row, some machine rows, and even the pulldown, though the chin is a better exercise assuming you have sufficient strength to perform it properly.

EXERCISE FORM AND SELECTION 13
I'm having a problem with 20-rep squats. The bar starts to slide down my back at about 10 reps, and by 15 it's killing me. I usually have to stop at about 18 because of the pain. Should I stick with 20 reps and hope that as my traps build up the bar will sit nicer? (I work shrugs once a week.) Or should I reduce reps and increase the weight?

FS13.1   There's nothing magical about 20 reps for the squat. Fifteen would work, or 16, or 12, or 8, or 21, or whatever, *providing you keep adding weight while keeping form tight, and providing you don't get injured.* Choose a number that you're comfortable with, and which is safe for you, stick with it for a long time, work hard, and get strong at it. More weight on the bar in consistently good form is what matters most, not rep count per se.

FS13.2   You may have the bar too low on your traps. If it feels like it's about to slip off your traps, raise the bar a tad, but it must *always* be below the boniest prominence at the base of your neck you can feel when you tilt your head forward. In addition, put chalk on your shirt where the bar rests. These tips should help the bar to stay in position better. Wear a couple of thick shirts for some artificial padding—but cut off the arms so that you don't get roasted while you squat. A cambered bar would likely make a big difference, both comfort wise and as far as keeping the bar in a fixed position on your traps. If it has knurling in the center, which it should, that will further help the bar to stay in place during a high-rep set. And as you build more muscle mass on your upper back, you'll acquire natural "padding" for the bar to rest on.

EXERCISE FORM AND SELECTION 14
Even when I squat with no weight I have a problem with balance and going to parallel. Can I use sissy

squats to replace squats, assuming I continue to deadlift? I want to do regular squats but how will they help me get big if I can't go to failure or go to parallel? They work my back more than my legs.

FS14.1   Sissy squats are a knee wrecker, and one of the worst. Some especially irresponsible trainers urge you to perform the movement while up on your toes, to apply even more stress to the lower quads (and knees). That sort of madness has ruined many pairs of knees. For every success story from that exercise, there are probably hundreds of trainees who end up with knee problems. I've been there myself. Look after your knees!

FS14.2   Regular squats won't do you any good unless you can do them well. While you may be one of the very few who can't squat well, you shouldn't give up yet. Good form modified to suit *you*, along with getting more flexible (all as described in my book on exercise form), building a stronger pair of spinal erectors, and using a cambered squat bar, can do wonders in making a "no squatter" into a good squatter. Don't give up on the barbell squat just because you experience a few initial problems.

FS14.3   If after *truly* applying all that's given in my exercise technique book on squatting form you still can't barbell squat well, *then* you need to look into two of the best alternatives—the trap bar/shrug bar deadlift (which is more of a squat substitute than a deadlift substitute), and the Tru-Squat machine, if available. The latter is high-tech and expensive, but the former is low-tech and cheap (relatively speaking, at under $200.00) but *perhaps more effective*. Both are described and illustrated in the second edition of my technique book. If you can't make one of those work, then go to the next level of alternatives to the barbell squat—ball squat, handle lift/modified straddle lift, or leg press, all of which are described and illustrated in my technique book. Other possibilities are the hip belt squat and step-up, as described elsewhere in this book.

EXERCISE FORM AND SELECTION 15
What's your opinion of using the Manta Ray to "cushion" the bar while squatting?

FS15.1   The Manta Ray appears to be a quick-fix solution to squatting difficulties, especially for trainees who are not using optimal squatting form. But with proper attention to improving squatting form, and some patience, the difficulties can be remedied without resorting to the Manta Ray. If you hold the bar lower on your traps, and build up your trap development so that you have more natural cushioning, and for some artificial padding wear a thick sweat shirt (with sleeves cut off) or a couple of T-shirts, use a cambered squatting bar, and improve your squatting form if it's not optimal for you, you shouldn't feel the need for the Manta Ray.

FS15.2   On the negative side, the Manta Ray places the bar higher than where it should go, which increases the distance between the resistance and the hips. Then if or when you "lose" a rep, and your torso leans forward more than usual, the stress on your lower back will increase greatly, and an injury will be the likely result, and perhaps a serious one.

EXERCISE FORM AND SELECTION 16
One could do the trap bar deadlift in such a way that it would emphasize the squat-like quality, or in a way that it would be more like a conventional bent-legged deadlift. Which do you recommend? In doing the trap bar deadlift in the squat style, i.e., squatting down low and involving the legs and hips more, does one miss out on something the conventional deadlift provides?

FS16.1   You could modify your degree of forward lean, and descent, to try to mimic more the squat or the deadlift. The style I recommend is what I describe in my exercise technique book, which is the style that's most natural for the trap bar/shrug bar—a squat lift. This style doesn't provide the degree of back musculature involvement that the straight bar deadlift does.

EXERCISE FORM AND SELECTION 17
I've often wondered about the difference between squats with dumbbells, and dumbbell deadlifts. They seem to be similar, but use a slightly different technique, either focusing more on the legs or more on the back. Please comment and advise. I'm trying to decide which to employ.

FS17.1   A dumbbell deadlift and a dumbbell squat are basically the same movement because the resistance is held in the same way. The movement can be varied by a special effort to either exaggerate or minimize back involvement, depending on whether it's to be more of a deadlift or a squat. Individual body structure is a big factor here. Some people, because of their body mechanics and proportions, can maintain a more upright torso than others, though some degree of forward lean is still required.

FS17.2   What matters most of all is finding the safest, strongest and most productive performance *for you*. Don't try to distort the exercise to make it favor the squat or the deadlift. Such a form distortion may put you at a leverage disadvantage that would expose you to a greatly increased risk of injury.

FS17.3   The dumbbell deadlift or squat is very similar to the trap bar/shrug bar deadlift. The major difference is that, because dumbbells are loaded with smaller diameter plates than what are usually loaded on a trap bar or shrug bar, the potential range of motion is greater with dumbbells. Putting the dumbbells onto the floor means you have to descend further than you would with a bar that has full-sized plates on it. This increased range of motion, for many if not most people, will lead to rounding of the lower back and perhaps excessive flexion of the legs too. Avoid this by raising the dumbbells on sturdy boxes.

FS17.4   A big problem with the dumbbell deadlift is finding sufficiently heavy resistance. Most gyms' 'bells only go up to 100 pounds or so.

EXERCISE FORM AND SELECTION 18
I can only train at a commercial gym, and am unable to barbell squat safely. The gym doesn't have a Tru-Squat, a shrug/trap bar or a decent leg press, and won't be getting any new equipment. What else can I do to work my legs and glutes productively?

FS18.1   The handle squat and the ball squat are possibilities, and both are described in my book on exercise form. Other possibilities which aren't included in that book are the step-up and one-legged squat.

FS18.2   The step-up is performed by stepping onto a platform or bench, with resistance. Done properly it will provide intensive and productive work for the thighs and glutes. While it's not the equal of the squat or trap/shrug bar deadlift, if you can't perform either of those, the comparison is irrelevant.

FS18.3   The step-up is rarely performed, but when it's illustrated in a
          book or magazine it's usually with a barbell across the
          shoulders. Using dumbbells is a *much* safer way of applying
          resistance. This is what I recommend, *not* a barbell. While the
          barbell version will produce more back involvement, safety is
          the priority, thus the use of dumbbells.

FS18.4   Find a bench or platform of sufficient height so that when you
          step onto it your upper thigh is no lower than parallel to the
          ground. (For reasons of safety, the surface needs to be wide—*not*
          the width of a bench.) If you have a history of knee problems, I
          suggest you use a lower bench or platform, to reduce the degree
          of flexion of your knees. This can be done by raising the height
          of the surface you step up from—e.g., put some non-slip matting
          on the floor, or a low platform. Over time you may want to
          gradually increase the degree of flexion to the parallel position,
          assuming that this is safe for you. If, however, you've had knee
          problems you'd probably be best off not to push your knees to
          their limit for this exercise, and thus stay at a degree of flexion a
          couple of inches or so above the parallel position.

FS18.5   Perform the step-up while wearing shoes with good cushioning
          and lateral support. In addition, put a "giving" material on the
          floor (or whatever surface you step up from), e.g., a rubber mat,
          to cushion the impact of your feet on the floor. The item you step
          onto must be sturdy, stable and with a non-slip surface.

FS18.6   You must not trip or stumble as you place your feet on the
          elevated surface. It's imperative that you keep your eyes fixed
          on the elevated surface and your feet as they move onto that
          surface. This, together with 100% mental focus on what you're
          doing, should keep the exercise safe.

FS18.7   A consequence of keeping your eyes on the elevated surface is
          that your cervical spine may be rounded, which would produce
          rounding of your lumbar spine. While this shouldn't be a
          problem for healthy trainees when *little or no resistance is used*,
          it's dangerous when demanding weights are used, and must be
          avoided. Keep your eyes on the elevated surface *without* leaning
          your head forward. Keep your head up; direct only your eyes
          downward. Maintain a flat or slightly arched back.

FS18.8   There are several methods of performing the step-up. All
          involve holding equally weighted dumbbells—one in each hand.

The first method is, for example, to lead with your right leg and then follow with your left. Then with both feet on the elevated surface, both legs locked out and straight, lead off with your right followed by your left. Then the right leg leads for the next rep, and so on. Both feet go up *and* come down, on each rep.

FS18.9 The second method starts like the first method. But with both feet on the elevated surface, the initial leading leg (right in this case) *stays* on the elevated surface for the duration of the set for the right leg. The left leg comes down and then the right takes the strain and elevates the trainee again. This continues until the required reps are performed. After a short rest the process is reversed for the other leg.

FS18.10 There's a third method: It's the same as the first one outlined in 18.8, but rather than do all the reps with the same leg leading for the entire set, alternate from rep to rep which leg leads. I suggest you try all three methods and choose the one you feel most comfortable with. At least for some people, the asymmetrical stress on the lower back and hips from the step-up may produce a negative response. If so, the third method of execution may be the best one. If there's still a negative reaction that persists, an alternative exercise needs to sought.

FS18.11 Place all the strain of elevation on the leading leg. Don't use a thrust of the "disengaged" leg to help out. Step up in a controlled manner, and step down in a controlled manner too. *Gently* place each foot onto the floor.

FS18.12 Don't work to total failure because a very final rep where you're almost caving in could be when you stumble and lose your footing. Train hard, for sure, but not to total failure. Increasing poundage on the dumbbells is the measure of progress. You need to train hard to achieve that, but not necessarily to failure.

FS18.13 With the first two methods of execution, you train one leg at a time. Finish with one leg, rest for a couple of minutes, and then train the other. If you finish one leg and then immediately move to the other, the fatigue in your first leg will compromise your ability to work the second leg hard, and expose you to a greater chance of stumbling or losing your balance in some way. *An alternative is to hold only one dumbbell (on the side of the working leg), and use the free hand to hold an upright for support. This involves a heavier single dumbbell than each 'bell of a pair, but may be safer.*

FS18.14 Don't rush into training the step-up intensively. While training twice a week, take a couple of months to gradually adjust to the movement. First find the degree of flexion—to parallel or a little above—that's safe for you. Then gradually pick up the poundage until you're really having to work. Later you may need to reduce the frequency to three times every two weeks, or just once a week. The bottom line is poundage progression in consistently good form. If, however, your back is anything other than very robust, the asymmetrical loading on your lower back from the weighted step-up *may* produce back problems, *especially if you don't take enough time to adapt to the exercise.*

FS18.15 While adapting to the step-up I suggest you keep your current major thigh exercise in your schedule. Once you're working hard on the step-up, and have picked up the poundage, then you can drop the other thigh movement and focus on the step-up.

FS18.16 Because each leg is working alone in the step-up, if you have a strength difference between your legs, this will show. By using the same resistance for each leg, and the same reps, a strength imbalance can be corrected. For the short term this would mean that your stronger leg won't be worked as hard as your other leg, at least until the imbalance has been corrected.

FS18.17 Another possibility if you don't have access to a trap/shrug bar, Tru-Squat or good leg press, is the one-legged squat on a bench. Put a bench near anything tall in the gym, such as an upright of a power rack. Stand on the bench with, for example, the rack upright on your right side. Hold the upright with your right hand, with your left foot off the bench. Then while keeping a flat or slightly arched lower back, squat. Hold the rack upright just sufficiently to keep your balance and prevent excessive forward lean; and be consistent from rep to rep, and set to set. (You'll need a bit of practice to get the hang of the movement.) At the end of the set for your right leg, take a short break and then reverse the setup and work your left leg. When you need additional resistance, hold a dumbbell in your free hand.

FS18.18 Avoid excessive forward travel of your knee in the one-legged squat (or any type of squat, or the step-up). Your knee must not travel beyond an imaginary vertical line drawn from the end of your big toe, and preferably *behind* that point. Use the support of the rack upright (or whatever else you use) to minimize forward lean of your torso, and also minimize forward travel of your knee. You also need to avoid excessive depth of descent. As with the barbell squat, you must not descend to a depth that produces rounding of your lower back or knee irritation *for you*.

EXERCISE FORM AND SELECTION 19
What's your opinion of dips between benches with weight on your lap. Is this a joint-wrecking exercise, or is there a safe form that can be used?

FS19.1   The problem with this exercise is the degree of forward movement of the shoulder, and the resulting high level of stress on the shoulder capsule. This produces unnecessary exaggerated stress on the shoulders. Of course, if the exercise is performed without an excessive range of motion, but with a controlled cadence and moderate hand spacing (neither too close nor too wide), the degree of stress on the shoulders won't be as exaggerated. But even when done in the reduced-risk fashion, this form of the dip is still inferior to the *properly-performed* parallel bar dip. Not only is the parallel bar dip superior from the safety point of view, but from the productivity angle too.

EXERCISE FORM AND SELECTION 20
I'm soon to embark on abbreviated training, but the one bodypart I'm not sure about is my neck. My plan is to use a neck harness, which will allow me to increase the weight in small increments, doing away with the uncertainty of progression that's inherent in manual resistance. My plan is to use one set in each direction (forward, backward, left and right) for 15 reps. What do you think?

FS20.1   You're right to be alert to the danger inherent in neck work. Some people have a natural bull neck, and won't injure it easily. But hard gainers usually have naturally thin and weak necks. A neck harness can be a fine way to work the neck, though depending on the particular design it may not turn out in practice to be as convenient and easy to use as expected. You may need to experiment a bit to find the best way to wear the harness. You may even need to try more than one harness.

FS20.2   I don't recommend the neck harness for lateral work, only for the other two directions (to the front, and to the rear). Lateral work with a neck harness is very risky because the resistance is so tricky to control. Manual resistance is much safer for lateral work, *providing it's done properly*. I recommend you apply it yourself—as you know your resistance limitations better than anyone—and even then you must *still* be very careful and conservative with progression.

FS20.3 Even for neck exercise that doesn't involve a harness, lateral flexion has a greater risk than work for the other two directions, so exercise *even* greater care for lateral work. You might want to work the forward and rearward directions alone for a month or two, if you feel that your neck is very weak to begin with. *Then* carefully introduce work in the other two directions.

FS20.4 For neck harness work, start out with no resistance, to get used to the movements. Use as full a motion as you can for the two directions but *without* exaggerating the range. Don't relax at the bottom of any rep. Stay tight or otherwise you may find, especially as you build up resistance, that if you relax just a little you'll get pulled into an excessive extra inch or so of motion you're not conditioned for. It's good to have a safety margin of an inch or so of motion, so that you're not working at the hilt of the movement.

FS20.5 *Slow* and *smooth* motion is vital for any type of neck work. Absolutely never thrust into a rep. *Ease* into each rep with a slow and consistent cadence. Take *at least* three seconds for each phase of each rep—that's at least six seconds total per rep.

FS20.6 I suggest you work your neck twice a week, at least for the early months, and perhaps drop to just once a week thereafter. When you can perform 15 *perfect* reps of consistent cadence for a given direction, add a tad of iron next week. By a tad of iron I mean just that—*not* a 5-pound jump. For harness work, add a pound maximum per increment—and a fraction of a pound at a time once you've been performing neck work for six months or so.

EXERCISE FORM AND SELECTION 21
Overhead lockouts have caused me shoulder irritation, even though I've attempted to perform them as described in your book on exercise technique. This may, however, be because I've not fully understood how to perform the exercise. After reading your guidelines I remain uncertain as to whether my arms (when locked out) should be at the same 75–80 degree angle as the body

(supported by a high-incline bench), or whether they should always remain vertical. I'm pushing my arms and shoulders quite far back. In fact, my lockout position is such that I can't really move my arms any further back (behind my head). Should my arms be brought forward a little so my shoulders are in a less extreme position, and my arms can then be kept vertical throughout the movement?

FS21.1 Your arms should be vertical or at least all but vertical—not 75 degrees of vertical. You've been moving your arms too far back. One of the reasons why I recommend the use of a Smith machine or power rack uprights for this exercise is to keep the bar moving vertically. Arrange your setup—move the bench back a little—so that your arms move vertically. And be sure to use controlled form. To try to put more stress on the delts without having to use as much resistance, perhaps shrug your shoulders at the top of *every* rep, and hold that top shrug position for a "one thousand and one" count.

FS21.2 As noted in FS6, the recommendation of the Smith machine for the overhead lockout is one of the very few instances where that piece of equipment can be safe to use.

EXERCISE FORM AND SELECTION 22
I don't think you mention this in your technique book, but I've a question on stiff-legged deadlifts. I like to turn my elbows in (having them pointing directly behind me instead of out to the sides) in order to increase the exercise's emphasis on my biceps. I've been doing this for about five months now; do you think this is a hazardous way to train?

FS22.1 To have your elbows pointing behind you, while using a straight bar and a pronated grip (knuckles to the front), will mean that you have to rotate your wrists to the maximum, thus putting your grip at a disadvantage, weakening it, and putting exaggerated stress on your wrists. If you use a supinated grip (knuckles to the rear), your elbows will automatically be pointing behind, but the price you'll pay will be a much diminished grip, especially relative to a mixed one that has one hand pronated and the other supinated. With a mixed grip you would have to make a special effort to keep the elbow of your pronated hand pointing to the rear, thus weakening your grip.

FS22.2 If you alternate a *normal* mixed grip from set to set, or workout to workout (right hand supinated at one set or workout, and next time the left hand would be supinated), you would achieve what you're targeting without weakening your grip or putting exaggerated stress on your wrists. Only the elbow of the supinated hand would point to the rear during any given set.

FS22.3 I don't recommend a pronated grip with the elbows rotated in, or both hands supinated, or a distorted mixed grip that forces the elbow of the pronated hand to point to the rear.

EXERCISE FORM AND SELECTION 23
It isn't recommended to put anything under the heels of your feet when squatting. But it's nearly impossible for me to do a correct squat without something to help my balance. When I squat flat footed I tend to round my back and lean forward a lot. Is putting a piece of wood under the heels of my feet when squatting really dangerous compared to the rounding effect upon my back from not having the board there?

FS23.1 Not only is it normal to lean forward while squatting, it's necessary, and part and parcel of the proper technique, though *exaggerated* forward lean is not desirable. The unwise effort to eliminate forward lean is one of the reasons why people turn to the Smith machine.

FS23.2 Don't risk trading knee problems in return for not injuring your lower back. You should be training with neither knee nor lower back problems in the pipeline. A lower back problem from round-back squatting is likely to be immediate and possibly very serious—semi-crippling you for a few days, and perhaps doing harm that lasts for months if not longer. The knee problems that usually arise from squatting with heels elevated take time to develop. Just because you might not feel much amiss in your knees from a few workouts can belie the damage that's accumulating but which may only show up after a few months. Once you have knee problems your training will be messed up big time. Look after your knees *and* your lower back.

FS23.3 If you can't squat without elevating your heels, you need to address the causes of the problem—including lack of flexibility in one or more of your ankles/calves, hamstrings and glutes.

FS23.4 There's more you can do to help your squatting ability other than improving your flexibility and exercise technique. Your spinal erectors may not be strong enough to maintain a flexed and flat lower back. The stiff-legged deadlift, when performed properly, can greatly and safely increase the strength of the spinal erectors. But for novices in particular, the back extension may be a better way to strengthen the spinal erectors, at least for the short term.

FS23.5 Your leverages may not be well suited to the squat, which means you need to work even harder on your flexibility, spinal erector strength, and on optimizing squatting form *for you*. Naturally terrific squatters often have short legs and long torsos, relatively speaking, and are rarely more than average height.

FS23.6 Even good natural squatters who are flexible and use excellent technique can still end up rounding their lower backs if they descend *too far*. Never descend further than the point a couple of inches *above* where your lower back rounds—this two inches builds in a margin of error. Establish the point at which your lower back rounds (with no weight on the bar) and set the power rack pins/safety bars so that you simply can't descend any deeper than a couple of inches above the critical point.

FS23.7 Especially for novices, but not exclusively so, as flexibility, spinal erector strength and squatting technique are all improved, the point at which you can descend to without rounding your lower back will be increased to some degree. So periodically check on this, and if your safe range of motion increases, gradually increase your depth of squatting accordingly. Be sure, however, that each time you increase your depth of squatting—and thus lower the rack pins/safety bar setting—you cut back your poundage and build it back up gradually over *at least* a few weeks. If you use your best current poundage for an increased range of motion, you're asking for injury.

EXERCISE FORM AND SELECTION 24
It seems that the higher in poundages I get in the squat, the more my lower back aches. I'm using good form. I don't want to give up the squat. Any suggestions?

FS24.1 You say that you're using good form. How can you be sure? Have you video taped yourself from the side, front and rear? Have you really scrutinized your form and compared it to what

I teach in my exercise technique book? If you have to elevate your heels, if your lower back aches a lot, if you're leaning forward a great deal, or if you feel the stress of the exercise through the front of your feet, all these are symptoms that your form is not good.

FS24.2 Focus on slowly and progressively increasing your ankle/calf, hamstring and glute flexibility. Your shoulders may be very tight, and prevent your holding the bar in the right position; so your shoulders may need more flexibility. Work on flexibility in general, and simultaneously increase your spinal erector strength. At the same time, put into practice form improvement. For example, you may need to widen your stance, turn out your toes more, and lower the bar placement on your upper back. Use a cambered bar rather than a straight bar. It will take *at least* a few weeks to produce the increase in flexibility and adaptation to revised form (using a bare bar, or just a little weight). If you try to return to hard training too quickly, your revised form will crumble, and you'll be back to square one. Become *able* to squat well, learn how to squat well, and then build up your squatting poundage gradually. Then after a few months you'll have laid the foundation for big gains in the future.

FS24.3 You may find some *very careful* stretching immediately prior to squatting helpful, to "loosen" the involved musculature. This is *not* the time to work on progressive stretching to increase your flexibility, but just to loosen yourself up to your current level should you feel any tightness at the time. Be sure, however, you've done some general warmup work first, and have broken into a sweat.

FS24.4 Some trigger point therapy may be needed to release congestion and tightness in the involved musculature. You need to be at your full current degree of "looseness" in order to be able to adopt your best current squatting form.

EXERCISE FORM AND SELECTION 25
You don't mention the leg curl for hamstring development? Is this exercise inherently bad?

FS25.1 The exercise isn't inherently bad unless it's performed in a hostile way, or on a machine that's poorly designed. It's just an inferior exercise compared with deadlift variations, especially the stiff-legged and Romanian varieties. Not only do you get hamstring involvement from forms of the deadlift, but a lot of other musculature is heavily worked too. While leg curls belong to the "train each muscle in isolation in order to hit the whole body" philosophy, the exercise hits aspects of the hamstrings that deadlift variations don't. As such, prudent use—e.g., four months out of each year—of a good leg curl setup can be valuable.

FS25.2 If you're physically incapable of any form of deadlifting, then *regular* use of the leg curl is needed—machine, or manual resistance from a partner. In such a case you're not going to get the *overall* muscular development you can from deadlift variations.

FS25.3 Leg curls, like leg extensions, pec flyes, pec deck work, laterals, cable crossovers and most isolation exercises, invariably distract people from the core movements that do the best job. As a result you'll not train hard enough on the core movements because a chunk of your effort would be taken up elsewhere. So you would get reduced growth stimulation; but the overall demands on your recovery system may be increased, whereas you want to *minimize* the demands there while stimulating growth.

FS25.4 The way to become strong and good at exercises such as the leg curl and leg extension, is to become good at deadlifts and squats—kill two birds with one stone, so to speak. But you'll never become good at deadlifts and squats by trying to become good at the leg curl and leg extension. So focus on the core exercises, and later on, *once you're big and strong*, you can spend more time on the isolation exercises, should you be interested.

EXERCISE FORM AND SELECTION 26
I've found that I can only use a foot angle of 10–15 degrees for trap bar deadlifts. When I use an angle greater than this, my legs tend to get in the way of the bar. Do you believe this restricted degree of flare will put undo stress on my knees? I've not had any problems initially, but I'm worried about the long term.

FS26.1 Maybe, maybe not. Only time will tell. Best to nip the problem in the bud, rather than take a chance on knee problems later on. If the trap bar deadlift stance you're forced to adopt due to the bar's design is substantially different to your barbell squatting stance, I'd take action pronto if I was you. Investigate the possibility of a custom-made trap bar with gripping sites wider than normal, to enable you to replicate your squatting stance. Or, probably easier, try a shrug bar instead. The hexagonal shaped shrug bar provides more knee room than the trap bar, comparing bars with gripping sites placed the same width apart.

FS26.2 Determine the width of stance you need at the widest point— from the outside edges of your shoes—and then investigate obtaining a bar to accommodate you. While the shrug bar allows more knee room than the trap bar, some people may still need a custom-made shrug bar with gripping sites wider apart than the norm, to accommodate their needs. There is, however, a limit to the width of the gripping sites, for reasons of strength and practicality. If you need a very wide stance, the shrug bar or trap bar may not be for you, at least not for squatting/deadlifting.

EXERCISE FORM AND SELECTION 27
Do you believe that I'm at any risk for injury by looking up slightly to see my form in the mirror during dumbbell rows? I believe that the mirror is a tool for checking my form.

FS27.1 Providing you keep your attention on maintaining good form, looking up slightly in the mirror while dumbbell rowing shouldn't increase your risk for injury *as long as you're not working under an intensive load.* Turning your head *to the side* while under even a moderate load is a risky activity that can easily lead to injury *even if your form is otherwise good.*

FS27.2 A mirror, at least for some exercises, can be a valuable teaching tool to see if you're really using proper form, but *only if you actually know what proper form is.* When you're training hard, the mirror is a distraction, and one that can easily lead to injury especially if you turn your head to the side to view your reflection. But even if you're face on to the mirror you can still run into problems. If you're focusing more on watching yourself than on the lifting, you may get sloppy and increase the risk of injury.

FS27.3 You should never be training hard *unless* you're already using perfect form. When you're training hard, the learning should be over, form should be down pat, and constant checking in the mirror shouldn't be necessary.

FS27.4 Checking your form on a periodic basis is, however, good and desirable. I'd prefer that you have someone video tape your training, from different angles, and then you can rigorously scrutinize your form using the play, rewind, slow motion and other features of a VCR. A permanent record of your training form to examine at home is more valuable than the fleeting image of yourself in a mirror.

EXERCISE FORM AND SELECTION 28
In BEYOND BRAWN you recommend using the Tru-Squat machine as a safe alternative to the squat. I've never tried or even seen a Tru-Squat except for the pictures you provide in the book, but it didn't look like being different to a hack squat except for maybe being more upright. In that case, wouldn't it be similar to the Smith machine variation?

FS28.1   Before I used a Tru-Squat I thought it looked like a glorified Smith machine squat. But when I tried the thing, all was revealed. There's *no comparison* with the Smith machine. With the Tru-Squat the resistance does *not* follow a vertical path. It follows an arc. The weight carriage travels down *and* back. That rearward travel makes a huge difference. The back is protected as long as lumbar support is used, and excessive forward travel of the knees is avoided as long as foot placement is correct for the individual.

FS28.2   I have knees that are very easily irritated. I can't barbell squat safely, and just the thought of Smith machine squatting gives me knee discomfort. But I can Tru-Squat safely—so the stress on the knees really must be greatly reduced relative to the barbell squat.

EXERCISE FORM AND SELECTION 29
You state a person should avoid pressing from behind the neck. I've always used this exercise in my routine as a mass builder, and feel awkward using front pressing. Why do you feel the press from behind the neck is a "wrong" exercise?

FS29.1   It's not that the press behind neck will definitely hurt *your* shoulders. Individual differences in structure, among other factors, can make one person's "dangerous" exercise another person's "safe" exercise. For most people for most of the time, the press behind neck increases the risk of shoulder and rotator cuff problems. Why take the extra risk when there are alternatives that don't carry the increased risk? I prefer to minimize risks. Many people have had to give up the press behind neck due to shoulder problems. By the time they were forced to give up the exercise they were left with shoulders that give them problems in other exercises. Best to avoid the problems in the first place. Look after your shoulders!

FS29.2 Some people find the press in front to be an awkward exercise. Use the dumbbell press—this positions the hands approximately midway between the front press and behind-neck press, in probably the most "natural" pressing position. The dumbbells also permit the wrists to find their most comfortable positioning. But be sure you control the dumbbells properly, and don't let them drift out to the sides.

EXERCISE FORM AND SELECTION 30
I've heard from several sources that overhead shoulder presses cause rotator cuff impingement, and are dangerous. What are your thoughts on this?

FS30.1 Behind neck presses are usually the most troublesome of the overhead presses. If you stick with the front barbell press or, preferably, the dumbbell press, and use impeccable form (without an excessive range of motion at the bottom) and a sensible poundage progression scheme, you shouldn't experience shoulder problems unless you're currently incubating some. Generally speaking, bench presses are more stressful on your shoulders and rotator cuffs than are front presses and dumbbell presses.

EXERCISE FORM AND SELECTION 31
You advise that trap bar deadlifts may not sufficiently train the lower back alone. Is the same true of the squat? I've noticed that many trainees have problems training both squats and deadlifts in the same program. It can be hard to make progress on both squats and bent-legged deadlifts at the same time, and some people are ill suited to, or daunted by the stiff-legged variation. What are the reasons, if any, why squats (perhaps with the assistance of back extensions) may not train the lower back intensively enough?

FS31.1 For some people, the squat, alone, won't be enough to work the lower back adequately. Different leverages affect the stress of the squat, and the effect on the lower back.

FS31.2 I'd prefer the lower back to be trained with one of the big exercises—and it could be the *partial* stiff-legged deadlift. The big back exercises intensively work more musculature than back extensions. I prefer back extensions to be an *addition* to the squat *and* a deadlift variation—and no more than two serious and intensive sets a week of back extensions can do the job. If you really feel you can't perform any deadlifting movement in the same program as the squat, then for sure you should include back extensions to give your lower back intensive work. The overall impact of back extensions won't be the equal of a deadlift, but if a deadlift can't be done, the comparison is irrelevant.

EXERCISE FORM AND SELECTION 32
I'm not structurally well suited to the bent-legged deadlift (I've never tried the trap bar), and the stiff-legged deadlift aggravates my back. If one is squatting hard enough, will that be enough work for the lower back and spinal erectors?

FS32.1 Maybe, maybe not. Some people get a lot of lower back and spinal erector work from the squat, but some don't. I suggest you explore other ways of deadlifting, to try to find one that doesn't aggravate your lower back.

FS32.2 When you say the stiff-legged deadlift aggravates your back, perhaps it's the specific way you perform it that's the problem, and a modification may make the exercise productive for you. Are you following the guidelines given in my book on exercise form? Are you avoiding an exaggerated range of motion? Are you keeping the bar very close to your legs? Are you using a controlled cadence? Are you maintaining a flat back?

FS32.3 If you can say yes to all those questions, try reducing the range of motion so that you do the exercise from just below your knee caps, inside a power rack—a partial stiff-legged deadlift, or even a Romanian deadlift (without setting the bar down on the rack's pins between reps). Taking a few inches out of the range of motion can make the world of difference.

FS32.4 The trap bar or shrug bar can make the world of difference when bent-legged deadlifting; and the sumo deadlift may make the straight-bar deadlift a much better movement for you. You may have incorrectly evaluated your ability to deadlift, and further efforts to correct the problem may yield a solution.

FS32.5 If you can't get a deadlift variation to work for you, use back extensions—regular or reverse—to make sure that your lower back and spinal erectors are worked thoroughly. Even if you can find a deadlift variation that's productive, it's *still* a good idea to perform an intensive set or two of the back extension once a week, *and treat it as a very serious strength builder.*

FS32.6 Back extensions work the glutes, hamstrings, thigh adductors, and the musculature, tendons and ligaments of the lower back differently to variations of the deadlift. That's why back extensions provide protection against back injuries, and are so valuable. They help keep your back in the robust condition needed to exploit the huge potential benefits from deadlift variations, and the squat.

FS32.7 If available, a hip-and-back machine can be used as an alternative to back extensions.

EXERCISE FORM AND SELECTION 33
What is your opinion on the T-bar setup with padded support on which one can lie at a 50% angle and do rows for the back?

FS33.1 The T-bar row I really dislike, and the one which has injured so many people, is the "freestyle" one where there's no back support and where the resistance can't be pulled into the waist area. The T-bar row the questioner asks about is a far less risky exercise, providing the design is such that there's no load taken on the lower back, and good controlled form is used.

EXERCISE FORM AND SELECTION 34
I understand that you consider the power clean to be a dangerous exercise that should be avoided. I'm reluctant to omit the power clean since, for me, it's the most enjoyable exercise. I do 2 x 15 reps once a week. I also do deadlifts, back extensions, side bends, and crunches, and I've never had problems with my back. What are the drawbacks of the power clean, and how important is it to avoid it?

FS34.1 The drawback with the power clean is that few people perform it correctly, and there are few people around who can teach it. I prefer to urge people to stick with exercises that are simpler to perform and easier to learn, especially since hardly anyone has an *expert* coach to keep an eye on them. The power clean is a more technically demanding lift than non-quick exercises. While all major exercises can benefit from an experienced and expert coach giving hands-on instruction, I feel that such coaching is a *necessity* for the Olympic lifts and their assistance moves. But if you really know what you're doing, have had expert hands-on coaching, can power clean with excellent technique, and can do it without getting injured, then by all means stick with it.

EXERCISE FORM AND SELECTION 35
I'm currently discovering the one-arm deadlift, which seems to be a terrific exercise. You recommended this exercise to me a few years ago, for climbing, but back then I could never manage to balance the bar. This exercise isn't covered in your book on exercise technique. How do I perform it?

FS35.1   I initially included the one-arm deadlift in the form book, but pulled it out prior to publication because of the asymmetrical nature of the movement, and thus the increased risk factor. But I kept the original description, and here it is, slightly revised:

FS35.2   This can be a great grip exercise (and erectors and traps). But if your lower back is not 100%, it's best not to do any one-hand deadlifting, to avoid its asymmetrical stress. Instead, do thick-bar deadlifts from knee height in a power rack, using two hands and a pronated (knuckles to the front) grip, or thick-bar holds.

FS35.3   The one-hand deadlift can be done with different diameter bars. It's most easily done with deadlift handles, or dumbbells, instead of a barbell.

FS35.4   When using a deadlift handle, or a dumbbell, there's nothing to concern you other than hanging onto the handle or dumbbell as you pull the plates off the deck. With the barbell there are more technique points to consider, due to the length of the bar and the chance of the bar tipping.

FS35.5   A two-inch diameter deadlift handle is not expensive to buy ready-made, or to have made locally. Instead you could put some two-inch diameter plumbing pipe around the center gripping area of a long dumbbell rod (or any longer bar), or use some other innovation to get a thick-handled bar. You could wrap a lot of tape around a bar until it becomes the required thickness.

FS35.6   When doing the one-hand deadlift with a handle or short rod, always brace your "free" hand on your thigh. For example, if you're pulling the weight with your right hand, brace your left just above your left knee. Initially, keep the fingers on the inside of your left thigh, not the outside. But experiment with different finger positioning to find what works best for you.

FS35.7   Don't stand up above the point at which you can no longer firmly brace your leg with your free hand. If you stand up completely erect, you'll shift most of the load to one side of your body and risk injury.

FS35.8   For the barbell one-hand deadlift, the barbell can be lifted either from in front of *both* feet, like with the regular deadlift using two hands or, as most performers prefer, from *between* the feet while *straddling* the bar.

FS35.9   With bent legs and flat back, grip the bar in dead center, and brace your disengaged hand on your thigh. "Squeeze" the bar off the floor using your back *and* legs in a synchronized movement, just like in the conventional deadlift. Don't just hold the bar or handle as you exercise, *crush* it. Keep your back flat, head up, and lead with your head. The bar doesn't have to be lifted as high as it does in the deadlift with two hands. For training purposes, *keep the disengaged hand firmly braced on your thigh during the entire lift.* This keeps the stress of the exercise distributed evenly over your lower back, and necessitates that you *don't* stand upright to the degree you do in the conventional deadlift.

FS35.10 Under the International All-Round Weightlifting Association's rules of competition, the braced position can't be maintained in the final position of the lift. The disengaged arm has to be held away from the body for a count of two before the lift is passed. Just holding the non-lifting hand a fraction of an inch away from the thigh would be quite sufficient, as long as the judge could see it.

FS35.11 If you stand upright you'll lose the bracing effect of your disengaged hand pressing on your thigh, take a lot of strain on one side of your back, and may risk injury due to the asymmetrical distribution of stress. *Only use the competition-style one-hand deadlift if you have a 100%-sound lower back, and have been progressively conditioned to this exercise.* For training purposes, finish the lift with your legs still bent sufficiently so that your disengaged arm can be *firmly* braced against your thigh. Avoid putting your disengaged hand too close to your knee, or otherwise you'll reduce your potential range of *safe* motion.

FS35.12 Keep the bar as near to horizontal as possible, or else it will tip and spoil the lift. Initially perform the exercise, with a light weight, side-on to a mirror. This will help you learn the technique. Find the spot your middle finger needs to cover for the deadlift to go smoothly and well. Mark this spot, if necessary and possible, so you know precisely where to find it each set. You'll not master the form immediately, so be patient until you do. Keep the poundage light and easy until you have the style right, the bar doesn't tip, and you can focus on style and pulling rather than on style alone.

FS35.13 At least to begin with, use the shortest barbell you have, for the minimum trouble with balance. *Always use collars.* Without collars, if the bar tips and the plates at one end slide just a little, the balance will be ruined and you'll probably lose the lift. If the plates slide sufficiently, the bar could be upended, with serious injury a possibility. Tight collars will keep the plates securely in place.

FS35.14 To avoid an excessive range of motion with a straight bar, don't use plates of a smaller diameter than a 20-kilo or 45-pound plate, unless you use a power rack and set the barbell on pins to mimic the height of the full-sized plates.

FS35.15 If you've access to a cambered bar, use that for one-hand deadlifts. It will need to have central knurling in order to maximize your grip potential. For the one-hand deadlift, a cambered bar is easier to handle than a straight barbell. The center of a cambered bar, when ready for pulling from the floor, is higher than the center of a straight bar, comparing bars loaded with the same diameter plates. If you want to keep the pulling distance the same for a cambered bar as a straight bar, use plates of a smaller diameter on the former. Alternatively you could stand on a low platform of the same height as the depth of the camber in the bar. Though in this way the pulling distance can be the same with both bars, you may not get the lowest end of a cambered bar above your knees, if you have long arms. This is because the ends of a cambered bar are not in line with the center, like they are with a straight bar.

FS35.16 Find a consistent style of performance that's safe for you, and stick to it, whether with a straight bar or cambered bar. For training purposes, it doesn't matter if you're not in strict accord with competition regulations.

FS35.17 While setting up, be sure *not* to have the bend in the cambered bar turned towards your disengaged arm, because that will turn your hand out of its ideal position once you start to pull the bar from the floor. While you set up your grip as the bar rests on the floor, it's best to have the bend in the bar turned slightly out to the side from which you're pulling. Alternatively you could have the bar placed so that it's not turned either way. Try both and choose the one that helps you most.

EXERCISE FORM AND SELECTION 36
The trap bar deadlift is the only major lower-body movement I can do, due to back and rotator cuff problems. I make it as much of a squatting movement as possible, but still feel next to nothing in my quads, and I'm hurting for size there. What do you suggest?

FS36.1 Many people find that they get more quad involvement from the trap bar/shrug bar deadlift than the squat, but "many" doesn't mean everyone. I'd say you should try a slightly increased range of motion, but tread very carefully because you have a history of back problems. Try half-inch increments.

FS36.2 Start by standing on a half-inch elevation—either a couple of thin plates turned flat-side up, or flat board. Have a 45-pound or 20-kilo plate on each end of the bar, plus whatever else that might be needed to produce half to two-thirds of your usual work set weight. If the bar will be too heavy for you when loaded with 45-pound or 20-kilo plates, you'll need to use smaller plates but put blocks underneath the plates, to limit movement in order to produce the same range of motion that you would have if you were using the big plates. Alternatively, use a trap bar or shrug bar that has "extensions" or long ends, to enable it to be used inside a power rack. Set the rack pins at the height to position the bar where it would be if loaded on the floor with full-sized plates. (The conventional trap bar and shrug bar are too short to use inside a power rack.)

FS36.3 Set up a tripod, or have someone help you out, and video tape your form from the side—zoom the camera in to get a close up of your back positioning. Also, get someone to crouch down—to get his eyes at your hip height when you're at the bottom position—to check out your back position.

FS36.4 If you can maintain a flat back at the bottom of the increased-range-of-motion deadlift, and have no immediate negative reaction, then try another set with an additional half an inch elevation—one inch total. Don't work to failure, but work enough to determine whether you feel more quad involvement. When at home, check out the video recording of your form, to see for yourself how your back was. If all is well, and you have no negative back reaction the following day or few, come back the following week and try another half an inch of elevation. If that goes well, then at your next workout try another half inch and thus a full two inches of elevation. Two inches can make a big difference for increasing quad involvement. I'd suggest you stick with that for a couple of months before considering going any higher, but only consider going higher if you still don't feel enough quad involvement.

FS36.5 Using 35-pound plates as your biggest diameter plates on the trap bar/shrug bar will produce an instant increase of about an inch and a half in range of motion (relative to that from a 45-pound plate), and that could be asking for trouble. Much better to play safe and take it half an inch at a time. Using smaller-diameter plates would increase the range of motion even further, and be a recipe for ruin for many people.

EXERCISE FORM AND SELECTION 37
I'm 6-0 tall and, relatively speaking, have a long torso and correspondingly short legs. What's the general rule for which is the better exercise—squats or bent-legged deadlifts—for my body type? I've had moderate success with both exercises but I'm looking to drop one of them from my program.

FS37.1 The general rule is that short legs and a long torso, relatively speaking, produce a better squatter than deadlifter. Long legs and a short torso, relatively speaking, produce a better deadlifter than squatter. This should show itself in terms of the poundages you can lift in the two exercises. Assuming the *same* degree of effort and commitment to both exercises, and a comparable degree of form expertise, a "better squatter" will squat more weight than he can deadlift (or use about the same for both), comparing the same reps; but a "better deadlifter" will be able to deadlift a lot more weight than he can squat.

EXERCISE FORM AND SELECTION 38
How can I increase my hamstrings involvement in the stiff-legged deadlift and Romanian deadlift?

FS38.1 In a nutshell, the Romanian deadlift is a stiff-legged deadlift from just below knee height, with no pause at the bottom of the movement—the bar is not rested on rack pins between reps. The stress is not unloaded in the bottom position, unlike how it often is in partial deadlifting, stiff-legged or otherwise. Also, the degree of knee flexion in the Romanian deadlift is minimal, probably less than most people use in the stiff-legged deadlift.

FS38.2 Regardless of which variation you use, and the Romanian variety will probably stress your hamstrings the most, keep your hips thrust to the rear, your back slightly arched, and legs bent just the minimum to take stress off your knees. The emphasis on keeping your hips pushed to the rear can make the difference between feeling a lot of strain on your hamstrings, and feeling very little.

FS38.3 Your back must never be allowed to round. Rounding of the back—as well as hugely increasing stress on your vertebrae and inter-vertebral discs, and making injury almost inevitable sooner rather than later—also takes stress off the hamstrings. Keeping your hips pushed to the rear, together with keeping your shoulder blades retracted, helps to keep your lower back in the strong slightly-arched position, which is essential both for safety and to maximize stress on the hamstrings.

EXERCISE FORM AND SELECTION 39
My right arm seems to want to flare outward on bench presses, but I would like to keep it against my lats. What do you think is the "weak link" causing this problem? I switched from barbells to dumbbells because the flare was causing me to bench press crookedly. The problem is not as extreme with dumbbells, but I would like my right and left sides to develop equally. Any suggestions?

FS39.1 From a distance I can't accurately answer this. A number of reasons may account for or contribute to this problem. I recommend that you find a chiropractor to check you out, preferably one with experience of weight training. An expert one should find whether or not you have any muscular imbalances or structural explanations that account for your problem. Then take the appropriate action to remedy matters. I've had enough experience of chiropractors to know that an expert one can perform near miracles, and find solutions to problems that you would never have discovered yourself. Sometimes the solutions are very fast. An expert chiropractor can be one of the most valuable allies you'll get to help you train productively over the long term.

FS39.2   Following the input of an expert therapist, and the appropriate corrective actions, I'd suggest you reduce your dumbbell poundage to that which you can easily handle while keeping your right elbow where it should be. Then slowly (over a couple of months, or longer) build up the weights while keeping the form perfect. If you rush the poundage progression you'll return to the old asymmetrical form.

EXERCISE FORM AND SELECTION 40
I read an article that advised trainees to use mental isolation (extreme concentration) to work the target muscle by keeping only the desired muscle (quadriceps in the case of squats) tense during a set, and letting other secondary muscles relax. What do you think?

FS40.1   This is a recipe for injury. For the big exercises it's imperative that *all* the naturally involved musculature is heavily involved in the movement. If you try to shift stress off some areas where it's naturally designed to be, and focus it on one area only, you'll distort form, apply exaggerated stress to one or more areas/joints, and make injury almost inevitable sooner or later.

EXERCISE FORM AND SELECTION 41
I'm thinking of buying a vertical leg press machine. I know that Hammer and some other companies make good machines, but I can't afford that type. I can't do squats as they hurt my lower back, and I can't go to parallel. I've found a vertical leg press that only costs $279.00, new. What do you think? I know I need to train my legs hard, but is this type of machine bad for the knees or the lower back?

FS41.1 What you can't afford most of all is a knee or back injury that wrecks your training. Vertical leg press machines are often among the worst of machines. One that costs less than $300.00, new, is almost certainly going to be bad news for your knees and lower back. Even much more costly non-vertical leg press machines can be very hostile to the knees and lower back.

FS41.2 For a little more than half of $279.00 you can get a shrug bar or trap bar, with which you can perform a squatlift. Though the exercise looks like a deadlift, it's really a squat with the bar in your hands. Not only is it safer than a vertical leg press—if used properly—but it's a much better training tool. There's absolutely no comparison. And relative to the barbell squat, the trap bar or shrug bar squatlift can give your legs lots of work *without* such heavy lower-back involvement.

EXERCISE FORM AND SELECTION 42
The Jefferson lift sounds like a very effective exercise, a la regular deadlifts, but is it a safe one? I'm concerned because no one seems to use this exercise. There must be some reason for this.

FS42.1 The Jefferson lift is a form of the deadlift, but with your legs straddling the bar, and one hand holding the bar in front of you, and the other holding to the rear. This is an awkward movement that produces a great deal of torque. This rotational force greatly increases the risk of injury. This movement is so inferior to a deadlift—regular, sumo, trap bar or shrug bar— that there's no comparison.

EXERCISE FORM AND SELECTION 43
I seem to able to do parallel bar dips with plenty of weight (over 60 kilos around my waist for 8 reps). My bodyweight is around 75–80 kilos. But my bench press has never really come on, and in my last twelve-week cycle I only managed to finish on 75 kilos for 7 reps. My routines are centered around the 20-rep squat and my squat poundage has improved to 140 kilos for the full 20 reps. Is it possible that my bench press technique is wrong, or will I never be able to bench press a lot of weight?

FS43.1 Your dip poundage (60 plus 75 kilos bodyweight) is well ahead of your bench (75 kilos). For a "typical" trainee, when comparing the same reps, the total weight for these two movements should be similar. You have 135 versus 75. That's a huge discrepancy which suggests something is amiss with the bench press in your case. I doubt that technique flaws alone could account for such a discrepancy, considering you're not a novice.

FS43.2 If I was you I'd ignore the bench press and focus on doing what I could do much better. Why knock yourself out on an exercise for little progress when you can do a comparable movement miles better? The dip, however, is actually a better exercise than the bench press because it works more musculature. In your case, the dip is a hugely more productive exercise. I wouldn't worry about the bench press. I'd focus on getting even better at the dip. Once you have bodyweight around your waist, for a set of perfect reps, you're going to have very decent triceps and chest development. Then if someone pokes fun at your not benching, just ask him if he can dip with his bodyweight around his waist. Very few people can dip with 45 kilos or 100 pounds around their waists, let alone their entire bodyweight.

EXERCISE FORM AND SELECTION 44
At least for me, the technique for the L-fly you describe in your form book feels awkward. Do you have any tips for making the exercise feel better?

FS44.1 Here's a tip care of John Christy, for the lying L-fly: Place a small rolled-up towel between your side and your upper arm. The thickness of the rolled-up towel should be no more than two inches. Try this tip and see if it helps.

EXERCISE FORM AND SELECTION 45
I'm able to do 40–45 crunches with strict form—but my neck is killing me. It's like I've a 90-pound plate attached to my head. I've no problem with my neck any other time, and it appears to recover just fine; but after hitting crunch #25 or so, my neck really gets sore. Are my neck muscles just weak and working to catch up, or is this an indicator I'm performing the crunch incorrectly?

FS45.1 It could be either, or even both. If you're following the instructions given in my exercise technique book, you'll not be pulling on your head with your hands, as many people do. So that can't be causing or contributing to a neck problem. That you're not suffering post-workout discomfort indicates you're probably not causing any lasting damage. But the neck soreness during the course of each set of crunch situps may mar your performance, and needs to be addressed.

FS45.2 You don't need to perform 40–45 crunches. When performing the crunch situp, the neck musculature is involved in holding your head in position. When the set is of a long duration—40–45 reps is a *long* set—your neck is going to get tired. You note that rep #25 is about the point where neck discomfort kicks in. I suggest you keep your rep count below 25, and add resistance sufficient to cut your reps from 40–45 to 25 maximum. Even 25 reps is a high number. You might want to try a ceiling of 15. When adding resistance, to cut your reps, don't add a lot of weight in one go so that you immediately struggle to get your new ceiling rep count. Build it up over several weeks, so that there's a gradual increase in resistance, and your body can adapt without any negative effects.

FS45.3 With the increased resistance you may experience neck discomfort at a lower rep count than around the 25 mark with no resistance. Some neck soreness shouldn't be a problem providing it goes away quickly and is not injurious. After a few weeks of acclimatization, you may find that you no longer have any neck discomfort. If neck discomfort continues, experiment with slightly different head positions—chin down more, or chin up more, for example. Try something a little different each workout, and see if it affects the degree of neck discomfort. Keep what helps, drop what hinders.

EXERCISE FORM AND SELECTION 46
I'm confused about pronated and supinated grips. In your book on technique, page 27, you describe a supinated grip as both palms facing you, and a pronated grip as both facing away from you. On page 132 a supinated grip is recommended, but in the picture on page 133 the model is shown with a grip where both palms are facing away from him. Is this not a pronated grip? Also, on page 66, a pronated grip is recommended for a deadlift. On page 73, the model is shown performing the sumo deadlift. His palms are facing him, which would seem to me to be a supinated grip.

FS46.1   The photo caption on page 133 of the book on exercise technique should have been "Pullups on a well-knurled bar of a Smith machine. Note the pronated grip."

FS46.2   On page 73 of the form book the model is using a pronated grip for the sumo deadlift. His palms *are* facing him. The "palms facing away from you" description of a pronated grip applies when you have your hands overhead (like in a pullup) or flexed (like in the top position of a reverse curl). I should have made this point clear in the technique book.

FS46.3   For exercises where the arms are not raised or flexed, such as the deadlift and shrug, a pronated grip has your palm facing towards you; and a supinated grip has your wrist turned inward so that your palm faces away from you.

FS46.4   A pronated grip for both hands is recommended for the deadlift until you reach your ceiling for that style; then you should move to a mixed grip. See T76 for help with your grip for the deadlift.

FS46.5   In the bottom position of the reverse curl, a pronated grip (like in the deadlift) has your palms facing you. But in the *top* position of the reverse curl, when your arms are fully flexed, the pronated grip has your palms facing away from you.

EXERCISE FORM AND SELECTION 47
What's the difference between chins and pullups, and which is the best to use in a program?

FS47.1   Chins are performed with a supinated grip (palms facing you while your arms are overhead), and pullups with a pronated grip (palms facing away from you while your arms are overhead).

FS47.2   "Which is best" depends on the individual. If the supinated grip produces wrist or elbow discomfort that doesn't desist following adaptation after a workout or few, but the pronated grip produces no negative reaction, then the latter is the one for you. But in most cases, a slightly closer or slightly wider hand spacing can make the supinated grip work. A slight change in hand spacing can make a big difference.

FS47.3   All things being equal—including both grips producing no negative reaction—chins are superior to pullups, because they put the body in a stronger position (especially the biceps),

work the lats through a longer range of motion, and usually
permit more resistance to be used. More resistance in good
form without reducing the range of motion, and without
compromising safety, means a more productive exercise.

EXERCISE FORM AND SELECTION 48
I need a summary of how to perform the eight exercises in my current program (spread over two different workouts), as a spot check so I can see whether or not I'm really using good form.

FS48.1 There's no substitute for the full scoop, which can be found in
THE INSIDER'S TELL-ALL HANDBOOK ON WEIGHT-TRAINING TECHNIQUE,
including many photographs. That said, here's a summary:

Squat
FS48.2 Is the bar really in the right place on your traps? Are your heels
really spaced properly, and your feet really flared enough? Are
you really never rounding your back, and are you really
exercising control?

FS48.3 Bend your head forward and place a hand at the base of your
neck. You should feel a vertebra that's noticeably more
prominent than the others above and below it. The bar must be
underneath that bony prominence, and as low on your traps as
you can comfortably hold it.

FS48.4 Your heels should be no closer than hip width. Many people
squat better with their heels further apart—more like 18–20
inches or so. This is an individual thing. Find what makes you
feel the most stable and comfortable. But heel spacing is only
part of getting the stance correct. Another major part is the
degree of foot flare—how far you have your toes turned out.
You need to experiment with both variables at the same time.

FS48.5 Many people squat with their feet almost parallel. Just turning
out their toes can make a world of difference. Imagine your feet
are the hands of a clock. Start with your feet positioned at five
minutes to one. Some people will need to turn their toes out a bit
more, so consider the five-to-one position the starting point, and
fine-tune from there.

FS48.6 With a good stance you can squat a bit deeper *without* rounding
your lower back, than you can with a poor stance. With an

unloaded bar, and using your optimal stance and toe flare, find the depth of descent at which your lower back *just* starts to round. Your maximum safe depth of squatting is about two inches above that point, to build in a margin for error. Set the power rack safety pins so that you can't go deeper than that point.

FS48.7   Keep your chest stuck out, head up, and knees travelling directly over your toes. Your knees should never come inward as you ascend. If they do, it's likely because your stance is wrong, and perhaps you have inflexible inner thighs (adductors) too.

Bench press

FS48.8   Are you really lowering the bar to your lower pec line? Are you really lowering the bar under full control and *gently* grazing your chest, as against bouncing it? Are you really keeping your elbows tucked in? Are you really avoiding an exaggerated grip?

FS48.9   At the bottom of the movement your forearms should be vertical, as seen from the side *and* the front (by an assistant). If they aren't, your grip spacing is amiss and/or your bar pathway is wrong. About 21 inches between index fingers is about right for most men, and about 4 inches closer for women. With the right grip, and lowering to the pec line (below the nipples), your forearms should be properly positioned at the bottom. On the ascent, push up and only *slightly* to the rear, keeping your elbows tucked in and directly below your hands—never let your elbows flare out.

Stiff-legged deadlift

FS48.10 Are you really keeping the bar brushing or almost brushing your legs on every ascent and descent? Are you really avoiding an excessive range of motion? Are you really *never* letting your back descend to beneath parallel to the ground (but better to stay a little *above* the parallel position)? Are you really using an impeccably smooth cadence, with absolutely no sudden movements? And are you really *never* rounding your back?

FS48.11 This exercise is often made into a back wrecker by performing it on a bench or box (to exaggerate the range of motion), and by using jerky movements. The *lowest* bar position should be where it is when resting on the floor loaded with 45-pound or 20-kilo plates. If you use smaller diameter plates, you'll need to elevate the plates (or bar) so that your range of motion is not exaggerated.

Chin

FS48.12 Have you really found the grip that best suits you and which doesn't produce any negative elbow reaction? Are you really keeping tight at the bottom, and *not* allowing your shoulders to relax? Are you really moving *smoothly* up and down? Are you really adding just a tad of iron every week or two or three—so little that you can't detect it, but doing it with consistency?

Seated dumbbell press

FS48.13 Are you really handling the dumbbells with control? If you can't get them into the starting position with perfect control, employ assistants. Are you really keeping the dumbbells above your shoulders, and *not* letting them drift to the sides? Are you really pressing with your back supported by a slightly inclined bench? Are you really avoiding an exaggerated arch in your lower back?

Side bend

FS48.14 Are you really moving to the sides *only*? Are you really moving smoothly without any snappy movements? Are you really avoiding an exaggerated depth of descent?

Dumbbell curl

FS48.15 Are you really only moving at your elbows and wrists? Are you really not arching your lower back? Are you really not allowing your elbows to travel forward, i.e., are you keeping them at your sides? Don't try to get your hands up to chin level—mid pec is the highest they should get to. Are you really lifting and lowering under perfect control, as against jerking and dropping?

Lying L-fly

FS48.16 Are you really moving with impeccably smooth, slow form? Are you really keeping your upper arm firmly against your side (or against a rolled up towel placed between your arm and side), and *never* allowing your upper arm to lose contact? Are you really putting form before resistance? Are you really raising the resistance as high as you can?

EXERCISE FORM AND SELECTION 49
In your technique book you described a stretch (page 196) for the Achilles tendons. Is this accurate?

FS49.1 It would have been better to have referred to it as an ankle and calf stretch. To squat and deadlift well you need flexible ankles and calves (*and* hamstrings, glutes and adductors).

If today you weigh about the same as you did six months ago, how can you have MUCH bigger muscles? It just isn't possible unless you've lost a lot of bodyfat. If you're on the lean side, you MUST become heavier if you want bigger muscles.

To develop much bigger muscles it's usually necessary to become a lot stronger. To become a lot stronger you need to build a lot of new tissue, which has WEIGHT. To become heavier you must consume a caloric and nutritional surplus. Don't slow your rate of progress to a snail's pace, or kill it altogether, by not consuming enough calories and nutrients. Perhaps a mere extra 500 calories (from high quality sources) and 50 grams of protein EVERY day can make the difference between good progress and no progress. But some trainees are undersupplying a lot more nutrition that that. GIVE YOUR ALL IN THE GYM, BUT DON'T CUT CORNERS OUT OF IT!

Nutrition

NUTRITION 1
Like you, I've experimented with vegetarianism and veganism. In fact, I've experimented with many other diets too: raw foodism, Atkins, CKD, etc. Presently, I'm following a paleolithic or "cave man" diet. Basically, the diet's main premise is to eat whatever would be available if all you had was a pointed stick: fruits, vegetables, meats, seafood, eggs and nuts; but no dairy (hence no whey protein or milk), grains, tubers, legumes, fermented products, processed products, etc. My question is, how "lifter friendly" is this diet?

N1.1   There's no universal answer because there are many individual variations. But ridding your diet of junk and processed food is an excellent thing to do. The diet may work well *providing* you can comfortably digest all the approved foods, enjoy them, and eat them in sufficient quantities and proportions to meet your dietary needs (calories *and* nutrients). But one person's meat can be another person's poison, so to speak, and what on paper may sound good may in practice not work. Personally, I'd struggle on this diet because I won't eat meat, and my digestive system can't handle nuts. The bottom line, as far as whether or not this diet is "lifter friendly" for you, is to test it for a sustained period.

NUTRITION 2
I was wondering what you think of a CKD-type regime. This would seem to be an extreme diet over what you put forth in your books.

N2.1   Personally, I'd not use a full cyclical ketogenic diet (CKD) as I believe that *for me* it's not healthy. People vary in the sort of diet that can work for them. What might work well for one person can have harmful effects for others. I prefer a mixed diet, though I don't eschew fats. I'm a strong believer is being generous with *healthful* fats—e.g., virgin olive oil, oily fish, avocados, raw seeds and nuts (if you can digest them well). Personally, I don't eat any meat, and meat is a staple for most people who follow a CKD.

N2.2   Skewed diets that almost eliminate one of the macronutrients will be harmful for many people, if not most people, *at least if carried out over the medium- or long-term.* A very low fat diet (fewer than 10% of calories as fats) is just as skewed as a diet that almost eliminates carbs. While short-term uses of skewed diets for specific purposes is one thing—and often a good thing for some people—sticking with them over the *long* term is something else. *Generally speaking,* a CKD is more suited to fat loss while holding muscular mass, than for overall gaining.

N2.3   If you do use a CKD schedule, albeit for a short period, avoid junk food, hydrogenated fat, fried food and heated fat/oils— especially when exposed to air, e.g., scrambled eggs. While the CKD schedule is primarily a percentages thing (approximately 25–35% protein, 5% carbs and 60–70% fat), and typically includes a 1–2 day(s) "carb-up" phase each week, there's *much more* to it than that. *How* you produce the percentages plays a huge role in the impact the diet makes on your body and health. If you get most of your fat from fried food, greasy meat, over-cooked meat, cured and processed food, scrambled eggs, margarine and junk food, then the effect of that on your health will be different to if you got most of your fat from much more healthful sources, *even though the overall percentages of macronutrients may be exactly the same in both cases.*

N2.4   Two of the potential problems of a CKD schedule are insufficient micronutrient and fiber intake. A dietary fiber supplement is a very good idea, but getting a decent amount of fiber from low-carb vegetables is better because along with the fiber comes a good supply of micronutrients. High-carb vegetables such as potatoes are out while in a CKD, but most vegetables (and salad items) are low-carb and can be eaten in large quantities.

NUTRITION 3
Is it important to consume 50 grams of protein and 50 grams of carbs within an hour after a workout? I try to keep my diet 40/40/20 (protein/carbs/fat). Is that right if want to gain muscle?

N3.1 Depending on your size, I'd strongly recommend that you consume 30–50 grams of protein and 60–100 grams of carbs within a quarter of an hour or so of finishing your workout. Drink plenty of water during training and immediately after. Make the post-workout feed a liquid one, for easier digestion. Then within two hours have another liquid feed, or a meal of solid food. It's very important to get quality easy-to-digest food in you soon after training.

N3.2 The 40/40/20 (protein/carbs/fat) schedule is very high on protein. Suppose you're consuming 3,600 calories, that would mean 1,440 calories from protein, which computes to 360 grams. That's vast (unless you're huge), and an expensive way of getting calories.

N3.3 As long as your diet is reasonable, and you're in caloric surplus, your bodybuilding progress will be almost totally a reflection of your training *and* how well you recover between workouts. Getting those two factors in terrific order should be your focus, not fine-tuning a few percentage points of any macronutrient.

NUTRITION 4
Should protein from vegetables and grain products form part of the one-gram-per-pound of lean bodyweight that's often advised for bodybuilders and strength trainees? I'm concerned I may be getting insufficient protein because I only take 85 grams per day from animal sources (fish and milk). My other 90 grams come from plant sources.

N4.1 Perhaps your progress is being limited by insufficient gross protein intake, or by insufficient animal protein consumption. Or perhaps it's more related to insufficient *caloric* intake in general. Many hard gainers simply don't consume enough calories, and no protein quantity or quality can compensate for a caloric deficit if you're trying to gain muscular mass. The first thing you need to check on is caloric intake.

N4.2 Follow a training program that's been proven productive for you in the recent past, and be sure you're in the intensive stage of the cycle (where there's growth potential), *not* merely the initial "breaking in" period. Measure your bodyfat percentage, or a single fat fold, or at the very minimum take your waist girth. Make a written record, and include the precise conditions you used for the measurement(s).

N4.3   Increase your daily caloric intake by 200 calories, from across all three macronutrients. Stick with that for a few weeks, and see if your rate of strength gain increases, and if your bodyfat increases (using the *exact* same method of measuring as previously). If there's a gain in bodyfat, then your initial caloric intake was about right, and you need to return to it. If there's no gain in bodyfat, increase by a further 100–200 calories, and keep repeating the process until you detect a bodyfat increase. Then cut back a little, and stick with that caloric intake for the immediate future.

N4.4   I'm writing here about the general training situation—slow and steady gains in muscle accompanied by minimal or no gain in bodyfat. For short-term modified "bulking" programs—during periods of "optimal" training and recovery where all the components are maximized (see BEYOND BRAWN Chapter 8)—a much faster rate of muscular gain *along with* an acceptance of more bodyfat too, is the agenda, so a greater caloric intake would be needed for that short period of a month or few.

N4.5   As your muscular bodyweight increases, so must your caloric intake if you want to gain further—by something like 30–40 calories per day per pound of additional muscle. The caloric intake that took you from 160 pounds to 170, for example, but *without* increasing your bodyfat noticeably, won't be enough to take you from 170 to 180 pounds.

N4.6   Once you're consuming the *maximum* caloric intake you can without gaining noticeable fat, *only then* should you start experimenting with protein quantity and quality. You must, however, be consistent with your caloric intake. If some days you skip a feed or two, that will throw the whole process out of whack, and put a brake on your progress. Many people are consistent with their training, but don't apply the same consistency to their nutrition. Then the latter plays havoc with the results that accrue from the former.

N4.7   Now that you're consuming the maximum caloric intake you can (without gaining noticeable fat), boost your *animal* protein intake so that you're taking in one gram per pound of bodyweight of it, or thereabouts. Make this adjustment over at least a few weeks, to give your digestive tract some time to adapt to the change. Then stick with this new intake for a sustained period, and keep other variables as constant as possible—training intensity, volume and frequency, caloric intake, and rest and sleeping habits. (If you change any of these variables, that will render the experiment meaningless.) See if the substantial protein boost accelerates your rate of progress in the gym. You'll need to be very meticulous with your nutritional "accounting" if this experiment is to be meaningful.

N4.8 This can't be a perfectly controlled experiment because there are many variables at play, but perform it as carefully as you can, and you should get an idea of the influence of changes in protein quantity and quality.

N4.9 I recommend you experiment with more protein than a gram of animal protein per pound or so of bodyweight. I suggest you increase your animal protein intake to 1.25 grams per pound of bodyweight for a couple of months, and compare training results. If you find that your training progress quickens, try even more protein. Perhaps you have a very big need for protein. Remember to keep increasing your caloric intake in line with increases in muscular bodyweight, otherwise your progress will grind to a halt.

NUTRITION 5
I've been a big consumer of cow's milk all of my life (including 18 years as a serious weight trainer) without any problems. It's a very convenient source of protein. Recently I've read that cow's milk may be bad for humans. I'm not sure I believe this. However, lately I've been substituting low-fat soy milk as it's meant to be helpful in preventing heart disease. Do you think soy milk is a reasonable substitute for cow's milk?

N5.1 Especially in the area of nutrition, there's a great deal of individual variation. One man's meat truly can be another's poison. One of my daughters, for example, likes soya products and they seem to agree with her digestive system. But the other girl, comparing the same meals that her younger sister eats too, experiences digestive tract discomfort from soya products. Soya products—including soya milk—give me digestive tract discomfort; and the same goes for my wife. So in the McRobert household, we've three "against" soya products, and one "for." No matter how "healthy" soya products are supposed to be, if they produce digestive tract discomfort for a given individual, they can't be healthy *for that person*.

N5.2   In Cyprus, soy milk is about four times the cost of cow's milk (at the time of writing, in 2000), and in the US soy milk is usually more expensive than cow's milk. Such a cost difference may make soy milk prohibitively expensive for people who drink a lot of milk while having to manage on a tight budget.

N5.3   I think soy milk is a reasonable substitute for cow's milk but only if the product produces no digestive tract discomfort.

NUTRITION 6
I know it's good to keep an everyday log on what I eat and the values in everything I consume. How can I find out about the calories, protein and fat values in the food I eat?

N6.1   Visit a library or bookstore, and go to the section on nutrition. There you should find a nutritional reference book that focuses on listing the caloric and nutritional values of individual foods. If you can't find a book that focuses only on caloric and nutritional content, check out the rear of a reputable book on nutrition. What's given there may be enough to meet your needs. What you especially need is the caloric value of food, along with macronutrient values—protein, carbohydrate and fat.

NUTRITION 7
I'm 200 pounds. I read that I need six meals each of approximately 42 grams of protein and 78 grams of carbs. If I consume say two pints of skimmed milk for my protein source—about 38–40 grams of protein—do I include the carbs from milk in my calculations, or do carbs have to be starch-type, like potato or rice? Also, is fruit a good source of carbs?

N7.1   I'm all for being organized over diet, and consuming the required caloric and macronutrient intakes each day. But don't take it to the extreme and get carried away. I'd rather you got carried away with making sure you give your all to training in an intensive, safe and progressive way on a handful of big exercises. Providing your diet is in good order, and you're consuming a caloric surplus, you'll gain well even if the protein and carbs quantities vary a bit from day to day.

N7.2   Providing you're getting a gram a day of animal protein per pound of bodyweight, it's highly unlikely that your gains are going to be negated by protein deficiency *assuming you're not short of calories* (but more protein *may* speed gains up). If you get overly focused on numbers in your diet, there's a good chance you'll lose some focus on your training. But for sure you should try an experiment where you consume more protein—see N4.

N7.3	Carbs are carbs regardless of whether you get them from milk, starchy food or fruit. They all have the same caloric value. You should get your carbs from a variety of food. Fruit is an excellent source of carbs *and* nutrients, and it makes sense to include fruit in your daily diet, and over time consume a variety of fruit.

NUTRITION 8
Did you notice a significant difference in your progress in the gym when you started eating fish? I'm a strict vegetarian (not a vegan though). I get most of my protein from milk, tofu, eggs, beans plus rice, cheese, and some brand-name protein drinks. From your experience with veganism and vegetarianism, do you think I'm holding back my bodybuilding progress by not eating meat? I usually get 160–230 grams of protein a day (I weigh 190 pounds). I also take a multivitamin (plus vitamins E and C) most days of the week.

N8.1	I didn't notice any difference in my progress in the gym when I started eating fish. The addition of the eggs made a dramatic difference, but no other dietary change has made any comparable difference. Had I added milk as my only source of animal protein after I broke with the strict veganism, or just fish, I think I'd have had the same dramatic change I experienced. It just happened to be eggs that I added first.

N8.2	If you keep at the upper end of the 160–230 grams range of protein intake per day, that may be more than enough for you but *only* if you're not short of calories overall, and the protein is mostly from animal sources. I'd suggest you experiment with increased protein intake, as outlined in N4.

N8.3	Is not eating meat holding back your progress? Maybe, maybe not. You'd have to experiment to see. Remove 60 grams of protein from non-meat sources, and substitute 60 grams from meat, keeping the total daily caloric intake the same; and keep your training program (and rest and sleep schedules) the same as before the dietary change. Then see if your progress in the gym changes. If it accelerates, the meat would appear to help. Before you try this, assuming you want to do such a thing, I suggest you try the experiment with fish rather than meat from land animals.

NUTRITION 9
Why don't you eat meat? What protein sources do you use? Can eating a lot of meat affect one's health? In the past I've thought of eating less meat, but assumed my lifting would be affected.

N9.1   I don't eat any kind of land animal, and haven't since about 1979. I don't eat these animals due to my own personal value system, which I'm not trying to impose on anyone. My meat-free diet is a fall back to my days as a total vegan (no meat, fish, eggs or dairy products) when I lived by a philosophy that wanted to cause the absolute minimum of suffering to animals. I paid an unacceptably high price physically for the veganism, and had to move to a mixed diet but one that still excluded land animals. Generally speaking, I believe animal protein is necessary for very good progress with the weights. There will be exceptions to the general rule, but even then the addition of some animal protein (perhaps not a lot) may hasten progress, *providing that caloric intake and total protein consumption are sufficient.*

N9.2   Even if eating land animals would help me to gain muscle and strength, I still wouldn't eat meat. My personal conscience comes before my appearance and performance. But perhaps eating meat wouldn't help me in the gym anyway. I've no comparison to make training wise between a diet that includes meat and one that excludes meat but while including other types of animal protein.

N9.3   I get animal protein from milk, eggs, fish and cheese. Some people seem more suited to meat than others, and are less likely to suffer negative effects. Meat varies in its quality, as does all food, and I don't doubt that an excess of meat, or the "wrong" sort of meat, is unhealthy. Of course, plenty of other food is harmful.

N9.4   A visit to a slaughterhouse (euphemistically called an abattoir) might affect your views on whether or not you eat meat.

NUTRITION 10
Do you think adding fish or chicken to a vegetarian (but not vegan) diet would help bodybuilding progress?

N10.1   Maybe, maybe not. It would depend on the individual, and
            what kind of vegetarian (but not vegan) diet was being
            followed. A vegetarian diet that includes a gallon of milk, six
            eggs and half a pound of cheese each day, along with fruit,
            vegetables and grains is very different to one that has no milk,
            and just one egg and a couple of slices of cheese each day,
            along with otherwise vegan fare. The vegetarian diet with the
            least animal protein in it is likely to get the most benefit from
            additional animal protein in the form of fish or chicken. The
            bottom line is individual experimentation, and finding what
            actually happens *for you*.

N10.2   On a personal front, I don't recall any noticeable benefit to my
            training progress when I added fish to my diet. At the time I
            was already consuming generous quantities of animal protein
            from dairy products and eggs.

NUTRITION 11
Any time you talk about your diet, you mention "and some cheeses." May I ask what particular cheeses you endorse, and which you avoid? Maybe some reasoning behind each?

N11.1   I'd "endorse" the mild cheeses that have not needed much
            maturing time, and ones with the fewest additives. I never eat
            any of the really mature "ripened" cheeses, such as the blue
            ones. And I prefer cheeses without coloring.

NUTRITION 12
You've written that a baseline is needed to determine your caloric needs for weight gain or loss. What if you don't eat right to begin with? Some days, meals are skipped and some are not up to par nutritionally to begin with. What should I do? If I'm not eating right to begin with, wouldn't my baseline be a false reading?

N12.1   You should begin by actually eating right in terms of meal
            consistency, frequency and quality. Once you're consistently
            eating five or preferably six times a day, of good quality food
            each time, and are pretty much consistent with your overall
            quantity of food each day, *then* it's time to find the baseline, and
            go from there. You can't determine an accurate baseline if your
            diet is inconsistent.

N12.2   The baseline, though apparently primarily about calories, is really a lot more than that. Where you get the calories from is critically important. I suggest you carry out an overhaul of your diet in all respects, make good nutrition a habit, and then go from there.

NUTRITION 13
I'm confused about the type of carbohydrates I should be ingesting for bodybuilding. On the one hand I've read that insulin is a fat storage hormone, and that I should avoid high-glycemic carbohydrates. Conversely, I understand that insulin is also an anabolic hormone and that it's needed to build muscle. Wouldn't that mean I should eat high-glycemic carbohydrates?

N13.1   I think you're overcomplicating nutrition, which isn't surprising considering how much information and misinformation there is in the mainstream that distracts people from applying themselves to the real priorities. Avoid junk carbohydrates and eat a selection of quality carbs you enjoy, eat well of healthful fats, consume lots of protein, and feed every three hours or so of a nutrient-rich diet (in a caloric surplus if you want to gain size), and then put your focus on training hard and progressively on the big exercises, and getting plenty of rest and sleep.

N13.2   Getting into the fine details of carbs won't make a significant difference, *unless* you're diabetic, in which case it *is* very important. There are another two groups of people that need to be very concerned with the glycemic index: those who are hypoglycemic, and those who are following a very low-carbohydrate diet (usually a temporary diet for fat loss). For most people, however, relative to the pivotal dietary issues of eating, where on the glycemic index your carbohydrates fall is so trivial as to be insignificant.

NUTRITION 14
In an earlier answer you stated that your main source of protein is milk. Can it be unhealthy to consume eight cups of skim milk a day?

N14.1   Milk is only one of my sources of animal protein—fish, eggs and a little cheese are the others.

N14.2   Unless you have an allergy to milk, or another problem with "processing" it, I don't think eight cups (or more) of skim milk each day will do you any harm whatsoever, or even semi-skimmed milk. But I wouldn't support drinking lots of *whole* milk for long periods.

NUTRITION 15
I'm 26 years old 5-8, 155 pounds. I don't have the time or interest to eat five or six times a day, but I stay with abbreviated routines. Can I increase my measurements without gaining weight, if I keep getting stronger for reps that build mass?

N15.1   You can't gain weight if you're not in a caloric and nutritional surplus. You won't be able to build muscle without increasing your bodyweight *unless* you simultaneously drop a lot of bodyfat. If you're new to weight training you may be able to increase your strength quite a lot without increasing your bodyweight. But once you've learned the skills of lifting, and have made it through the period of adaptation to the new demands of weight training, you'll need to develop muscle if you're to go further.

N15.2   If you're say 15% bodyfat at 155 pounds, that means you have 23 pounds of fat. If you were to maintain a bodyweight of 155 pounds by paring your fat down to say 8% (which is very lean), and simultaneously increasing your muscle mass (to maintain your bodyweight at 155 pounds), you'd be down to 12 pounds of fat. That would equate to 11 pounds of additional muscle (23 minus 12), which could account for a substantial increase in strength. Such a body composition change would have a dramatic effect on your appearance.

N15.3   Gaining muscle while losing fat may be possible but probably only if you're a beginner and/or have genetics better than average. Most hard gainers are unlikely to be able to build 11 pounds of muscle while *simultaneously* losing 12 pounds of fat, down to an 8% bodyfat count. Most hard gainers are better off focusing on fat loss (while holding muscle mass) *or* muscle gain (while minimizing fat gain), rather than trying to lose fat and gain muscle simultaneously.

N15.4   Assuming you make the body composition change noted in N15.2, to go further in your development (in order to keep getting stronger), you'd have to increase your bodyweight because additional muscle would add to your 155 pounds. The alternative of dropping under 8% bodyfat while also adding muscle is something usually reserved only for drug-fed genetic phenomena.

N15.5   By limiting your dietary intake in order to maintain a bodyweight of 155 pounds at 5-8, for a male, you'd risk undersupplying important nutrients, which in turn would slow if not kill your progress in physique and strength because you'd be impairing your recovery "machinery."

NUTRITION 16
You always recommend that a trainee consume calories in excess of maintenance needs, to become bigger and stronger. What if a trainee wants to become stronger but not bigger? Should he eat a maintenance diet? What if the trainee wants to become smaller, yet stronger?

N16.1   Use abbreviated training with a focus on adding poundage in good form, but *don't* consume a caloric surplus. Consume a diet rich in nutrients, but not enough calories to cause weight gain. If your strength increases substantially, and assuming you're not a novice, your bodyfat level should decrease, and you'll stay the same weight but your body composition will change—you'll become leaner at the same weight. Further, use strength-focus training techniques that build strength but not necessarily much size—e.g., low reps, partial reps, low-rep rest-pause work.

N16.2   *If* you have good genetics, and the will to train intelligently and hard, you should be able to get a good deal stronger but without getting heavier, depending on the level you're at now. If you're already very strong with 8% bodyfat, you may be close to your limit at your *current* bodyweight, though strength-focus training may take you farther still. If you're a novice with 15% bodyfat, you have room for considerable strength gain, and body composition change, with no increase in bodyweight.

N16.3   To become *smaller* yet substantially stronger, there would have to be plenty of bodyfat to get rid of. If you're already 8% bodyfat, and an experienced trainee, that doesn't give you room for further strength gain *and* loss of bodyweight. But if you're a male with 20+% bodyfat, that gives you a lot of slack for loss of fat and hence bodyweight. By losing 20 pounds of fat, and gaining 10 pounds of muscle, for example, you could gain a lot of strength while losing bodyweight overall, and thus greatly improve your physique.

N16.4   A ceiling will eventually be reached. Your bodyfat can only go so low, and there's a limit to how much strength you can build at a given bodyweight and the same bodyfat percentage. At that point you would need to increase muscle mass to yield a substantial increase in strength.

NUTRITION 17
Do you agree with bulking up?

N17.1   To try to gain a lot of muscle while keeping bodyfat very low is a nigh-on impossible task for hard gainers. It's much easier to gain muscle while also adding some fat. Bulking up, providing it's not overdone, is the way to go for *fast* gains. A gain of a pound of fat for every 2–3 pounds of muscle is a good proportion to target. But some people get so carried away that they add 2–3 pounds of fat (or even more) for every pound of muscle. Then they end up looking more like the Michelin Man than a bodybuilder. Like with many things in life, the key is in balance and proportion.

N17.2   Bulking up can be unhealthy. Some bulkers massively increase their dietary intake over a short period of time. This is too rapid a change. For many people it will cause digestive tract distress, to put it mildly. Some bulkers eat generously of junk food, justifying it as a way to satisfy the high caloric needs they have.

N17.3   When the following three-part strategy is adopted, bulking up can be good: First, build up the increased food intake *gradually*, to allow your digestive tract time to adapt. Second, such an increase *must* coincide with very intensive, abbreviated weight training along with plenty of recovery time. If you're not stimulating growth by adding at least 5 pounds per week to your top work set of squats and deadlifts, the nutritional surplus is going to be stored as fat rather than be used to build muscle. And if you're not getting enough recovery time and sleep between workouts, you won't have the time to build muscle in response to the growth stimulation. Even a great surplus of food can't make up for insufficient recovery time and sleep between workouts. Third, eat a healthful diet.

N17.4   Just because you have increased caloric and protein needs
        doesn't mean that eating poor quality food is justified. Quality
        food is not only best for your health, it's also best for your
        training and recovery. Keep tabs on your bodyfat, and adjust
        your caloric intake accordingly. If bodyfat is coming on faster
        than muscle, then cut back on your caloric intake.

N17.5   Bulking up is a short-term strategy you use now and then, for
        periods of accelerated gains. It's very demanding because you
        need to be living a relatively leisurely life where just about all
        you do is train, eat (and drink milk), rest and sleep. There's no
        room for anything less than great generosity in all aspects.

N17.6   If done properly, bulking up can yield 10–20 pounds of muscle
        in three months or so (along with 5–10 pounds of bodyfat, which
        you'd need to trim back). Generally speaking, however, most
        people for most of the time are better off sticking with the slow
        and steady method of gaining because it's more practical.

NUTRITION 18
Isn't accurate bodyfat measuring important when regulating food intake?

N18.1   Let's say you're male and following a bulking and trimming
        schedule whereby you minimize fat gain while building size,
        and once you reach a ceiling of say 15% (for a male) you slowly
        trim back bodyfat while maintaining your muscular mass. Then
        once you're at the 10% bodyfat level you revert to bulking with
        minimum fat gain. If your bodyfat measuring is way out, what
        you may think, for example, is a percentage of 15% may actually
        only be 12%, so you'd be ending a gaining cycle prematurely. Or
        perhaps you think you're at 10% bodyfat and thus ready to start
        on a gaining cycle, but in fact your bodyfat may already be 15%
        and thus you have no leeway for a gaining cycle.

N18.2   Bodyfat measurement is important so you know where you stand,
        and how much scope you have for some fat gain while you pile
        on the muscle. But accurate bodyfat measurement is very difficult.

N18.3   For most people, use of calipers and multiple skinfolds is all that
        is practical. While you may not be able to determine your
        bodyfat percentage accurately, if you're consistent in your
        technique you can detect changes in your bodyfat; and that can
        be enough to help you. With experience you'll discover what

you consider your maximum acceptable level of bodyfat, and be able to correlate that with a percentage *according to your measurement procedure and technique*. While what you measure as 12% may in fact be more like 15%, if you deem that to be your maximum, you'll know what your (inaccurate) 12% correlates to visually. Then prior to a bulking period you'd be able to work out where you stand relative to where you need to be in order to provide the slack to be able to gain some fat while you pack on the muscular pounds *without taking you over your fat ceiling*.

N18.4   There's a problem, however, with putting a *rigid* ceiling on the point at which you move into "trimming" mode and out of "gaining" mode. Your training may be going very well, and muscular size coming on very nicely, with potential for quite a bit more in the current cycle. If you end the cycle just because you've gotten to a given bodyfat percentage, you'd be terminating that cycle prematurely, as against milking it dry.

N18.5   If fat gains are coming along too quickly, trim your caloric intake enough to curtail fat gains but without actually going into deficit that would kill size gains. One of the hardest aspects of a gaining cycle is consuming enough food to grow on but not so much that you gain too much fat and are forced to terminate the cycle prematurely.

N18.6   With experience, many people know their maximum acceptable bodyfat percentage simply by the appearance of their abs, and their waist girth—so no bodyfat measurement is actually needed.

N18.7   There's no need to get paranoid about this, but do set limits on bodyfat/waist girth, and regulate your caloric intake so that you *creep* to your upper limit of bodyfat, to permit maximum muscular gain and the full exploitation of a gaining cycle.

NUTRITION 19
What are some good concoctions for liquid feeds? I know milk is the base, but what else should I add, and how much should I drink for each feed? What do you drink for your liquid feeds?

N19.1   As far as concoctions go, you need to find mixtures that work *for you*. I just drink milk by itself (semi skim). If I add anything to it, my digestion would be hampered. Hampered digestion means fewer feeds, which means a reduction in total caloric intake.

N19.2   Quantity wise, and combination wise, if you don't get a return of hunger about two hours after the liquid feed, then you either had too much, or the combination didn't suit you.

N19.3   I suggest you add skim milk powder to the fresh milk as the first option, and perhaps a bit of vanilla flavor. Then perhaps try yogurt and/or cottage cheese. You could try a commercial protein powder if you can find one that "agrees" with your stomach.

N19.4   Keep things on the simple side, as the more ingredients you put in, the more likely you're going to run into digestive tract distress. I suggest you put in just one ingredient (and at most two) on top of the milk, other than flavoring, and find several different combinations that agree with you. Then you'll have some variety. Fruit/fruit juice when mixed with milk is an incompatible combination for the digestive systems of many people, as are yeast powder and soya products.

N19.5   If no matter what you try, the concoctions still hamper your digestion, just stick with plain milk, perhaps with a bit of flavoring for taste.

NUTRITION 20
What's your opinion on food supplements? Might they help me?

N20.1   The major problem with food supplements is that as soon as bodybuilders in particular start thinking about the things, they usually think less about matters that are most important to their progress. Then even if the diet is strengthened by food supplements, the inadequate attention on hard training, proper form, poundage progression, food nutrition, and sufficient rest and sleep, will impair if not kill gains.

N20.2   Many trainees have become walking encyclopedias on the food supplement industry and the ever-changing state of affairs there. They study articles and books on supplements with greater vigor than they study information on training. They discuss food supplements when they are with fellow lifters or bodybuilders, rather than how to make their training more productive. Yet many of these people don't know how to squat properly, never deadlift let alone know *how* to deadlift, grossly overtrain volume wise but loaf on the intensity front, skip meals, and only rarely sleep more than eight hours a night. Even if food supplements could account for a 20% "edge" on their training progress, that wouldn't compensate for cutting corners in the other areas.

N20.3   If you truly use excellent exercise form, truly train hard on an abbreviated training routine that has been tailored to meet your individual circumstances and goals, truly consume six meals/feeds a day that supply an excess of protein and calories in line with your needs, truly rest well on your off days, and truly sleep *at least* eight hours every night, you should be able to consistently add weight to each exercise, and as the months go by your muscles will grow steadily. Keep it up for a few years and you'll achieve a metamorphosis. *That* is the formula that works, *guaranteed*, and it can be done *sans* food supplements.

N20.4   *But*, as long as you have that overall package in truly sound order, *are* making good progress, and there's no risk of corner cutting in any aspect of your overall strategy, *then* you may experiment with supplements, to try to *increase* your rate of gain.

N20.5   Food supplements shouldn't be used to try to make an unproductive package into a productive one. But this is how many people use them—to try to patch up something that's no good to begin with, rather than overhaul their whole approach.

N20.6   I'm not anti-food supplements. I *am* anti a loss of focus on the pivotal priority of excellent exercise form, hard work on abbreviated routines dominated by the biggest compound exercises, a superb diet of five or preferably six quality feeds daily, lots of rest, and at least eight hours sleep per night every night.

N20.7   The problem with food supplements is not merely limited to the fact that they distract many people from much more important issues, although that alone is very serious and enough to stymie progress. Some supplements simply don't contain the listed ingredients and quantities. When some companies lie about the contents of what they produce, you can be certain that they will also lie about what the supplements are supposed to do.

N20.8   Some supplement manufacturers and marketers, in order to present an appearance of credibility, use that great marketing phrase "research has shown," make up research studies or results, select research that has nothing to do with healthy hard-training humans, or draw on research that's based on methodology utterly devoid of any scientific credibility.

N20.9   I'm *not* saying that all supplement manufacturers and marketers are guilty as above, but many are, and the bodybuilding food supplement industry has a sorry record on credibility front. As far as experimenting with bodybuilding food supplements goes, here's some of what I had to say in BEYOND BRAWN:

N20.10   "If or when you experiment with bodybuilding supplements, do not use a shotgun approach. Try one supplement for a month or so, during an intensive period of training. Only buy a minimum supply for the test period, and choose a reputable company that offers a money-back guarantee. If the supplement helps, keep it in and possibly add another. If that helps, keep it in. If a supplement makes no difference, drop it (and get your money back!) Do not use year round supplements that you find helpful. Save them for periods when you need a boost, i.e., at the end of training cycles. But still remember to keep 99% of your focus on the basic combination of training, rest and food."

NUTRITION 21
Is protein powder high on your "to try" list?

N21.1   It's one of the items to consider, but *only* as long as you've put into force what I described in the previous answer. The extra protein may or may not help you. You can only know by trial and error, assuming that all other variables are kept constant. If you go adding a lot of protein to a diet that's currently short of calories, you may produce gains, but they would be from the boost in calories that the protein supplied. If your diet is currently short of calories, you've no business experimenting with bodybuilding food supplements. You must first get *food* nutrition in 100% sound order, along with training, rest and sleep.

N21.2   A protein powder will only *potentially* help if you can digest and assimilate it well. If it produces digestive tract discomfort— stomach ache, gas, diarrhea, or delays digestion time—it can't be doing you any good. A quart of semi-skim milk every two hours, for example, would give you more nutrition than a quart every four hours with protein powder mixed in it (which ends up hindering digestion). Much better to get extra protein from increased quantities of milk and solid food, if protein powders don't "agree" with you.

N21.3   If you're lactose intolerant, avoid milk or take action as outlined in BEYOND BRAWN pages 415–417 to deal with the intolerance.

N21.4 Even the expensive "designer" protein powders produce digestive tract discomfort for many people—advertising hype doesn't give you the full story. In such cases these powders are not only a waste of money but a *hindrance* to training progress. If, however, you try several different protein powders, you may find one that "agrees" with you. The ingredient that causes a problem in one powder may not be present in another. Some trial and error will likely be needed.

N21.5 Food supplements hog the attention far too much in the training world, and way out of proportion to what the supplements can potentially deliver as far as improving strength and physique progress is concerned. But this is intentional. Food supplements are the big money earners in the training world, not training instruction or gym equipment. Food supplements offer huge potential for *repeat* sales. So the supplement hawkers are going to keep ramming their exaggerated and often criminally dishonest claims down the throats of muscle mag readers.

N21.6 For "inside" information on the commercial importance of food supplements—along with a disclosure of dishonest marketing tactics, drugs, and the good, bad and ugly of Bob Hoffman and his York Barbell Company (the former hub of the training world)—read John D. Fair's 1999 book MUSCLETOWN USA. Here are excerpts relative to food supplements:

N21.7 "By the mid-1950s York had not only survived the challenges confronting it since the war but was thriving...Business, owing largely to Hi-Proteen, was prospering again.

N21.8 "What kept York buoyant in the sixties was protein supplements. Hi-Proteen, a best seller in the 1950s, exceeded the million-dollar mark in 1960 and soon accounted for half of Hoffman's sales.

N21.9 "Hoffman had no recourse but to develop a larger stake in diet foods, where less manufacturing, shipping, and overhead left more room for profit."

N21.10 Exaggerated claims, dishonest reporting, abuse of editorial responsibility in its magazines, and utter nonsense were necessary to produce huge sales of food supplements for York. The commercial success and reprehensible marketing tactics were the forerunners for what we have today.

N21.11 I take food supplements myself, and have done so for many years—but for health benefits, not supposed bodybuilding benefits. I take supplements to ensure I get plenty of anti-oxidants—especially beta carotene, vitamins C and E, and selenium—and trace minerals. I recommend that other people take these supplements too.

N21.12 I've tried many so-called bodybuilding food supplements over the years, including several of the very big name ones, but I'm still waiting to find one that helps. I'm not unique in these experiences—ask around among people with no vested interest in food supplements.

NUTRITION 22
I've been lifting weights for over a year now and have seen very little progress. I've tried tons of supplements, every kind of creatine, and got nowhere. I'm 6-1 and 180 pounds, and would like to get to about 210, but every time I try, I just get a big gut. I've very skinny legs and can barely squat 135 pounds. Please help.

N22.1 There are many things that are wrong with the bodybuilding world. Just one of them is the stress placed on food supplements. It's an outrage that some beginners think more about how to use creatine "properly" than how to squat properly, or deadlift properly, or recover properly. Fortunes are being made from food supplement sales. The marketing bull is doing a darn good job in conning people and distracting them from the real priorities. Even rank beginners often give more attention to food supplements than how to train.

N22.2 At least for the foreseeable future, forget creatine and all other "bodybuilding food supplements." I'm not saying that prudent use of *a few* of them won't help you. But I *am* saying that no quantity or "quality" of food supplements can compensate for shortcomings in *the package* of abbreviated training, focus on the big exercises (including the squat *or* trap bar/shrug bar deadlift *or* Tru-Squat), plenty of knife-and-fork food (and milk), lots of rest and eight or more hours of sleep *every day*, and adhering to the creed of more weight on the bar in good form.

N22.3 This package of factors *works* big time. But if you cut corners on any of the factors, you risk *killing* the productivity of the whole thing. No creatine, designer whey protein, or God knows what else food supplement will compensate for compromising on any of the factors that make up *the package*.

N22.4 That you can barely squat 135 pounds is significant. Learn how to squat, then squat hard and consistently for a couple of years or so, along with a handful of other exercises. When you can squat 350 x 20 or so, then you'll be at least 210 pounds bodyweight.

N22.5 If you try to get to 210 pounds bodyweight quickly, you'll get a big gut and a lot of frustration. You want to be 210 pounds at no more than 15% bodyfat; 210 pounds at 25% bodyfat won't make you satisfied. Forget all the food supplement "solutions" and slick marketing chicanery, and stick with what really works.

NUTRITION 23
In your opinion, if everything else in your training life is correct first, can creatine monohydrate be beneficial to the hard gainer?

N23.1 Creatine monohydrate has been one of the biggest money earners in the training world, and many supplement companies have been milking it dry. Notice how so many "improved" versions of the product have been touted, often with better "delivery" systems, to get extra mileage out of sales. Here's what I say about creatine in BEYOND BRAWN, and my views haven't changed:

N23.2 "Creatine in its numerous forms has become perhaps the most popular bodybuilding supplement of the nineties (together with whey protein). For many users creatine does produce a fast gain in bodyweight over the first week or two of consumption, during the 'loading' phase. But when they go off it, they experience a loss of bodyweight. So what sort of weight did they add? Certainly not 'solid' lasting muscle. To keep that water-weight people have to keep taking creatine.

N23.3 "Creatine does not work for all users, even the genuine creatine, and even when used exactly as directed by the manufacturer. Creatine has greatly distracted many people from the priorities of proper training and food-nutrition. Rather than learning about and then applying proven strategies of how to add 10–20 pounds of solid muscle yearly, for consecutive years, many people have got caught up in the excitement of the possibility of gaining 5–10 pounds of water weight over just 1–2 weeks. But then there's the downside—the impossibility of holding all that weight while going off creatine for a long period, and the impossibility of repeating the 5–10 pounds gain experience on a cumulative basis. And of greatest importance is the fact that long-term creatine supplementation has not been proven as safe."

N23.4　Now to specifically address a point in the question: If everything in your training life is correct, you'll be gaining so well and steadily, especially for a beginner or intermediate trainee, that the appeal of a one-off gain of a few pounds of water weight won't have any attraction. Accumulating 10 or more pounds of real muscle each year for a few years will be the big attraction.

N23.5　I've heard lots of negative things about creatine—doesn't work for many people, causes diarrhea, and when it does work the gains usually but gradually fade when the creatine is dropped.

N23.6　Should creatine "work" for you, you need to keep taking it to maintain any benefits *over the long-term*, and the effects on the body of years of use are unknown. There can even be *short-term* alarming side-effects, and powerful reasons not to dabble with creatine or fall foul of the hoopla and shenanigans of its hawkers. Father William Keebler, Jr.—a priest of the Catholic Diocese of Peoria, IL, USA—wrote, unsolicited, to let me know the following:

N23.7　"I'm 44 years old and had a physical for some life insurance program, and while the blood work was fantastic, the blood pressure was horrible and there was blood in the stool. The doctor ran complete tests and found nothing and asked if I was '...GNC'n it...' and if so, get off the creatine. I got off the creatine (why I continued taking it after reading BEYOND BRAWN was foolishness, I admit) and lost no strength or muscle, but I did lose the high blood pressure and the blood in the stool.

N23.8　"No kidding, on creatine my blood pressure was terrible and within three weeks of getting off creatine—never to be touched again—my blood pressure is almost too good, with an athlete's resting pulse. My resting pulse has dropped twenty beats per minute, and that's a fact. Thank goodness I had a good doctor who identified the problem."

N23.9　This is serious. Heed the warning.

NUTRITION 24
Which are the best supplements for fat loss?

N24.1   Relative to the role of diet in general, and energy in and energy out (and staying in caloric deficit), the potential value of supplements "for fat loss" is so insignificant as to be negligible. I'd urge you to focus on the 99+% of what matters.

N24.2   The mainstream training literature distracts people from the basics, and gives excessive attention to the maybes of nutrition and training. Much of the mainstream has a vested interest in the sale of food supplements. Consider that some of the big magazines are published by/intertwined with food supplement companies. Such magazines are hardly sources of unbiased information on food supplements. Quite the opposite, of course, and some of their articles are poorly disguised ads for the supplements that their sister or master companies sell.

NUTRITION 25
How much protein can I assimilate at a given meal?

N25.1   I can't say because this is an individual matter. Individuals vary in their abilities to digest and assimilate food. Further, how a given quantity of protein is supplied can affect digestion and assimilation greatly. A quart of milk and a large meat sandwich may each supply a similar quantity of protein, but one may digest a lot faster than the other.

N25.2   An 19-year old in hard training may be able to process 50+ grams of protein and be ravenous for more food inside two hours. But come age 35, things will have changed. While as a teenager the 50+ grams of protein could have come from any mixture of food, by age 35 the digestive efficiency will have decreased markedly, and some food combinations will likely take much longer to digest than others.

N25.3   What matters is what *you* can comfortably process now. If you want to grow bigger muscles, you need to be in caloric and nutrient surplus, and consume nourishment every three hours or so, with a good amount of protein at each feed. Select food types, quantities and combinations so you can process nourishment well enough for your appetite to return within three hours. If you can't achieve this, you're going to have a big problem consuming *and* assimilating a caloric and nutrient surplus.

If you know you're slacking in the effort department, give more importance to the little exercises than the big ones, never strive to add poundage to the bar, take liberties with exercise form, or treat the gym as more of a social club than a place of serious work, then you're seriously missing the boat in the gym and no degree of attention to the elements of recovery will make that pseudo training work.

Even if you've a perfectly designed training program, and have fully attended to all the recovery factors, if you don't have the ferocious passion to train hard in a disciplined way—using consistently perfect form— then all the "perfect" program design and satisfaction of the components of recovery will be wasted. Successful bodybuilding and strength training is the result of getting the WHOLE package in good order.

Other Topics

OTHER TOPICS 1
What's the difference between the trap bar and the shrug bar?

OT1.1 On the functionality front, there are no really *major* differences, assuming that the spacing between gripping sites is the same. Both bars enable you to stand "inside" the bar, and are especially suited to the deadlift and shrug. I've written at length on the value of the trap bar in BEYOND BRAWN and THE INSIDER'S TELL-ALL HANDBOOK ON WEIGHT-TRAINING TECHNIQUE. All that I've written about the trap bar applies to the more recently produced shrug bar too. The two bars are produced by different manufacturers, and inevitably there are differences in the quality of workmanship, design, customer service, and delivery.

OT1.2 On the appearance front, the trap bar is a rhombus with two gripping sites welded on inside, and bars welded on the outside for loading plates on. The shrug bar is similar, with the major difference being that instead of a rhombus design, the shape is that of a hexagon. This hexagonal design provides a bit more room "inside" the bar, and thus more space for the knees to move in.

OT1.3 If the gripping sites on either of these bars are placed too close, that will limit foot placement and proscribe the deadlift for some people. Just what's "too close" will vary among individuals, depending on the stance used for squatting—which should be replicated when trap bar or shrug bar deadlifting, unless a closer stance can be used without knee or back problems. If you need to use a stance wider than about hip width, you may need to have the gripping sites a little wider than standard (depending on your height and body size). I suggest you discuss this matter with the manufacturers, in case you need a custom-made bar.

OT1.4   There's a limit to how wide you can have the gripping sites placed, for reasons of strength and practicality—as noted in FS26. The standard shrug bar has the gripping sites placed about 25 inches apart.

OT1.5   On the other hand, for short trainees, perhaps the standard trap bar or shrug bar has the gripping sites too wide apart, and a custom bar with the gripping sites placed a few inches closer than standard may be better. Again, discuss this matter with the manufacturers before you place an order. A shrug bar manufacturer let me know that about 30% of the shrug bars he makes are custom made with regards to hand spacing.

OT1.6   If you want to use the bar inside a power rack, and be able to set it down on the pins, you'd need a custom-made bar with much more width.

OTHER TOPICS 2
I've difficulty getting to sleep on the night after I do 20-rep squats. When I get to sleep it's a fitful one and I end up wide awake by 4 or 5 am. I don't have this problem after my second workout where I do deadlifts; and I'm normally a good sleeper. Have you come across this problem? What's causing it?

OT2.1   Intensive 20-rep squats can have an effect beyond what goes on in the gym and the growth produced. When the intensity is severe, and you're in new poundage territory, the mental and physical demands are great. For some people, and I've experience myself, this leads to disturbed sleep the night *before* a workout—due to anxiety over the workout to come. It can also lead to a disturbed night's sleep *following* the workout because the body gets so stirred up. I've also experienced this, but only when I squatted in the late afternoon or evening.

OT2.2   The night before squatting, try mental "tricks" to play down the anticipation of the workout and convince yourself that relative to really major struggles, the 20-rep squat is trivial. In six months time you'll be handling a lot more weight, and thus your next target weight is no big deal. Do whatever works for playing down the anticipation of training, so that you can sleep well.

OT2.3   *Very importantly*, providing you're notching up poundage increases on the 20-rep squat *slowly*, there should be no detectable increases in effort needed each week. If, however, you're bumping up the weight faster than you can properly adapt to, you'll perceive an increase in effort needed each workout, and then almost for sure you'll have anxiety attacks.

OT2.4   If you almost needed to die in the effort to make all 20 reps with say 290 pounds, and then you have to do 295 next time, that's too much of an increase. If, however, you have the progression off to an art—very hard work, but not "life-taking" stuff—and are adding just a pound or two a week, you can keep on doing that for a *long* period, *without any perceptible increase in effort needed*. "Just" stay at the very hard level, again and again and again, with a pound or two more on the bar each week.

OT2.5   Having just *a little* left in you at the end of each work set of 20-rep squats gives you the confidence to tackle a tad more iron next time. *But please don't misinterpret this.* While I'm not urging the "take your life with a barbell" type of 20-rep squatting, I *am* advocating very hard work. Hard work is a necessity, but over the long term the very-hard-but-with-just-a-little-left-in-you approach will take most people further than the take-your-life-with-a-barbell method. Most people burn out on the latter before they realize the full potential of the current cycle, but can keep on going and going and going with the former.

OT2.6   You need to sleep especially well the night after a 20-rep squat workout. Sleeping problems the night after squatting are usually due to squatting too late in the day, thus not leaving enough time for your body to wind down prior to sleeping. Ideally, arrange your workout schedule so that you can squat in the morning, a couple of hours or so after breakfast. Many if not most people can't train at their best very early in the morning, so allow enough time to be "up" for training. For most people, having their 20-rep squat workout at the weekend is probably best, to give the opportunity to train in the morning. For your other weekly workout, try to time it in the afternoon *at the latest*. Even workouts that don't involve the squat can lead to disturbed sleep if performed shortly before bedtime.

OTHER TOPICS 3
As a tennis player playing 2–3 hours every day, and weight training three times a week, how much sleep do I need? And what about naps? I'm currently 23 years of age.

OT3.1   You can either get all your sleep in one shot—at night—or have a nap during the day and get the balance of sleep at night. Take your pick, according to what's most practical or efficient for you. Personally, naps make me feel groggy and disorientated, but some people feel good after them, and napping is a big tradition in Cyprus.

OT3.2   There's a danger with napping. Let's say, as an illustration, you only had three hours sleep one night. A nap for a couple of hours the following day may make you feel as if you're fully rested. But you'd have had only five hours sleep in total, as against your required quota of at least eight if you're training hard. So the nap can give an *illusion* that you've slept enough, while in fact you're running a sleep deficit.

OT3.3   Naps can, however, be life savers, literally. If you're drowsy, and are due to drive or operate heavy machinery, for example, then a nap for just an hour or so can return you to full alertness even though you may still be running a sleep deficit. In such a case, the emergency or preventative nap should be taken, as it could mean the difference between safety and a possibly fatal accident. Many people have died as a result of drivers falling asleep at the wheels of vehicles.

OT3.4   You need as much sleep as you need. Sleep, to a degree, is an individual thing. Go to sleep when you start to feel drowsy, and get up when you wake naturally. If you're woken in the morning artificially—either by an alarm clock, or by a person, for example—you can't have had enough sleep. Precisely how many hours sleep that will amount to, only you can tell, but I'd guess that it will be at least nine hours considering how active you are. Most people go to bed too late, and shortchange themselves of sleep. Being woken before you wake naturally is a sure sign you're not getting enough sleep, and that you need to get to sleep earlier each night.

OTHER TOPICS 4
I keep hearing that genetics are important in bodybuilding. Precisely in what ways are genetic factors important?

OT4.1   Genetics are your inherited "instructions" that provide the "blueprint" responsible for your construction—eye and hair colour, for example. As far as bodybuilding and strength training go, some of the most important genetically determined factors include bone structure, muscle cell numbers, muscle fiber type and number, muscular "aesthetics," and length of muscle bellies.

OT4.2   The length of your muscle bellies is hugely important—the muscle belly is the "meaty" part of your muscle, whereas the tendons are the white fibrous tissue that connect a muscle to bones. Long tendons and short muscle bellies mean that the muscles will be small, and only have a small potential for growth. Short tendons and long muscle bellies produce muscles with great potential for growth.

OT4.3   Most people have average-sized muscle bellies. Easy gainers usually have longer muscle bellies than average. Freakishly gifted bodybuilders of the ilk of Sergio Oliva, Arnold Schwarzenegger, Mike Mentzer and Ronnie Coleman have very long muscle bellies throughout or almost throughout their bodies. This factor alone makes building big muscles a piece of cake *relative to how it is for people with average or below-average length bellies*. Other factors which are heavily influenced by genetic factors are recovery capacity, tolerance of exercise-induced discomfort, and neuromuscular efficiency.

OTHER TOPICS 5
Just what is an easy gainer, and will an easy gainer always achieve more than a hard gainer?

OT5.1   The term "hard gainer" is a misnomer, implying that there's something abnormal about the "condition" of hard gaining. A hard gainer is really a normal gainer. Easy gainers are the "abnormal" ones, but of course this is a good type of "abnormality," and one I wish I had.

OT5.2   A very few people have the "abnormality" in spades—Oliva, Schwarzenegger, Mentzer brothers, Yates, Coleman, etc. A significant proportion of trainees, which I guesstimate at around 10%, have the "abnormality" to a significant degree, but not spectacularly. They have it sufficiently so that they have a substantially greater potential than hard gainers; but just having the potential doesn't mean anything. To *realize* the potential, the investment in training and related factors needs to be provided.

OT5.3   Successful hard gainers can achieve more than easy gainers who never put in what's needed to get anywhere. Easy gainers, due to their greater responsiveness to training, can make good gains without the same degree of commitment that hard gainers have to invest. There's far less room for error for a hard gainer than for an easy gainer.

OT5.4 A hard gainer needs to get his training spot on, focusing totally or mostly on just a few big exercises. The easy gainer can use a much more expanded program and yet still gain—his tolerance of exercise, and recovery ability, are superior. The hard gainer needs to get his diet almost perfect all the time—surplus of calories, protein and other nutrients every day. Any corner cutting will limit if not kill gains. The easy gainer can get away with some corner cutting on the nutritional front, and yet still gain. Some easy gainers progress well despite following very poor diets. The hard gainer needs to rest and sleep well all the time, or otherwise his progress will be seriously impaired, if not killed. The easy gainer can break the rules on this front, and yet still gain well (but not optimally).

OT5.5 When an easy gainer provides the commitment that a hard gainer needs if he's to realize his potential, you get stellar progress (in the easy gainer), and the disparity of genetic factors is graphic.

OT5.6 A *well-trained* hard gainer can gain so steadily and well that he may think he's an easy gainer. And a very badly trained easy gainer may make such slow progress that he may think he's a hard gainer. "Gainingness" is a relative condition. But compare a hard gainer and an easy gainer, on a similar training regimen (tailored to the individual, to "optimize" it), and with comparable dedication to meeting fully all the components of recovery, and then you'll see the difference that the genetic component makes. In the same time that a hard gainer makes his way to say a 300-pound bench press, the easy gainer will be up to 400+ pounds; and in the same time that a *really well-trained* hard gainer builds up to a 16-inch arm, the easy gainer can get to 18 inches or bigger.

OT5.7 Discussing the matter of "gainingness" is a very sensitive one for most of the high achievers in the training world. Few people will acknowledge they had a better hand of genetics to start with, and thus a more responsive physique, because they prefer to think that they got where they are because they were more dedicated and harder trainers than the rest of us. Only a bona fide hard gainer who delivered 100% commitment knows the real score.

OT5.8 It's true, however, that many hard gainers get nowhere because they simply don't apply the basic rules of successful abbreviated training. But that doesn't mean all hard gainers don't achieve great things purely because they don't apply the necessary commitment. Many have applied the necessary commitment, but commitment can go only so far. Woody Allen could never have matched Schwarzenegger on the posing dais, for example, no matter how much dedication he'd invested.

OT5.9 Unless, however, you're interested in "elite" level competition, even "mere" achievement at the limit of a hard gainer's potential is magnificent, and one that will make almost everyone at a beach or pool stare at you in amazement, if you're just in shorts. Further, a successful hard gainer who stays lean can end up with a lot better physique than a much stronger and bigger easy gainer who carries an additional 10% of bodyfat. Overall strength and size aren't the whole story when it comes to appearance.

OT5.10 Easy gainers are blessed and fortunate as far as bodybuilding and strength training are concerned. That they are blessed shouldn't mean that they can see how many of the "rules" of sensible training they can break and yet still make progress. They too should follow abbreviated training, pretty much as hard gainers should. It's not just that easy gainers will make faster progress on an abbreviated program than they would from a more expanded and frequent training regimen— perhaps enough to take them to a spectacular level of achievement, drug-free. As a bonus they will achieve that progress with less time commitment, thus leaving more time for a life outside of the gym. It's an all-win situation—better gains, from less training.

OT5.11 As I wrote in BEYOND BRAWN: "Whatever genetic potpourri you have been dealt is all you are going to get. Whatever shortcomings you may have, you have to live with. Rather than spend time complaining about your genetic fate, pour your energy into achieving your genetic potential. An average or even a less-than-average potential for bodybuilding, *if achieved*, is stunning to an untrained person, and respected by almost any trained individual.

OT5.12 "Focus on achieving *your* potential, *not* on comparing yourself with ideals. Apply yourself intelligently and you may discover that what you thought was a modest potential is actually a lot more.

OT5.13 "If you are consumed with the achievements of others, enviously look at the natural talents of a gifted but tiny minority, and bemoan your own genetic fate, you will never deliver the consistent and savvy dedication needed to do what will satisfy you most of all—*the achievement of your own full potential for muscle and might.*"

OTHER TOPICS 6
Is muscular soreness a good indicator that I've had a good workout?

OT6.1   Maybe. Soreness in the bellies of the muscles is good, as long as you're not crushed systemically. If you're totally wiped out, the chances are that you used too much training volume (or even intensity in a few cases) and you're overtrained. Overtraining doesn't build bigger muscles.

OT6.2   If the soreness is primarily in the tendons/attachments around the joints, you're lining up joint problems. In such a case, you need to correct the form liberties you may be guilty of, and/or slow down your rep speed; or, if you're using high-risk exercises such as hack squats, cut them out.

OT6.3   Some people get sore easily, some don't. In fact, some people hardly ever get sore. I used to get sore very easily in my teens and twenties. But in my mid thirties and beyond I rarely got sore muscles, even when training as hard as I did in my youth, or even after changing exercises.

OTHER TOPICS 7
I recently began training in kung fu three days a week. I train with weights one day per week doing a hard but abbreviated workout. Is there a specific type of routine I should follow if I only have one day per week to train with weights?

OT7.1   I don't think so. You need to strengthen all your major bodyparts in a balanced way, using an abbreviated routine focusing on the big exercises. You have the same bottom line as most people who lift weights in a serious way, unless you're already big and strong enough—progress in strength and development over the long term. Either way, you must train safely and without overtraining. This is especially so considering the rigors of kung fu training.

OTHER TOPICS 8
How much of an effect would taking a martial arts class two or three times a week have on the ability of a hard gainer to make strength and size gains?

OT8.1 The degree to which the martial arts training will affect your progress with the weights depends on many things, including the intensity of the martial arts work, and its volume and frequency. It will also be affected by how well you're weight training, and your recovery "machinery" as influenced by your diet, rest and sleep schedules. It's also affected by your overall conditioning and ability to tolerate exercise.

OT8.2 If you're already overtraining on your weight training, the martial arts work will make a bad situation worse. If your weight training is in sound order, then providing you don't really overdo the martial arts training, and you work it in *progressively*, you may be able to get a good mix of both activities, though eventually one may affect the other negatively, depending on how you go about your overall training program and the degree of commitment to the martial arts. If you want to be a master of one activity, you'll have to focus on the one of your choice, and keep the other as a "second string" pursuit only.

OT8.3 Strength training will *always* help you in any activity that requires strength and speed, *as long as you go about it properly*. If you really go after martial arts training with a vengeance, the commitment involved would compromise the ultimate results you could expect from your strength training. If, however, martial arts training is your priority, that compromise wouldn't be a problem. But to repeat myself, the strength training would still be a big asset for you in your martial arts even if you couldn't realize your full strength potential.

OT8.4 Martial arts training two or three times a week, assuming it's very demanding physically, will be enough to kill the gains of many hard gainers, depending on the individual. Before you get into demanding martial arts training, first learn how to weight train to produce good steady gains in muscle and might.

OT8.5 Once you know what really delivers the gains for you, *then* add in the martial arts work, and see the impact on your weight-training progress. Add the martial arts work in a *progressive* and *gradual* way, to give your body time to adapt to the increased load. And pay *even more* attention to your dietary and sleeping habits. You'll need to increase your caloric intake, and get an extra hour or so of sleep each night.

OT8.6 What if your weight-training progress slows or stalls as you take up martial arts work? Abbreviating your weight-training program, and paying even more attention to your diet and sleep, may rekindle your gains in the gym. If not, and you don't adapt to the increased workload over a few months, you're going to have to decide on your priorities, and make changes in your program accordingly.

OTHER TOPICS 9
I've had hernia surgery for an inguinal hernia, using the bard plug mesh method, as an out-patient. About nine months later, when I deadlift I feel it a little in the surgery site. When I squat (20-rep style) I feel great. What are your suggestions for recovering from this condition?

OT9.1 I've never had a hernia, so have no personal experience here. But I've had many injuries over the years. Caution and good sense are the keys.

OT9.2 Find what doesn't cause a problem, and avoid what irritates you. I'd say you should push hard on the squat, because you don't get a negative reaction from it, and temporarily drop the deadlift. I suggest you try the stiff-legged deadlift from two inches below knee height. That might not produce the irritation the regular deadlift does. But if it does irritate you, stay away from that too.

OT9.3 The squat is a great lower body exercise, and if you can do it safely you'll get plenty of thigh, glute and lower back work, at least for the time being. After 2–3 months, carefully reintroduce the variation of the deadlift that produces the least discomfort for you *now*. By then, what causes a little discomfort now, may not produce any discomfort because you'll have had 2–3 months of hard squatting to "toughen" you up and prepare your body for the deadlift. But start light with the deadlift, and build up slowly and carefully.

OT9.4 The two biggest problems that stymie recovery from injury and/or surgery are selection of the wrong (for the moment) exercises, and coming back too quickly. Come back slowly, and you should get there. Rush, and you'll end up getting hurt, and have to lay off and then restart the recovery process again, thus greatly increasing the overall recovery period.

OT9.5 I'm assuming you're using impeccable form in whatever exercises you perform. Technique liberties will be your downfall even under normal circumstances, sooner or later. But when coming back from injury or surgery, technique liberties will produce problems even faster.

OTHER TOPICS 10
I'm 47. I started lifting late (age 37) but I love it and have been faithful for 10 years. Can someone my age get big, strong and lean?

OT10.1 Depends on what you mean by "big, strong and lean." For sure you can get bigger, stronger and at a lower bodyfat level. The question is to what degree. All you can do is train sensibly, responsibly, progressively and consistently, and follow good nutritional habits. Then be patient as the changes take place, and you'll find out how far you can go. The older you get—and you're not old yet—the more you'll set yourself apart from most of your peers, as they continue to go downhill and you improve. Even if you were "just" to maintain yourself as you are now, then at age 65 you would be awesome relative to most other people of the same age. Train for life, sensibly, and you'll add life to your years, years to your life, and maintain a physique that your peers will be in awe of.

OTHER TOPICS 11
The day after squatting I usually have more soreness in my right leg than left. Am I descending a little more to the right, or does it have to do with bone structure or alignment of spine?

OT11.1 I'd say you're either favoring your right leg over your left consciously or due to a technique error, or there's some structural or positional anomaly that's forcing your body to squat in an asymmetrical way. This is an illustration of the sort of problem that has led me to urge people to get themselves checked out by an expert chiropractor. It may be that the cause of this problem can easily be fixed by an expert chiropractor, but you won't know unless you investigate. Chiropractors don't just treat back pain. What you're describing is an injury waiting to happen, perhaps a serious one. You need to get to the root of this problem, as soon as possible, before it becomes a serious one.

OTHER TOPICS 12
How much do smoking and alcohol affect my ability to gain muscle? I'm trying to quit desperately, but I'm just curious. I've searched everywhere and have not found an answer to my question.

OT12.1 Depends on your age, current health, and extent of smoking and alcohol drinking. For sure your training progress will be compromised. The question is, to what degree? What's more important is the fact that smoking is very harmful to your health, and so is heavy drinking. That alone should be incentive enough for anyone to put matters right. You'll never fully appreciate how important good health is until you no longer have it. Once you no longer have your health, it will ruin many aspects of your life, not just your ability to gain muscle. In fact, gaining muscle will be one of the *least* of your concerns.

OT12.2 Stop smoking, and either don't drink alcohol, or only drink in moderation. My father tried to give up smoking many times, and I can recall having many arguments about his smoking. He finally did stop smoking, but only when he died from a smoking-related problem, aged just 59. The longer you wait to give up smoking, the harder it will be. Come to your senses, and stop now. Don't *try* to quit. Just quit! I know it's easier said than done. But I bet my father wished he'd actually stopped long before age 59, rather than merely *tried* to stop.

OTHER TOPICS 13
Is it possible to add additional muscle mass (not simply recover muscle lost from inactivity) past the age of 50? At the ripe old age of 51 I've learned much and have gotten the resolve to make as much progress as I possibly can, but fear that I'm too old—diminishing of growth hormone, testosterone, etc.—and shouldn't get my hopes up too high. Please advise me.

OT13.1 Yes it's possible to add additional muscle mass (not simply recover muscle lost from inactivity) past the age of 50. The question is not "if," but "to what degree?"

OT13.2 That you've never trained well and consistently is a sure sign that you've a lot of potential for building muscle and might. Of course your ultimate potential is less now than it was when you were age 30, but that's irrelevant. You can't turn the clock back. Please don't let anyone try to discourage you with comments about diminishing growth hormone, testosterone, etc. What matters is making the most with what you've got, and for someone who has made little progress in the past you've tremendous room for improvement now, *but only if you train in a sensible, responsible, safe and personalized way.*

OT13.3 The older you are, the more savvy you need to be about training. Empower yourself with appropriate and practical knowledge, stoke up the fires of desire, and then get training. Exercise is probably the nearest thing we have to the fountain of youth. After a few years of sensible training you should possess a physique that will have your peers gaping at you in envy.

OTHER TOPICS 14
I'm 35 years old. Talk to us about the differences in results us older guys can expect compared to someone in his early twenties. Is a different diet or a different workout style needed? Does my body have less growth hormone, and if so what products or foods can I eat to help?

OT14.1 At 35 years old you're not old. Sure you're not a teenager, but you're still young. Of course you have fewer years ahead of you than has a 22-year old before you hit legitimate old age, but you're still young.

OT14.2 As you age, you need to be even more knowledgeable about and careful with your training. I don't believe in taking liberties in training even by teenagers and trainees in their early twenties. But very young people usually pay a less heavy price for liberty taking than older people do. At 35 you absolutely should *not* risk taking any liberties. Two or three months out to recuperate from an injury may not seem such a big deal if you're only 22 with so many years in front of you, but it's a big deal when you're 13 years further on in your life. *And the older you get, the harder it usually is to come back after injury.*

OT14.3 Your age isn't what really matters. What you have or haven't done in the past doesn't matter. What you might or might not do in the future shouldn't occupy your thoughts much. What matters is what you're doing *now*. The only thing you have control over is *today*. Get each *today* right, repeatedly, and then you're doing all that you can to get your future in good order. Get your next meal right, get your next night's sleep right, and get your next workout right, and then do all of that again and again and again...

OT14.4 If you spend a lot of time pondering over the factor of age, and the "problems" that come with it, you may never get around to the 100% consistent dedication to getting each day right that's needed to stay on track to achieve your goals.

OT14.5 The physique improvement process is the same for any age—muscle and training response are not age specific. The older you get, the fewer the years you have ahead of you, relatively speaking, so the more important it is that you don't go wasting time with unproductive training methods, or from getting injured.

OT14.6 Perfect form is critical at all ages, but even more so as you age. Small weight increases on the bar are even more important as you age. Avoiding overtraining is even more important as you age. Eating healthfully and not taking liberties with your diet is even more important as you age. Resting and sleeping adequately are even more important as you age. You need to become sufficiently knowledgeable on training and on your own body—including its strengths and limitations—to become your own expert trainer.

OT14.7 Hormone secretions change as you age, but possible action to alter the secretions should only be taken by an endocrinologist. *Even then, such action is potentially very high-risk.* Much of the current hype over hormone boosters is just advertising bull to plunder the pockets of gullible bodybuilders. Eat well every meal, train well and safely every workout, sleep well every night, and follow a training program that's truly personalized and productive for you. Then you'll make good progress.

OTHER TOPICS 15
I've been training for 13 years and have recently found that no matter how light I train I seem to hit a wall and find it very difficult to recover. I've taken a month off but when I return to training there's no improvement. Have you any advice on how to

overcome this problem? I'm 34 years old, married with three children and have been training three times every fortnight.

OT15.1 Unless you're near the hilt of your genetic potential—which is highly unlikely—or you've some serious medical condition, you should be able to make steady gains as long as you satisfy *all* the necessary requirements. Even for a very hard gainer, providing he rests well, sleeps eight or more hours each night, really eats well every day and consumes a surplus of calories and protein, and trains hard on an abbreviated program of big exercises, gains should happen. If you're run ragged in your life, don't rest well between workouts, cut corners with your diet, rarely get eight hours of sleep a night, or don't squat, deadlift and dip/bench press, you're never going to gain well, if at all.

OT15.2 With recovery factors—rest, sleep and nutrition—in really good order, training three times every *two* weeks on say the squat, stiff-legged deadlift, dip and chin should do the trick, *or* perhaps train twice a week but spread the four exercises over two workouts (squat and stiff-legged deadlift one workout, and dip and chin at the other) and alternate the workouts from session to session. The latter very abbreviated strategy would give you a week between hitting each exercise, whereas the other strategy only gives you 4–5 days between hitting the same exercises. I'd suggest that you include the L-fly and calf work at one workout, and some ab work at the other, on the divided program strategy.

OT15.3 From a distance it's difficult to put my finger *precisely* on why someone doesn't gain, as the questioner's interpretation of his training, nutrition and sleeping habits may be different to mine. What someone might think is good eating may actually be deficient. What someone thinks is good form in the squat may actually be a mess. What someone thinks is plenty of sleep could be an hour or two short per night. What someone thinks is lots of protein could actually be less than half a gram of it per pound of bodyweight. What someone thinks is hard work could actually be a travesty of effort.

OT15.4 I'm not saying that the questioner is guilty of these deficiencies. I'm just making the point that some people haven't accurately assessed their training and lifestyle, and the reasons for their lack of physique and strength progress could be staring them in the face if only they could see things objectively and critically.

OT15.5 Long layoffs from training, other than for recovery from serious injury, should be avoided like the plague. The older you get, the harder it is to come back from long layoffs.

OTHER TOPICS 16
My question relates to fat loss and all these little "metabolic tricks" you hear about. No carbs after 6pm; eat a little protein, wait two hours and then do your aerobics; do aerobics on an empty stomach, then don't eat for another hour. Do any of these things have any _significant_ effect on fat loss?

OT16.1 The little "metabolic tricks" you mentioned, and others along the same lines, usually have minimal or no benefits. Some may even have negative effects in the sense that they will help accelerate *gross* weight loss, but part of that loss will be muscle, which is the last thing you want to lose. Overdoing aerobics will lead to overtraining in general, and an inability to sustain the intensive weight training you need to retain your muscle mass. In short, excessive aerobic work will lead to muscle loss as well as fat loss. I suggest you stay clear of the "tricks" and stick with the basic "calories taken in vs. calories burned up over the course of the day" strategy (and being in a caloric deficit), in combination with intensive abbreviated weight training, regular aerobic work, and the patience to achieve the fat loss slowly over the medium to long term, rather than quickly over the short term.

OTHER TOPICS 17
I'm in the position of moving to a new house. This is the ideal opportunity to obtain my own gym. I would have bought a power rack for self-spotting, as I train alone; however, the height of the cellar where the gym will be is only about 6 foot. This is clearly below the height required for the average power rack. My partner wouldn't allow the gym in any other area, and we won't have a garage. What other self-spotting devices could I use for squatting and bench pressing, etc?

OT17.1 A "half rack" or "open rack" may be your best option There's a picture of one type on page 43 of my book on exercise technique. Alternatively, you could get a custom-made four-post power rack built to fit in your cellar. These options will permit you to squat and bench press in safety, assuming you set up the equipment properly, and train sensibly. Whether you'll be able to perform seated overhead presses (without hitting the ceiling) will depend on your height and arm length, the height of the bench you sit on, and the diameter of the plates you use. I recommend you set things up so that you can perform the seated overhead press, either with a barbell or dumbbells.

OTHER TOPICS 18
I just recently started a difficult manual labor job. I'm lifting relatively heavy objects (15–40 pounds) all day. By the time the workday is through, I'm too exhausted to work out. I work Monday to Friday with only the weekends off. Do you have any suggestions as to how I can increase my stamina?

OT18.1 If your job is getting you down, I urge you to come up with a plan to change jobs so that you find one that's satisfying. I know this is easier said than done, but if you set your mind to it, acquire new training/education, or motivation, you can change more than you may currently think you can.

OT18.2 In the meantime you need to make the most of the present situation. If you've just started the manual job, then with time you should adapt to the rigors of the job, and develop at least some of the stamina you need. Give yourself the best chance of doing this by sleeping more than usual each night, and eating especially well. If you cut corners with your nutrition and rest schedules, the rigors of the manual labor will take a greater toll.

OT18.3 Training wise, I suggest you get to bed early on Friday night, and sleep as late as possible on Saturday, and rest up all day Saturday. Then following a good night's sleep on Saturday, you should be fully rested and raring to go for training on Sunday. Then train hard on a full-body abbreviated routine, e.g., squat, parallel bar dip, stiff-legged deadlift (from the floor, not an elevated surface) and chin, rounded out with calf and ab work. Really make the once-a-week workout count. As long as you add a little iron to each of the four major exercises every week, you'll make progress. To do that you'll need to sleep well every night, and eat well every day—no corner cutting! Never mind that you're not training more frequently, or that you're doing a lot of manual labor during the week. Hard work that delivers progressive poundages in good form in a handful of big compound exercises is what strength training and bodybuilding are all about.

OTHER TOPICS 19
I just started the HIT style of training, working two days a week. I've been making excellent gains but had to skip two workouts due to soreness. Should I just lift through the soreness, or is my body still recovering? If I should wait, is there anything else I should do, or should I redesign my workouts? I cut out cardio completely but will go back to it later on.

OT19.1 The soreness is probably due to initial (shock) response to the changed training format. Training while you're still sore is risky from an injury point of view—a sore muscle is more easily injured. Also, such a degree of soreness may be an indication that you're not recovering fully. I suggest you ease back a bit—stop your sets one rep short of what you would otherwise do. Then once you've adapted to that degree of intensity, without much if any soreness, then perhaps crank up the intensity a tad. But poundage progression should be your guide, not just training intensity per se. *Get on the progression trip, not just an intensity trip.*

OT19.2 Another thing you should consider is putting overlapping exercises in the same workout, so that each major bodypart gets trained only once a week. For example, by benching on Wednesday and close-grip benching and shoulder pressing on Sunday, you'd really be bench pressing twice a week, and may not fully recover from either workout. This would set you up for overtraining and stagnation.

OTHER TOPICS 20
As well as bodybuilding I'm interested in some sports. Can I do justice to all activities, or will I have to accept some trade off?

OT20.1 Among other factors, this depends on how many activities you're involved in, how physically active they are, how often you participate, how you weight train, what sort of condition you're in, your genetic talent for the activities in question, your age, and how well you attend to recovery factors.

OT20.2 If you follow an abbreviated weight-training program of only three big exercises per workout, train hard and short *no more* than twice a week (different threesome of exercises at each of the two workouts), you should leave adequate recovery "space" for some serious sporting activity. Perhaps just a single workout every 5–7 days may be better, to allow more recovery days. But it's very important that you introduce the sport(s) in a gradual way (if you're not already well conditioned to it/them), to permit your body to condition itself to the increased demands.

OT20.3 As I noted in OT8 with specific respect to martial arts work in combination with weight training, the body has a tremendous capacity to adapt to increased demands, *but only if the extra demands are progressive and in small increments*. As pointed out in T41, what some people consider to be overtraining is, in fact, merely a lack of conditioning. If you add a lot of extra stress in a short time, you're highly likely to exceed your current capacity, overtrain, risk wear and tear injuries, and suffer fatigue, frustration and disappointment.

OT20.4 To enable your body to adapt to increased demands, you must be consistent and uncompromising in providing adequate nutrition every day, and plenty of sleep. You'll need more sleep than you would if weight training was your only vigorous physical activity, and more food too. Increased demands mean an increased need for supply of raw materials to meet energy needs and produce full recovery.

OT20.5 The chances are that you'll need to make a value judgement. You may be able to get near your potential at bodybuilding and a *single* sport (so long as it's not an endurance sport), but to realize your *full* potential at either you would probably have to focus on a single activity and have the second one play second fiddle (at least for some of the time). But perhaps the fun, camaraderie and socializing aspect of a physically demanding team sport that you may not get from bodybuilding is sufficiently important for you that you would willingly accept a trade off of say 80 pounds off your squat, and 10–15 pounds less muscular bodyweight. Alternatively, change the sport to one that's not physically very challenging, but really demanding only on the skills front, so that your bodybuilding isn't compromised any.

OT20.6 If you want to add two or more vigorous sports to an already stressful and progressive weight-training program, you'll push yourself beyond what you can cope with unless you're a very gifted individual. Then you would put decent progress at any of the activities at risk unless you contented yourself with "maintenance" training at one or two of them.

OT20.7 You have to determine what you want and how much you want of it, and then tailor your weight training and other activities accordingly, while keeping in mind your individual strengths, limitations, preferences, time available, lifestyle, etc.

OTHER TOPICS 21
You often suggest 300-400-500 pounds as strength goals for male hard gainers in the bench press, squat and deadlift. Are these limits?

OT21.1 While it can be interesting making this sort of comparison, and other number crunching, please don't get so carried away that you get deflected from the real priority—making incremental progress in strength and physique improvement on a month-by-month basis. No medium- or long-term goal, realistic or otherwise, has any meaning unless you knock off small bits of progress on a month-by-month basis. To make that progress you need to get each workout right, each day of nutrition right, and each day of rest and sleep right. The day-by-day units of life are where your focus should be. Get those units in good order, consistently, and the medium- and long-term goals will take care of themselves.

OT21.2 The 300-400-500 numbers are *not* given as limits, but as marks of respectability for hard gainers. Most hard gainers who are not limited by age should be able to exceed these achievements, in at least one of the movements, if not two or even all three. *But they will need to be very determined, very committed, very persistent, and very knowledgeable on how to train themselves.*

OTHER TOPICS 22
In BEYOND BRAWN, page 84, as a comparable performance to a bench press single with 300 pounds, a chin of bodyweight plus an extra 30 pounds. Isn't this too little?

OT22.1 In most cases, yes. The extra weight should be more like 50–60 pounds. Of course, I'm referring to full reps and controlled form.

OTHER TOPICS 23
I've seen your list of target poundages in BEYOND BRAWN. Is there a another set, this one given in terms of bodyweight, that's also written from the perspective of the hard gainer?

OT23.1 Yes, and the list is in HARDGAINER issue #56 (September-October 1998), from Rich Rydin and Dave Maurice, in their "Questions & Answers" series:

OT23.2 "...here are guideline strength levels we consider attainable by most male hard gainers. These are long-term guidelines—you can get there, but it takes time. Be patient and enjoy the process. Squat: 125–150% of bodyweight for 15–20 reps; deadlift: 150–175% of bodyweight for 15–20 reps; Trap Bar Deadlift: 150–200% of bodyweight for 15–20 reps; bench press: 125% of bodyweight for 6–8 reps; dumbbell bench press: 45% of bodyweight per dumbbell for 6–8 reps; chin up: bodyweight to bodyweight-plus-25% in weight for 6–8 reps; dumbbell row: 50% of bodyweight for 6–8 reps; overhead press: 75% of bodyweight for 6–8 reps; dumbbell overhead press: 35% of bodyweight for 6–8 reps; dips: bodyweight plus 25% in weight for 8–10 reps.

OT23.3 "The above are for male trainees of up to about 40 years old. After that, maybe take 10% off these figures for each decade past 40, up until the age of about 60. After that we don't care to guess. Again these are not intended to be the pinnacle of what you can do, but are levels we think almost all of you should be able to reach. Women might adopt goals of weights roughly 50% of the above goals, though they may be able in selected cases to reach 70–80% of the above weights.

OT23.4 "These strength guidelines are based on hard gainers, i.e., those with bodies with less than perfect leverages, those who don't gain muscle easily. Maybe you will be more suited to some movements and will do better; maybe some exercises will be harder for you, but we believe that if you can safely perform these moves you can get to these strength levels. We've listed many movements simply so that you can find a few that work for you. We don't expect that everybody can reach all of them. Certainly there are those who can exceed all of these goals, and our best wishes to those folks as well."

OTHER TOPICS 24
You mentioned in BEYOND BRAWN about how myotherapy and working out your trigger points helped you recover from your injuries. How do I know if after a training session that my form was bad or if my trigger points have just flared up? After my recent hard leg training session I thought

my form was great, but the next day I had some knee pain. My knees were not sore, but I had an occasional uncomfortable twinge.

OT24.1 Just because your trigger points flared up doesn't necessarily mean you used poor form, though you may have. While you think your form was good, you may be in for a surprise if you could see a video recording of your workout. Recruit someone's help and have your next workout taped, including side, front and rear views of each exercise. Then scrutinize your form and compare it with what THE INSIDER'S TELL-ALL HANDBOOK ON WEIGHT-TRAINING TECHNIQUE teaches. You'll likely find more than a thing or two amiss. If your form continues to be off, you're going to be continually racked with highly irritated trigger points, discomfort or even pain.

OT24.2 If, after examination, your form is good, you need to investigate other reasons for trigger point flare-ups. These could include injury, structural faults or overtraining. Injury and structural faults should be investigated by an expert chiropractor. If or when you're free of injury, structural faults or overtraining, trigger point therapy alone may be all you need to rid yourself of pain. Then maintain the therapy to keep yourself pain free.

OTHER TOPICS 25
Reading BEYOND BRAWN was my first exposure to myotherapy. I've had a few sessions with a certified myotherapist, and found it very helpful with some hip and knee problems. I wonder if you might describe the areas housing trigger points which were causing your shoulder problems.

OT25.1 It's been a few years since I treated those shoulder problems. Generally speaking I used a shotgun approach—I hunted for all the trigger points I could find, and hit them all hard and often. I never suffered bruising, and only very rarely suffered any tenderness on the subsequent days, so I was able to hit the trigger points as often as I wanted. (That I didn't bruise may have something to do with my high intake of vitamin C—4 grams or so a day.) For my shoulder problems I hit every trigger point I could find in my delts (all heads), triceps (I remember some agonizingly painful ones there), and upper back including the traps.

OTHER TOPICS 26
I've been training on abbreviated routines for a number of years, but have not progressed very well because every time I reach heavy weights for me, I pull my back. I then have to stop training, recover and restart my cycle. I've pulled my back three times, twice because of squatting, and another time at work. How can avoid this cycle of frustration?

OT26.1 That you've had repeated back problems once you've reached "heavy" weights indicates there's a problem with your back (or supporting structure) and/or your form. If you're being limited in your training by your back, you're probably always going to hit a wall at a certain threshold, and that will mean you're never going to be able to move the sort of weights needed in order to build substantial muscular mass. Many trainees resign themselves to living with a back problem, and don't take the required action to correct it, and thus their training is indefinitely compromised. A back problem is a major limitation. Take action to put it right.

OT26.2 I urge you to get yourself checked out by a chiropractor with experience in weight training. While any truly competent chiropractor should be able to help you to some extent, if he/she doesn't have experience in weight training, the extent of the help is probably going to be severely limited. Even if you don't think you have a structural problem, *still* get yourself checked out. It's possible there's something amiss you're simply not aware of, and if it can be fixed (as many structural problems can if you find the right help), you may find you get a new lease on training life.

OT26.3 You also need a thorough investigation of your exercise form. I urge you to have a video recording made of your entire training *while making no special effort to "tighten" your form*, including different views of each exercise, especially the big movements. You must record your *usual* form if it's to be a fair representation of what you do in the gym. Then rigorously analyze the recording and compare your form (and bar control) with what's described in my exercise form book. If you find a chiropractor with weight-training experience, get him in on the analysis process. I can almost guarantee that there'll be room for improvement in your form and bar control, and probably a great deal of it.

OT26.4 There are a number of very specific possible explanations for your problem. For example, it may be that you can't use good (and thus safe) form in the squat and deadlift *because your hamstrings are too tight*. An increase in flexibility in general, but specifically in your hamstrings, may make a big difference to the form you can adopt. And a strengthening of your spinal erectors, through back extensions (as noted in some answers in the *Exercise Form and Selection* section) may be a big help too.

OT26.5 Depending on what your back problem is, if you have one, the side bend may not be a good inclusion in your training program. Asymmetrical exercises produce a degree of stress on the back that may be too much for you. Discuss that with the chiropractor you consult.

OT26.6 Trigger point therapy may prove a valuable help both in treating the problem and then keeping you free of it in the future. I cover trigger point therapy in great detail in BEYOND BRAWN, Chapter 18.

OT26.7 Trigger point therapy is *not* an alternative to chiropractic adjustment, or even medical attention in some cases. For example, if you have a problem with a malpositioned vertebra, treating it with trigger point therapy will only deal with symptoms. You'd need to have a chiropractic adjustment to correct the problem. That said, there are many physical problems that do not need manipulative adjustment and which will benefit greatly from trigger point therapy alone. You'd need to consult a competent therapist for guidance.

OTHER TOPICS 27
Since writing BEYOND BRAWN have you modified any of your views on trigger point therapy?

OT27.1 I now use a different technique, at least some of the time. Rather than pressing in a steady way on the trigger point with no movement over the skin, I now often prefer to press hard (as before) and *simultaneously* move up and down on the skin, or laterally—"vibrating pressure," for want of a better description. It's the technique that Dr. Efstathios Papadopoulos uses, and that's where I got it from. As a bonus, the technique may not be as painful as it can be when pressing in a "non-vibrational" way on a trigger point.

OT27.2 Another refinement is that, where possible, I put the muscle being treated in a stretched position, *keep* it in that stretched position, and *then* perform the trigger point therapy. I got this tip from Dr. Gregory Steiner.

OT27.3 When hunting for trigger points you treated at a previous session, or earlier on in the same session, you need to *replicate* the position you had your body in for the previous "hunt." For example, the precise position of a given trigger point in the thigh of a flexed leg may not be the same if you have your leg straight.

OTHER TOPICS 28
At 5-8 and 160 pounds, if I could bench press say 250 pounds for 10 reps, squat 300 for 20, curl 150 for 10, and so on, could I get around 16-inch arms, 24-inch thighs, 44-inch chest, in your opinion?

OT28.1 To make those lifts at 5-8 and 160 pounds would be very impressive, and you'd have to be very lean in order to have the musculature to handle that load. Unless you're very gifted, I'd say you'd have to be at least 20 pounds heavier in order to be able to make those lifts and get the girths you note.

OTHER TOPICS 29
I've read a lot about different types of stretching. Should I be stretching for muscular growth? Does it really help? If so, how often?

OT29.1 Stretching doesn't produce muscular growth, but sensible stretching can help "injury-proof" your body, thus helping to create the conditions needed for the consistent, progressive training that *will* produce muscular growth. Also, if you're inflexible in the hamstrings, for example, you won't be able to use good and safe form in the squat and deadlift. So stretching is especially important if you're inflexible at present.

OT29.2 Some very strong men never perform specific stretching work; and they maintain the required degree of flexibility without any formal stretching. Some very serious strength trainees have diligently made themselves very flexible but are nothing special strength wise. Unusual flexibility is not necessary for a high level of strength. A sensible stretching program is, however, a recommended addition to an overall training program because a moderate level of flexibility is very important. Most people require regular stretching in order to maintain the necessary degree of flexibility needed for successful weight training.

OT29.3 Too hasty stretching, use of risky movements/techniques, forced stretching, or becoming excessively flexible, will hurt you and set your training back. Too little has been written about the potential for stretching to cause injuries. I recommend a sensible, progressive strategy of stretches that are suited to the individual. A stretch that might be fine for you could hurt someone else, and vice versa.

OT29.4 I'd recommend stretching at least twice a week, preferably after your weights workout, or spread out between sets during the workout. You must be already warm when you stretch. Never stretch while you're "cold." And never try to move straight to your current limit of flexibility. Take several progressive "reps" before you get to your "work rep" hold for a given stretch. Hold each "rep" for at least 10 seconds, and better more like 25 or more seconds, or until you feel the muscular tension diminish. You'll need 3 or 4 reps per stretch—2 or 3 progressive preparatory stretches, and then the "work" rep/stretch. You could even do 2 "work" reps/stretches, if you prefer.

OTHER TOPICS 30
After my last workout, the very top of my shoulders (near and around my rotator cuff) was very sore—no pain when I move my shoulders, but sore to the touch. I didn't do any movement that put my shoulders in a severe position, and I can't figure out why this soreness has occurred. Is this a bad soreness, like if my knees were sore? Or is it like any other muscle (if this is muscular), that if I let recover, will get stronger?

OT30.1 This may be very "bad" soreness, unless it goes away within three days or so, and *doesn't* return after the repeat of the workout/activity that triggered off the problem. If so, and it was a one-off, you're probably all right. If not, you need to investigate the problem and cause, and take action. Don't train through or around this sort of pain, or else you could set up a more serious problem. You would need to seek out a competent chiropractor with experience in weight training. You may also need to change an exercise or two.

OTHER TOPICS 31
I squat once a week religiously, as suggested in your books. However, no matter what measures I take (such as light exercise and stretching before my squatting session, and stretching lightly afterwards) I experience quite a bit of local soreness in my quads and buttocks the next day. Have you found a sure-fire way to combat soreness? I'm not overtraining because I don't experience any of the symptoms associated with overtraining.

OT31.1 A "healthy" degree of soreness is one of the rewards of quality training. If, however, it's enough to severely restrict your movements for a day or two, that's too much. Some people get sore easily, others don't. If your soreness doesn't restrict your movements, I'd suggest you enjoy the reward of a good workout. But if the soreness is a problem, I'd recommend trying the following suggestions, but there's no guarantee that they will help in your particular case.

OT31.2 After your squatting session, perform a set of freehand squats— enough reps to get some blood moving in your thighs and glutes—followed immediately by careful stretching of your hamstrings, quads and glutes. Quickly have your post-workout liquid feed, and as soon as possible soak in a hot bath for a while, followed by further stretching. Shortly after waking on the following morning, perform another set of freehand squats, to get blood moving again. If the combination of all of this eliminates severe soreness, stick with it. If it makes no difference, I suggest you add a second squatting session each week, three days prior to your major squatting session. But at this second session, only perform your warmup sets of squats. At least for many people, if the first strategy doesn't help, the second one will, and you won't get so sore after your major squatting session each week.

OTHER TOPICS 32
I read in BEYOND BRAWN that a man with a medium frame (wrist size of 6.75–7.25 inches) and height of 6-4 should carry 225 pounds. Do I really have a medium frame? My wrist measures 7.25, while my ankle measures 9.125 which, as you quote David Willoughby, implies that I've a balanced upper- to lower-body bone structure (a relationship of

approximately 79–82%). Does a 7.25 inch wrist at 6-4 indicate a medium frame? If not, is it possible to expand your theory to interpolate based on exact wrist/ankle measurements?

OT32.1 I feel you're giving too much thought to the "on paper" figures. Whether or not you're medium frame, etc., doesn't matter. The figures I gave are guidelines only, to give people an approximation of what to expect from serious training.

OT32.2 What matters is what you do with whatever you've got. Just build the best physique you can. Whether it's a bit under or a bit over what the "on paper" figures say, doesn't matter. Don't let yourself carry surplus fat just to be able to satisfy someone's figures for what you "should" weigh. Keep yourself on the lean side if you want to look your best. For example, at 200 pounds and 10% bodyfat you'd look more impressive than at 220 pounds and 18% bodyfat, even though your muscle mass would be the same at both bodyweights.

OT32.3 Comparing yourself with a genetic phenomenon (Steve Reeves, in the questioner's case) usually leads to discouragement. Train hard, intelligently and consistently on abbreviated training routines, fully satisfy out-of-gym factors, and you'll be doing all that you can. Don't get overly caught up in the maybes and possibilities. Focus on the definites.

OTHER TOPICS 33
A point of interest is strength gains relative to muscle mass growth. I feel that in order to gain 10 solid pounds one has to increase his bench press by about 35 pounds while his squat should go up about 50 pounds. What do you think?

OT33.1 The relationship between strength and muscular mass is not a consistent one. Some people can get a lot stronger without getting much bigger. Others can get quite big, relatively speaking, without getting anywhere near as strong. These differences are in part genetic and in part a reflection of training procedures used and diet followed. By all means try to work out a strength-to-mass relationship that seems to hold true for you, but don't get so concerned by it that you get limited or constrained by numbers or expectations. The numbers that work for you may work for some others too, but will be well off the mark for many people.

OT33.2 There's no need to perform actual maximum singles—a high risk activity—in order to work out a maximum-strength-to-size relationship. Use the conversion tables given in BEYOND BRAWN, page 95, where singles can be converted to multiple reps, and vice versa.

OTHER TOPICS 34
Is it possible to be a hard gainer and exhibit signs of a naturally high testosterone level?

OT34.1 There are many components of "hardgainingness," so it would be possible to be above average in one variable, but to be disadvantaged in others, with the overall diagnosis being "a hard gainer." Further, the variables of hardgainingness are not steady over time.

OT34.2 A hard gainer who's a student without employment and family responsibilities, with enough money to meet his needs comfortably, who can sleep ten hours a night, and has a leisurely lifestyle, is not going to feel his hardgainingness at all *relative* to how his identical twin brother does who's married with twin babies, never gets an undisturbed night's sleep, and has to work at two jobs to make ends meet.

OT34.3 If someone is run ragged in his life, never sleeps enough, persistently cuts corners with his diet, and focuses on isolation exercises rather than the big compound ones, he will be a hard gainer even if he has a naturally high testosterone level and other attributes of an easy gainer.

OT34.4 Much more important than musing over the role of testosterone production and one's level of "hardgainingness" is ensuring that the variables over which we have control—especially exercise selection, effort level, sleep and nutrition—are in top-notch order. Focus on doing what you can to maximize your responsiveness to exercise, and don't get overly concerned with the maybes of bodybuilding and lifting, or factors out of your control. By doing this you'll give yourself the best chance of actually getting the strong and impressive physique you want.

OT34.5 I'm not saying that the questioner is guilty of the following, but many people are—they get so distracted that they invariably fail to train hard on the best exercises, fail to follow a generous rest and sleep schedule, fail to eat and drink a great nutritional program, and fail to use a good progression scheme. Thus they never get around to experiencing the great gains they could if only they would get their acts together.

OTHER TOPICS 35
I'm a 16-year-old bodybuilder and I've been lifting for about a year. But I didn't feel I was putting on much size. I was taking protein powder and I started taking actisyn, but then I heard about andro and its effects on testosterone. I also heard about its side effects—acne, deeper voice and increased estrogen levels, which can lead to "bitch tits." Well, I heard that norandro doesn't have any side effects so I started taking that for about a month (two 100 mg pills before I worked out). Immediately I noticed the difference while lifting, but I didn't feel that anymore after about a week unless I increased the dosage to three or four pills, but I knew that was dangerous so I stopped taking the norandro. Then I started taking androstenene pills, but about a week into taking them I started noticing little pimples on my back, and my nipples were kind of swelling up. I took the andro for about another week, but then my nipples started sticking out more, and they were getting really sensitive. So I thought that before this gets any worse I would stop taking the andro. The pimples on my back have since gone away, but my nipples are still swollen and sensitive. What can I do or take to get rid of the excess estrogen in my body?

OT35.1 Get off the hormone "boosters"/drugs, and stay off the things. You've done damage after just a few weeks of foolishness. Visit a doctor to see what can be done to correct the damage, and then learn to train properly so that you don't feel the need for any artificial help.

OT35.2 For a relative novice at training you can make almost linear progress for several years, providing you know how to train productively. *Don't expect to build a terrific physique in just a few months, but set your stall out for a few years of disciplined dedication.* Learn how to train properly using abbreviated routines, and pay your dues. Then you'll build a terrific physique while *improving* your health, not while putting it at risk. Good health is the priority—don't wait until you no longer have it before learning this big lesson. When you no longer have your health, big muscles will be very low on your list of priorities.

OTHER TOPICS 36
I think I've some muscle imbalances in my body. My right shoulder may be lower than my left, similar to a problem you had. Who should I see to investigate this and possibly fix it?

OT36.1 More than one type of physical therapist may be able to help you. Therapists vary greatly in their level of training, expertise and experience. I actually had my hip tilt fixed by a dentist who had an interest in chiropractic, and had watched a chiropractor fix a hip tilt in his (the dentist's) wife. I gambled on letting such a unqualified man work on me. As it happened, my gamble turned out well. But some amateur therapists have wreaked havoc on trusting "patients." Don't let anyone other than a legitimate, licensed and experienced chiropractor perform adjustments on you.

OT36.2 Chiropractors, like other professionals, vary greatly in their level of expertise and qualifications beyond the basic training. The near miraculous hip tilt adjustment I had done on me involved procedures that are not part of the standard chiropractic course. So all chiropractors wouldn't be able to perform that adjustment. Chiropractors are experts in spinal biomechanics and will definitely help with your problems. There are some who specialize in sports injuries.

OT36.3 You may need to contact more than one chiropractor before you find one with the experience and perhaps special training needed to be able to help you with your particular problems.

OTHER TOPICS 37
Do you know anything about pelvic tilts? If so, do you think excessive focus on squats can cause this problem? Do you have any suggestions for correcting or preventing the problem from getting worse?

OT37.1 Muscular imbalance, and flexibility imbalances can certainly contribute to a pelvic tilt. A number of factors can be involved, and expert attention from a therapist with experience in this area should be consulted. I have personal experience with a pelvic tilt, though my particular brand of it won't have been the same as yours. I wrote about this in my editorial of HARDGAINER issue #60 (May-June 1999), and I hope it will encourage you to take action to correct your own pelvic tilt. My correction was almost instant, yet lasting—nearly two years later and I'm still "corrected." Because it's such an unusual subject, despite many people suffering from pelvic tilts, here's the entire editorial:

OT37.2 "For at least fifteen years, my left shoulder has been nearly an inch higher than the right. I never thought much of it. Over recent years, since discovering in 1992 that I suffer from 'borderline serious' scoliosis, I thought that the shoulder tilt was a side effect of my unusually curved spine. The shoulder tilt was very noticeable, and a T-shirt always looked to have been pulled over to one side.

OT37.3 "Last year, HARDGAINER author Mike Thompson paid a visit to Nicosia, along with a friend. Kevin, a dentist with an interest in healing skills, had learned some techniques from a chiropractor he'd seen at work in London. Kevin noticed I had a hip tilt—one hip higher than the other. Because my hips were tilted laterally, so were my shoulders.

OT37.4 "Kevin had me lay face down on the veranda table, and performed a minute or two of work on my lower back and the area at the base of my sternum. What he did, I learned afterwards, was to normalize the nerve flow to balance the musculature of my body, as well as normalize my 'chi.' (Chi is the vital life force in the body that's regulated by, for example, acupuncture.)

OT37.5 "After the minute or two of work, and absolutely no forceful noise-making adjustments, I stood up and looked at the reflection on one of the veranda glass doors. I was stunned! For the first time I could remember, my shoulders were horizontal. For the few days following the correction I would gaze in a bathroom mirror in utter amazement at my properly lined up shoulders. The reflection of the bathroom tiles provides a 'grid' I use to check my shoulder alignment. Nearly a year later, my shoulders are still perfectly aligned, and I've had no further work on my hips. And since the day of adjustment, T-shirts have laid on my shoulders symmetrically.

OT37.6 "I trained a few days after the adjustment, and was shocked to discover I'd 'lost' so much strength. I'd cut the poundages back to about 85%, but 85% for the usual reps felt harder than my previous week's 100% weights. Not only that, but I experienced post-workout pain in my knees. I was depressed, and regretted Kevin's work.

OT37.7 "Though the corrective adjustments seemed so minor, the effect on my body was major. My body went into shock and was inhibiting my strength. My body had major neuromuscular adjustments and realignment to make. New 'grooves' had to be adjusted to for each exercise. And slightly changed stresses in joints, especially my knees, had to be adapted to. Over about 6–8 weeks my strength came back, and the knee problems faded away. Then I was back to normal, but with properly aligned hips and shoulders, less pronounced scoliosis and, I believe, a better potential for sustained gains and a reduced probability of degenerative changes to my spine as the years go by. I'm very happy that Mike and Kevin paid their visit.

OT37.8 "If you have tilted hips—especially noticeable if the tilt is a lateral one—and/or shoulders that are tilted, seek a chiropractor for possible correction. Chiropractors, however, vary in their competence and areas of special interests, and only some are trained in the normalizing of chi. You may need to hunt around to find a really good one. A good chiropractor is a miracle worker!"

OT37.9 As an addendum, the speed with which a hip tilt can be fixed will vary according to the degree of damage or imbalance that needs to be corrected, and the expertise of the therapist. Each case is unique.

OTHER TOPICS 38
When I was younger I achieved great results from squatting and deadlifting. In my early twenties I hurt my back at work, leaving me unable to perform either exercise. I can find no two exercises that stimulate as much growth. Is there anything I could do to work around this chronic injury in order to squat and deadlift?

OT38.1 You probably never will find an exercise duo that are as productive as the squat and deadlift. I don't know of your specific back problem. The best advice I can give you is to find an expert chiropractor, ideally one with a background in weight training, and follow his advice. I know from personal experience that an expert chiropractor can make you believe in miracles. The chiropractor I've had most experience of has no background in weight training, but still helped me out no end. All chiropractors are not equally competent, so you may need to hunt around to find a good one.

OTHER TOPICS 39
I'm a 25-year-old male and for a few years have had a need to "crack" my back when getting up in morning (every morning) or after sitting down for long periods. I do kind of a half circle swinging motion, arms out and looking back, and that gets it "back in place." It's a similar sound and feeling like when you visit a chiropractor and he cracks it for you. As recommended in BEYOND BRAWN, I consulted a sports chiropractor before starting to increase my weight on the deadlift and was told it's okay.

Have you come across the above "cracking" before, and is it really okay to keep on lifting as long as I don't have any pain from it? About 95% of the time I can fix it myself immediately, and when not I can usually do it after a while.

OT39.1 The noises you refer to are called crepitations. I've certainly come across the exact same need to "crack" the back—both in myself, and others. If you have a consistent need to "crack" your back, that's a sure sign something is amiss, and needs proper adjustment or correction. After proper adjustment by a competent chiropractor you shouldn't feel the urge to keep "cracking" your own back, unless the problem was hypermobility of your vertebrae.

OT39.2 As it is, you're not correcting the problem, but apparently just relieving the problem for a few hours, and then you feel the need to "crack" it again. A single visit to a chiropractor may not fix the problem. After an adjustment, a period of a few days or a week or so is usually needed for the adjustment to "fix." During that interim period, the adjustment can be at least partially "undone" relatively easily. So another adjustment would be need. But that one—which would probably be a more minor adjustment than the first one, because less work needed to be done—would "stick" better, and all may be well, at least for a while. But things "slip," especially if you have a major structural problem (such as scoliosis); so a regular "tune up" every 6–8 weeks or so can keep you in sufficient good shape to avoid things "coming out of place."

OTHER TOPICS 40
I'm thinking about using a chiropractor because of pain in my lower back and shoulder. Most of my associates say it doesn't work since you have to keep going back. It's a temporary fix and a waste of money, they say. I'm having trouble making gains because I keep getting hurt. I've small joints and my body just can't handle high amounts of weight. I've already stopped squats since my legs are long and I never could get to parallel, and it was very painful for me. I'd hate to give up deadlifts but if my lower back keeps getting hurt, I'll be forced to give that up also. Any advice?

OT40.1 Some money-first chiropractors have given the profession a bad reputation in many people's minds (just as some doctors have in other professions), because they abused their responsibility and took advantage of patients. The doctors had the patients come in for unnecessary "treatments," or perhaps didn't actually fully treat the problems so the patients have to keep coming back. But just like in all professions, there are bad examples. You mustn't tar all practitioners with the same brush. I've said this many times, and I'll keep saying it—a competent chiropractor is a wizard, and one of the very best friends you'll ever make. I know this from first-hand experience. Chiropractic works!

OT40.2 I urge you to ignore your cynical associates, and hunt for a good chiropractor. Your cynical associates are seriously hindering your progress in the gym. By keeping you from chiropractic help they are denying you the possibility of relief from the problems that are seriously holding you back.

OT40.3 Hard gainers are more easily injured than easy gainers. Some of the anti-chiropractic faction are easy gainers who haven't had much if any need to consult a chiropractor. Especially watch out if the cynics are big mesomorphs who can never get in the shoes of genuine hard gainers. Hard gainers typically don't have the strength of structure that easy gainers do, and are more in need of chiropractic "tune ups" and attention in general.

OT40.4 As a bona fide hard gainer with a major structural problem (scoliosis), I can hand-on-heart let you know that Efstathios Papadopoulos, DC, of Nicosia, Cyprus is one of my most valuable associates. Again, chiropractic works big time, *if you find a good chiropractor*. Anyone who tells you otherwise is guilty of an outrage, and doing you a major disservice.

OT40.5 I hasten to add that a chiropractor shouldn't be seen as a "fix it" person to treat symptoms of poor training methods. You must still train sensibly, and with perfect form, etc. But many people need the help of a chiropractor to enable them to keep training safely, *even when using perfect form*.

OTHER TOPICS 41
I've had thoracic scoliosis since I was 14 years old. My orthopedic surgeon always told me that I shouldn't do squats or deadlifts as it could make my scoliosis worse. Has doing squats and deadlifts worsened your condition, and what exercises do you recommend I avoid? I believe that if I begin a resistance training program I could strengthen the multiple muscles of the back and torso that could straighten the spine *slightly*, thus reducing the scoliosis' curvature. What are your opinions and recommendations?

OT41.1 Because you have scoliosis you *must* maintain strong back musculature. This is essential to minimize, if not prevent problems from the scoliosis. You also need to find a competent chiropractor. Because you have scoliosis, it means you're more likely to have problems with your vertebrae than is someone who has a normal spine. Due to the unusual lateral curvatures on your spine, the vertebrae are more likely to move out of position on the outer side of the arcs. Such malpositions need to be corrected, or otherwise additional problems will be produced.

OT41.2 Just what exercises are best for you, I can't say. But I'd not be happy with the "don't squat or deadlift" dictate. I'd urge you to find a chiropractor with both experience of scoliosis *and* weight training. One, if not both of the squat and deadlift may be exactly what you need, providing you use impeccable form, and don't take any of the liberties that I foolishly did in years gone by that led to my downfall. I would, however, urge you to avoid rotational exercises that use resistance, and asymmetrical exercises such as the side bend. They have been excluded from my exercise program because they injure me, no matter how careful I am with progression. My chiropractor says this is because of the scoliosis.

OT41.3 Consult a competent chiropractor about the possibility of your having a hip tilt. This can be fixed, at least in many cases, and can reduce the impact of scoliosis on your body. I had a dramatic improvement as a result of a hip tilt adjustment. See OT37 for detail.

OT41.4 I'd urge all parents who have scoliosis to have their children checked out, and seek professional advice from a chiropractor for action to take to minimize the degree of scoliosis that develops. Regular chiropractic care can ensure that all the vertebrae are kept in the right positions, and thus keep scoliosis from deteriorating to a serious degree. In addition, the children should perform resistance training to strengthen their backs and abdominal musculature. They also should avoid poor posture and asymmetrical weight carrying, as both encourage scoliosis to become more exaggerated, especially in a child. (As a boy I used to walk to and from school with my bag on just one shoulder, which produced a slightly skewed gait that probably contributed to the degree of scoliosis I now have.)

OTHER TOPICS 42
What are the major differences between chiropractic, osteopathy and physiotherapy?

OT42.1 *I'm not qualified to give an answer to this question. I sought out someone who is qualified—Dr. Efstathios Papadopoulos, a practicing US-trained chiropractor. He's approved my reporting in this answer of what he told me.*

OT42.2 The major differences between chiropractic and osteopathy vary according to where you live. In North America, an osteopath is generally a medical doctor who has taken an elective in osteopathy. Osteopaths trained *outside* of North America obtain a non-medical qualification that makes them closer to chiropractors. But the courses provided in schools of osteopathy outside of North America vary greatly, because there isn't standardization. As a result, osteopaths can vary greatly in their level of training and expertise.

OT42.3 Chiropractic has standardized training courses throughout its schools, and thus its graduates have a uniform training at the degree level. You can be sure of a standardized training for licensed chiropractors. While this is no guarantee that you'll find a high level of competence in all chiropractors, it should weed out bogus practitioners. The same can't be said of osteopaths, however, where the lack of standardized training in all of its schools has produced serious problems of great inconsistency among practitioners—from the excellent, to the bogus.

OT42.4 Chiropractic should be your first stop for non-invasive drug-free treatment of injuries and other physical problems. This is not to say that chiropractic can deal with all such problems, but a chiropractor should be able to let you know if he/she can help you, and if not, where you should seek help. Chiropractic can't, for example, correct muscle and tendon tears, or bone fractures. An orthopedic sports medicine doctor would be appropriate there. A chiropractor could, however, correct any structural misalignment that may have occurred during the accident or event that produced the injury.

OT42.5 Individual chiropractors may take specialties after they have fulfilled their basic training. Sports chiropractic is one of the possible post-graduate specialties, along with radiology or orthopedics, as other examples.

OT42.6 Physiotherapists usually work under a doctor, and aren't qualified to diagnose, unlike chiropractors. Some physiotherapists may, however, *attempt* to diagnose "off the record." Chiropractors are actually trained in physiotherapy as part of their chiropractic schooling—the physiotherapy is sometimes called "physiologic therapeutics." However, most chiropractors choose not to practice physiotherapy. They prefer to stick with work that physiotherapists can't do, and delegate physiotherapy to physiotherapists. In this way the chiropractors have more time to focus on the skills unique to chiropractic.

OT42.7 Chiropractors are trained to perform "adjustments." Osteopaths use general mobilization techniques, and their treatment has a different theoretical and practical basis to that of chiropractic. Physiotherapists are not trained in adjustments, though some perform manipulations despite not having the training and expertise of chiropractors and osteopaths. If you need physiotherapy, a chiropractor is qualified to give the required instructions and a referral to a physiotherapist. Some chiropractors, however, employ in-house physiotherapists. [In the UK, *chartered* physiotherapists have *standardized* training, and qualifications greater than those of non-chartered physios. The training includes diagnosis.]

OT42.8 Be sure only to let *legitimate fully-trained and licensed* professionals work on you. There are quacks who claim to be experts at spinal and other adjustments and manipulations, and "practice" freely (especially outside of North America). Some of these have produced severe damage in patients, and made problems much worse. Many a chiropractor has had to correct the damage carried out by quacks. Contact your country's appropriate professional association, or the international head office, for information on legitimate professionals in your area.

OT42.9 A number of medical doctors have taken brief courses in manipulation techniques (*not* chiropractic), and some of these doctors claim to have far greater competence in manipulative work than they actually possess. *The only type of chiropractor you should consult is the real thing—one who holds the full degree qualification from an accredited chiropractic college.*

OTHER TOPICS 43
I constantly think about my training and physique. It's become the focus of my life. I'm depressed that I'm not in better shape than I am. Relative to the time, effort and dedication I've invested, I'm not good enough. If I don't get a lot better soon, I fear a major depression. What am I going to do?

OT43.1 I can recall a few years of my life when I was on the same wavelength that you are now. As important as strength and physique are to you now, relative to the big picture they truly are on the trivial side. A major negative event in your *own* life would quickly gets things in perspective. You're so concerned about where you want to go, that you're not enjoying where you are now. I'm going to quote from my editorial in HARDGAINER issue #62 (September-October 1999), as it deals with your question:

OT43.2 "Training is a process full of future expectations, e.g., 'I'll be content when I make a 500-pound deadlift, or build a 17-inch arm.' I'm all for setting goals, and giving one's utmost to realize the things. But if you believe that you'll only be content when you get to a given goal, you'll never be content now. But life is now, not in the future. And once you get to a given goal, you'll probably set a new one and only when you get to that one will you be content, so you think. Contentment is always around the next corner.

OT43.3 "This mentality works in other areas of life. 'I'll be happy when I've finished paying off the mortgage.' 'I'll be happy when the kids are off my hands and I can take it easy.' 'I'll be happy when I've finished my final exams.' Most people seem to live while believing that they will only be really happy and content after a certain achievement or acquisition.

OT43.4 "I too was like this until I learned the big lesson that my life is dealing with day-to-day trials and tribulations. This is the reality of life, and it's the same for you, though your circumstances, concerns and activities will be different to mine. Life doesn't have to be 'perfect' in order to produce happiness and contentment. Other than in truly extreme situations—but even then a silver lining can often be found—it's time to be happy and content *now*. If you can't do it now, you probably never will.

OT43.5 "Projecting an imaginary future where all problems and difficulties have been dealt with, procrastinates contentment and happiness, so you never actually fully enjoy your life as it happens. It's taken me until age forty before I finally clicked with this. Don't wait till you've been through this process a million times before realizing that a stream of problems and difficulties is your life, and won't end until you end.

OT43.6 "When I wrote the first draft of this editorial I had what I used to consider a frustrating day full of discontent, because of so many things getting in the way of my planned activities. But when I ran through these 'frustrations' with a different mindset, I was happy despite all the 'irritations.'

OT43.7 "Due to my wife's car being repaired, I had to taxi the children around—five round trips, amounting to a couple of hours or so. (My wife doesn't want to drive my vehicle.) But we're fortunate to have two vehicles, and far more fortunate to have children to taxi around. My workout was disturbed by a number of things, but I'm fortunate to have the health and opportunity to train and be disturbed. Time to deal with business matters was devastated that day, but I'm blessed with having a business to be disturbed. And that I'm not 230+ pounds of lean muscle (at 5-9) doesn't mean I can't be happy with what I do have, but while still seeking improvement. With an adjustment to my attitude, the everyday problems of life don't take the toll they would otherwise.

OT43.8 "See if the above rings a bell in your life. See how you can be happy and content but while still taking action to improve your life, health, physique and strength. But you need to be continually alert regarding your attitude, as life is unrelenting in its challenges, and will quickly take you back to square one if you're not ever-vigilant."

OT43.9 If that piece doesn't strike a chord with you, then please consider the following, from HARDGAINER issue #55 (July-August 1998):

OT43.10 "Two recent events have provided me with a double reality check that has left a mark on my life. I would like to share these events with you.

OT43.11 "Over the last two years I've amassed a substantial collection of weight-training magazines from the thirties, forties, fifties and sixties. This is a tremendous treasury of knowledge and history. But a major reality check accompanies the magazines. Most of the prominent figures in these magazines, who were in their prime at the time of publication, are now dead.

OT43.12 "A second reality check arises from the new location of my office. It's within ear shot of a church. Funerals are held there every week. The tolling of funeral bells is a big reality check.

OT43.13 "Life is limited, and fragile. It can't be taken for granted no matter how young one may be. A number of supermen who were in their prime when the old magazines were published, died as relatively young men.

OT43.14 "Each of us had better get on with making the most of the present while the going is good. And we should be sure to look after ourselves as well as possible in order to preserve relative youth for as long as possible. Being big and strong is no guarantee of good health, though of course it's much better to be strong and well-developed than weak and underdeveloped.

OT43.15 "I know I've written on this theme before, but it's so important that I'm returning to it. Really make the most of your health, youth and well-being while you have them. Really look after yourself. Really make the most of your training. Really enjoy your life.

OT43.16 "Stop putting off doing the things you know you should be doing. Especially stop procrastinating those actions that you know would be good for your health. And fix up your training program so that you really apply productive routines. But include cardiorespiratory training and eat a healthful diet. And take actions to make your life a happier one. A fit and strong physique can be ruined by unhappiness. Work to solve the problems that trouble you. Don't let them fester.

OT43.17 "Developing big and strong muscles is extremely satisfying. Don't miss the opportunity to get your share of muscle and might. But you need to apply abbreviated and intensive training on a consistent and long-term basis. Really focus on the big exercises—on ones that are safe and productive for you. Really weight train only twice a week, on a different set of exercises at each of the two workouts. Really work hard. Really apply small weight increments on a steady basis. Really fully attend to recovery factors—sleep well each night and consume five or six healthful meals a day that satisfy your caloric needs. Then you'll experience good gains.

OT43.18 "Very few people make the most of their training. Mark yourself out as one of the exceptions—invest the dedication, and then achieve your own physical excellence.

OT43.19 "The Grim Reaper will eventually come for each of us. Do your very best to take whatever actions you can so that when the day comes you'll not be racked with regrets for having not made the most of your life. Don't delay!"

OTHER TOPICS 44
My gym's lowest weight increment is 2.5 pounds, so what I've been doing is building to hitting all my target reps for *all* sets on a certain exercise. Once I've hit all reps for all work sets, I increase the weight by the smallest increment possible, drop some reps, and then build towards hitting all target reps again. Do you think this is wise, or do you think I would benefit more from micro weights?

OT44.1 What you're doing (double progression system) can work well, though in some exercises a 2.5-pound increment is a lot, especially for women. Adding that increment to the deadlift is one thing, but adding it to the L-fly is another. It can also be a lot for any exercise when you're near your current hilt of new poundage territory. It can cause your reps to drop a lot, and then you may suffer frustration and have trouble building up the reps again.

OT44.2 You may find that sticking with constant reps and just a pound or less on the bar each week or two is more practical and effective than adding 2.5 pounds, dropping reps, and then building up the count. The pound or less on the bar is so little as not to be perceived (other than on exercises that use small weights), whereas 2.5 pounds can be perceived.

OT44.3 I can't recommend micro weights enough. They will help you no end if you use them properly—they enable you to add just a single pound at a time, or even just half a pound.

OTHER TOPICS 45
My gym doesn't have 1-pound weights to add to the bar, so how can I increase my poundage by 2 pounds? Bring store-bought 1-pound weights to the gym with me and ignore the puzzled glances?

OT45.1 That's right. As well as helping you to add weight in manageable doses, the experience of getting used to puzzled glances and comments will give you good training for ignoring the same things when you apply other aspects of sensible and responsible abbreviated training.

OTHER TOPICS 46
I train at a commercial gym, and there are no "little gems" there. How can I add small increments without using small discs?

OT46.1 Use the following method, as reported by Scott Silva in "Forum" of HARDGAINER. It's critical, however, that the plates you use are calibrated. If the plates are not calibrated, then just a slight discrepancy in actual weight as against what the plates are supposed to be, will render the method worthless. The method assumes, however, that plates are available in pounds and kilograms denominations.

OT46.2 "A friend who works out in a function-first gym that costs only $50.00 a year, brought the following to my attention. In order to make one-pound jumps in weight, you only need two 2.5-kilo plates and four 5-kilo plates, along with the usual plates machined in pounds.
5 kilos = 11 pounds
2.5 kilos = 5.5 pounds

OT46.3 "Here's an example of how it works, though of course the process can be used with other poundages, in order to make gains in one-pound jumps.

OT46.4 "For 301 pounds you need 290 pounds plus a 2.5-kilo plate on each side. For 302 pounds you need 280 plus a 5-kilo plate on each side. For 303 pounds you need 270 plus a 5-kilo and a 2.5-kilo plate on each side. For 304 pounds you need 260 plus two 5-kilo plates on each side."

OTHER TOPICS 47
I'm using microloads and wondering about hitting a plateau. Will I hit one and need to drop the weight and start a new cycle, or could I keep increasing week by week? I'm asking because every week I'm able to increase the load even if by only half a pound.

OT47.1 Eventually, whenever that is, you'll reach a limit. You can't add even just half a pound every week for thirty years. But providing you get your recovery in good order, don't overtrain, etc., then you can realistically keep adding a tad of iron every week or two for year after year—on the very big movements that is, not the smaller ones. Just how long you can go will depend on how close you are to your full potential, and whether or not you're overreaching what your body can cope with training load wise.

OT47.2 I urge you to gear your entire training and recovery schedule so that you *can* keep adding a tad of iron every week or two to your major exercises. If you can't add it, then adjust your training, and/or rest and sleep more, and deliver better on the nutrition front, so that the adding of bits of iron starts happening again.

OTHER TOPICS 48
I've been training for almost six years, and while squatting I've been taking three deep breaths at the top between reps, for rib cage enlargement.

But instead of my upper rib cage being expanded, my lower rib cage and upper abs have become bigger. Please explain why this has happened, and how it might be corrected.

OT48.1 It sounds like you've been breathing from your "stomach" rather than by lifting your chest and filling your upper chest. As you sit now, breathe while not raising your chest but by allowing your abdomen to distend. Then breathe while keeping your abs tucked in, but by lifting your chest. Then you'll see that it's possible to breathe without any lifting of the rib cage.

OT48.2 Change your breathing habits, while squatting. Suck the air into your upper chest, keep your abs tucked in, and lift your chest as high as possible. As a bonus, a high chest and full set of lungs helps to maintain the posture you need while making a good descent and ascent while squatting. Breathing "through the abs" encourages rounding of the upper back, and a loss of the strong, contracted back musculature that's needed to keep the spine in a secure position.

OTHER TOPICS 49
How much increase in strength do I need to gain in the squat, bench press and barbell curl to see an inch on my chest and thighs, and half an inch on my arms?

OT49.1 This will vary among individuals, but as a *very rough* approximation, I'd say about 30–40 pounds on the bench press, 50–60 on the squat, and 15–20 on the barbell curl. This assumes the use of consistently *impeccable* form, use of five or more *continuous* reps per set, that you're comparing the increases with your current best weights for the same rep counts, are *not* using strength-focus techniques (low reps, partial reps, and low-rep rest-pause work, which can build a lot of strength but not much size), are not recovering from injury or coming back from a voluntary layoff, and you're well beyond the novice stage.

OTHER TOPICS 50
I've been using a belt (from my jeans, not a special purpose-made belt) for loading plates for dips and chins, but it's getting awkward to use. Any tips?

OT50.1 Hang the plates behind your body. Put the belt through the holes in the plates, and fasten the buckle at the front of you. Let the belt hang on your hips rather than tighten it onto your waist. These tips should enable you to add more plates without it becoming especially awkward until you hit around 60–80 pounds. But you can't beat the right accessory for the job. Move to a purpose-made dipping belt and you'll find the difference in convenience and comfort so substantial that you'll probably wish you'd made the move earlier. Such a belt is not expensive—the price of a book or two—and well worth the investment.

OTHER TOPICS 51
Aren't you as guilty as some other people in being dogmatically rigid in your training views?

OT51.1 I *am* rigid on some points, such as training safety, training over the long term (for life-long benefits from exercise), focusing on the big compound exercises, using impeccable form, and keeping training progressive for as long as you want to make gains in strength and size. Within this general framework there's leeway for a great deal of individual interpretation and open-mindedness. I don't say, for example, that only one rep range is correct, or that only one interpretation of intensity is right. Few writers in the training world have hammered away as hard as I have on the need for *individual interpretation* of training, to best suit individual needs, strengths, limitations, lifestyles, goals, and so on.

OT51.2 Here's a relevant excerpt from BEYOND BRAWN: "This is not a quickly written book of simple prescriptions and proscriptions, or a single plan that is supposed to work universally. Cut-and-dried, neat-and-tidy programs are misleading. There are important components common to all programs that work for typical trainees, but people respond differently to the same program even assuming that each person interprets the program in the same way. Generic 'one size fits all' programs are utterly unfit for mass use.

OT51.3 "This book presents different interpretations of abbreviated training routines that focus on core exercises. This versatile eclecticism produces a great depth and breadth of instruction. Draw upon this to educate yourself about how best to exploit weight training. While there's always the trial-and-error component of weight training, this book teaches you enough to spare your having to go through the degree of trial-and-error that most trainees have to before learning what works for them.

OT51.4 "This book intentionally provides radical training strategies, and even some methods and tips that are downright blasphemous relative to gym norms. This is done for *one reason only*—to provide all hard-gaining trainees, even *extreme* hard gainers, with the instructional tools they need in order to make good progress. Building impressive physiques and strength levels should not be the right of just the gifted minority.

OT51.5 "Learn from the very costly experiences of those who have been through the mill of desperate frustration with conventional training advice. This book is not based on only one man's journey, *but is a distillation of the experiences and acquired wisdom of generations of people.*"

OTHER TOPICS 52
In BEYOND BRAWN, p. 168, item "m," it seems to state that people get fatter as they gain muscle. But if someone is gaining more muscle than fat (2–3 pounds of muscle and 1 pound of fat), doesn't that mean he's getting leaner, since he's increasing his muscle mass faster than his fat mass?

OT52.1 While you can have an increase in gross bodyfat as expressed in pounds, your percentage of bodyfat may decrease if you increase your muscular mass *sufficiently* more than your bodyfat. The key word is "sufficiently." The proportion of muscle to fat needs to be a lot more than the 2–3:1 ratio referred to by the questioner.

OT52.2 For an illustration, let's say you're 180 pounds and 12% bodyfat. That computes to 21.6 pounds of fat. If over several years you increase your lean bodyweight by 25 pounds, and keep your bodyfat constant, you'll end up at 205 pounds with 21.6 pounds of fat That same amount of fat, when expressed as a percentage of your new bodyweight, is now 10.5%. Due to the increased lean mass over which the same amount of bodyfat is spread, you'll appear leaner.

OT52.3 Now let's say, from the same starting point, you increase your lean bodyweight by 25 pounds and your bodyfat by 5 pounds. So you now become 210 pounds, with 26.6 pounds of bodyfat. That increased amount of fat computes to 12.7%. A big difference in lean mass and a small increase in bodyfat has still produced an overall increase in bodyfat percentage, albeit tiny. Why?

OT52.4 Out of the 30 pounds gain, 5 of it was fat and 25 muscle. So 16.7% of the 30-pound gain was fat. That 16.7%, when spread over the *whole* bodymass, produces a tiny overall percentage increase in bodyfat.

OT52.5 At the 2.5:1 ratio of muscle to fat gain the questioner refers to, that would compute to, for example, 25 pounds of muscle and 10 pounds of fat. That 35 pounds would take the illustration from 180 pounds to 215, and increase bodyfat weight from 21.6 pounds to 31.6. That 31.6 pounds is 14.7% of bodyfat when expressed in terms of overall bodyweight. Such a gain would need to be finished off by trimming back the bodyfat to produce a physique of the same degree of leanness as in the "before" condition at 180 pounds and 12% bodyfat.

OTHER TOPICS 53
I'm 15 years old. Will intensive and heavy weight training stunt my growth?

OT53.1 Maybe, maybe not. If you've not yet reached your full adult height, especially if you're many inches away from it, I'd say that exercising with progressively heavier weights over a period of years in exercises that have weight bearing down on you—e.g., squat and overhead press—is not going to encourage the realization of your full potential height. A potential for reaching 5-11 doesn't mean that you'll reach 5-11. A number of factors could contribute to "losing" an inch or two of that potential height.

OT53.2 No one can really say that if they had not weight trained heavily in their mid teens they would have grown an extra inch or two. We'd need to have identical teenage twins, living in an identical way other than one of them participating in intensive weight training including lots of weight-bearing exercise. If the one not weight training ends up three inches taller than the other, then that would be strong evidence that the heavy weight bearing exercise did stunt growth.

OT53.3 If height is a big concern for you, and you can't afford to "lose" an inch or two, I'd suggest that you avoid heavy weight-bearing exercises until you're at least age 18. In addition, I'd urge you to do some stretching, hanging from an overhead bar, and inversion work—e.g., suspend yourself from your hips while on a back extension setup—several times per week, to try to help you to reach your full potential height.

OT53.4 If, however, you did the just-mentioned supplementary work, perhaps that alone would balance out any effects from compression due to weight-bearing work, and it would thus not be necessary to remove compressive exercises from your program.

OTHER TOPICS 54
Don't you think you might be exaggerating the need for sleep, at eight or more hours per night?

OT54.1 No. Hard-training bodybuilders and strength athletes need more sleep than inactive people of comparable age and lifestyle. Intensive exercise increases the need for sleep. If "average" people need, say, 7–8 hours of sleep per night, then weight trainees need at least an hour more. Count your hours of sleep each night over the last few days, and average it out. Do you better *the minimum* of eight hours a night? I'm referring, of course, to good quality sleep, not just hours lying down. Eight hours lying down, tossing and turning and sleeping in fits is not the same as eight hours of sleep. Anything less than eight hours of good quality sleep will contribute to compromising your recovery ability and slowing your progress.

OT54.2 Because we live in a world that provides so many interesting activities to occupy leisure time, and because artificial light is so cheap and available, many people repeatedly shortchange themselves of sleep, and not just weight trainees. It just happens that weight trainees need more sleep, and more sleep means less time available for other things, and thus the need for more discipline in regulating sleeping hours. For many trainees, hard work in the gym is easier to deliver on than switching off the TV and going to bed at a decent hour. That so many people depend on coffee to keep themselves alert, is one of the clearest signs of how a sleep deficit is masked on a daily basis.

OT54.3 All trainees who shortchange themselves in the sleep department not only slow their rate of progress at best, and negate it at worst, but more importantly they also compromise their health and well-being.

OT54.4 If my words are not persuasive enough on the importance of adequate sleep, please read the 1999 book THE PROMISE OF SLEEP, by William C. Dement, M.D., Ph.D., one of the world's leading authorities on sleep, with over 40 years of research experience. To quote from the book:

OT54.5 "Healthy sleep has been empirically proven to be the single most important determinant in predicting longevity, *more influential than diet, exercise, or heredity,* but our modern culture has become an alarming study in sleep deprivation and ignorance...Sleep is sacrificed to meet the demands of our endless days. Unnoticed, deadly sleep disorders shorten countless lives...Doctors regard sleep deprivation as a fact of life and do little to promote sleep health or awareness. Meanwhile, the physical, emotional, and psychological costs of unhealthy sleep continue to mount."

OT54.6 As important as eating healthfully is, along with taking anti-oxidant food supplements, exercising regularly and avoiding harmful activities, it may be that obtaining good quality sleep on a regular basis occupies an even higher priority. Ideally you should get everything in good order, but a sleep debt can't be compensated for by anything other than sleeping more. Not clocking up a sleep deficit doesn't just benefit your training and long-term health, but your day-to-day alertness, creativity, attentiveness and capacity to learn. What many people consider as fatigue, insufficient energy, boredom and lack of attentiveness are nothing other than *the effects of a sleep debt.*

OT54.7 If you're running a sleep debt—and the chances are that you are to some degree—you'll not be living at your best. *Once you've caught up on your sleep debt,* which may need an extra couple of hours or so sleep each night for a week or two (perhaps time this during a vacation), just an extra 45–60 minutes of sleep each night relative to what you get now may be all that it takes to keep you running in real good order. Though you'll be active for an hour or so less each day, you'll be able to get more out of those reduced hours than you did from the extended day, make better training progress, and feel a lot better to boot.

OT54.8 Sleep needs vary at least to a degree among different people. To begin with you'll have to sleep more than your normal daily need, in order to clear your sleep debt. Thereafter, whenever you're woken before you wake of your own accord, you've not slept enough. But there's a caveat here. You have your own internal clock, and your body may wake at a given time merely because it's programmed that way. For example, you may be able to "beat" your alarm clock and wake a few minutes before the horrible ringing would otherwise start. But that doesn't mean you really woke naturally.

OT54.9 Once your sleep debt is cleared, keep a sleep log for at least a week. Wake naturally each morning, and calculate your average sleep per night. While eight hours may do the job under normal circumstances, periods of intensified training, or increased overall physical demands, will increase your sleep needs.

OT54.10 Getting more quality sleep may not be a simple as it sounds. For many people, just going to bed earlier is all that's needed. For others, quality sleep doesn't come so easily. Even the general rule of sleeping till you wake naturally each morning doesn't work for many people, especially those in and beyond middle age. If you nod off easily during the day, become drowsy while driving, or need to drink a stimulant such as coffee to remain alert, you're not sleeping enough and/or in sufficient quality, no matter how many hours you spend in bed each night. If the tips given in BEYOND BRAWN don't do the trick, consult a sleep clinic.

OT54.11 Here's a summary of the tips given in BEYOND BRAWN:

   a. Don't weight train late in the day.
   b. Low-intensity cardiorespiratory work late in the day may help you to fall asleep.
   c. Don't drink coffee, tea or any other stimulant within several hours before sleeping. It's best to avoid stimulants completely.
   d. Sleep in a dark room.
   e. Eliminate as much as possible all sources of noise, and sound proof your bedroom as well as you can.
   f. A warm shower or bath before going to bed should help prepare your body for sleeping.
   g. Stretching immediately before going to bed may you to relax.
   h. Before closing your eyes and trying to go to sleep, read something that relaxes you.
   i Shortly before bedtime, don't watch anything on TV or at a cinema that stirs up your emotions in a major way.
   j. Establish regular sleeping habits. Going to sleep at 11 pm one night and 1 am the next is not regularity. Make it 10.30 pm till 7 am on a regular basis, for example. Much better than catching up on lost sleep is not losing any sleep in the first place.

OT54.12 Another important factor is climate control. If you're too warm or too cool, that could seriously disturb your quality of sleep *even if you feel that you're neither too warm nor too cool.* Even though, for example, you might think you're warm enough, you may benefit from an extra blanket. Experiment to see.

OT54.13 If you're a shift worker, moving from one shift to another over time, this is likely to ruin your sleeping patterns. The only solution may be to get off changing shifts, to provide your body with the consistency of going to sleep at a regular hour.

OTHER TOPICS 55
I follow all the guidelines for better sleep you give in BEYOND BRAWN, and I'm even in bed for at least eight hours a night, sometimes as many as ten hours, but still I don't sleep well. I feel tired during the day, nod off easily when I'm not physically active, and I'm sure I'm not recovering optimally from my training. What else could be wrong?

OT55.1 For many people, sleeping well is much easier said than done. The problem is almost certainly that you're suffering from a sleep disorder. Sleep disorders are very common. If you snore, for example, you have a sleep disorder. The chances are that about 50% of people who read this book are regular snorers to some degree. While snoring often causes amusement, and is taken as just an everyday fact of life for many people, it's actually a serious disorder that's heavily involved in the creation of many health problems *and* some of the *perceived* effects of aging. All that is on top of serious impairment of recovery from training, which exaggerates your "hardgainingness."

OT55.2 As this is such a serious issue, I'm going to quote several times (non-consecutive paragraphs) from one of the world's leading experts on sleep disorders—Dr. William Dement—care of Chapter 7 of his book THE PROMISE OF SLEEP. My purpose is to spotlight a much neglected health problem. Dement has spent most of his adult life researching sleep problems and "battling" the medical establishment and government bodies into giving proper recognition to a health problem that's so common and serious, yet astonishingly ignored.

OT55.3 "Snoring is a sign that your breathing is impaired while you sleep... Not everyone who snores has sleep apnea, but in general, the louder the snoring, the more likely that the sleeper has apnea."

OT55.4 Apnea is a temporary suspension of breathing while sleeping—"missed" breaths. There are two types of sleep apnea—central apnea (uncommon) and obstructive apnea (far more common). Obstructive apnea is what's going to be discussed here. This isn't something to ignore or trifle with, and the problem won't go away by itself. Apnea can lead to serious health problems no matter how big or strong you may be. If left untreated, sleep apnea can be life-threatening, with many severe cases having died in their sleep. This is *in addition* to the high risk of accidents while driving and nodding off at the wheel. A shocking number of deaths and injuries have happened because of drivers falling asleep at the wheel. If you depend on a stimulant such as coffee to maintain wakefulness, then almost for sure you suffer from sleep apnea.

OT55.5 Apnea ruins the quality of your sleep, hence why sufferers never get fully rested no matter how many hours they spend in bed, and why they accumulate a big sleep deficit. To make up for "missed" breaths, your body inhales in an exaggerated way that can be so forceful that your whole body shudders and even "jumps" off the mattress. Despite your being disturbed if not actually woken *very briefly* during each mini crisis, *you're not aware of it* (but your spouse/partner may be), and you return to sleep immediately. Then after further snoring the cycle may be repeated. This can occur dozens of times per night, if not over a hundred times in severe cases. This produces a fragmented, poor quality of sleep because your rest is continually disturbed. The extent of this depends, of course, on the severity of the apnea.

OT55.6 Mild snoring leads to the heavy snoring that can be compared to a jackhammer. Mild snoring is a sign that action needs to be taken to prevent the decline into heavy snoring. Heavy snoring is an urgent cry for action, as it can even lead to premature death. During the years of decline to advanced apnea and very heavy snoring, an increasing toll is taken on your day-to-day well-being and efficiency, and the ability to recover from your training.

OT55.7 In addition to snoring and daytime fatigue and drowsiness, consider some of the other symptoms for apnea patients, as Dement reports them: "A variety of other difficulties are common, including esophageal reflux, frequent nocturnal urination, heavy sweating at night, morning headaches, raspy throat, personality changes...And yet when patients go to doctors with these apnea-induced symptoms, their physicians nearly always miss the true cause. Even the by-products of excessive daytime sleepiness—diminished performance, diminished mental acuity, forgetfulness, poor concentration, disorientation—frequently are ascribed to some other problem, like Alzheimer's disease."

OT55.8 "The severe consequences of this sleep disorder and its very high prevalence make it one of the most serious general health problems in America."

OT55.9 "Nearly 40% of the population has some sleep apnea, and half of those cases are clinically significant. That means that at least 20% of the people walking to see their family physician have a dangerous level of apnea. The number of doctor visits attributable to apnea is probably much higher, because apnea cases a wide range of health problems that force people to see their doctors."

OT55.10 "In all of medicine, I can't think of a single other serious condition that is so common, life-threatening, treatable, and yet so unrecognized."

OT55.11 "By now I and my colleagues at Stanford have saved thousands of lives...And yet we have barely started to address the tens of millions of apnea victims right here in the world's most medically sophisticated nation who continue to suffer without diagnosis or treatment."

OT55.12 "The danger of apnea stems not only from heart problems and high blood pressure, but also from the incredible sleep debt that apnea suffers carry around with them since they get almost no continuous sleep at night."

OT55.13 "I am absolutely convinced that obstructive sleep apnea plays a major role in causing high blood pressure, heart disease, and stroke...I expect that this warning will be largely ignored, just as early warnings about the health risks of tobacco were ignored."

OT55.14 Many people ignore the signs of sleep apnea, rely on a stimulant to keep them alert, and "soldier on" while thinking that sleepiness and loud snoring are just part of the normal course of aging.

OT55.15 Considering how very common sleep disorders are, and how very serious they can be, it's an outrage how so little publicity is given to them, and an indictment of skewed priorities (and/or ignorance) in the medical world. Far less serious health problems get lots of publicity.

OT55.16 Visit a sleep clinic, *and* explore "alternative" therapies too, and take non-surgical action to correct sleep disorders of which apnea is only one, though probably the most serious in terms of the number of people it affects and the extent of its impact. Not only will you improve your recovery ability and results from your training, but much more importantly you'll improve your health and quality of life. You may even add many years to your life.

OTHER TOPICS 56
I've heard reports of some people having heart attacks when engaged in intensive exercise, with a few of them actually dying. Is this for real?

OT56.1 In nearly all cases the heart attacks have taken place in people who had several risk factors and/or who were not accustomed to vigorous exercise. If an out-of-shape, overweight, middle-aged man with other risk factors such as high blood pressure, cholesterol and triglycerides, jumps into a demanding exercise program, he's asking for big trouble due to the *vast* increase in demand on his unhealthy and unconditioned body. The exercise need not be something done in a gym, but a bout of snow shoveling, for example. Especially for people in middle age and beyond, it's *imperative* that a thorough physical checkup be performed before an exercise program is started. The exercise program must be done under the counsel of a doctor, started out very low key, *and* be accompanied by action to reduce any risk factors that may be present. The volume and intensity of exercise must be increased in a very slow, incremental, progressive and sensible way.

OT56.2 Being fit and strong doesn't mean you're necessarily healthy *internally*. A few *very* fit people have suffered heart attacks during intensive exercise because they were unaware of the risk factors they had, and were not taking action to control those risk factors while *simultaneously* moderating their exercise intensity and volume. Thorough annual checkups are urged for *everyone* over age 35, to check on internal health *and* sleep-related problems, and to determine the vital action needed to correct whatever is amiss.

OTHER TOPICS 57
In BEYOND BRAWN you praised the Tru-Squat machine. Do you still feel the same way today?

OT57.1 I still feel the machine is terrific for people who either can't barbell squat safely, or can't squat well. I still use a Tru-Squat, and like it very much. The barbell squat (preferably with a *cambered* bar) is a more productive exercise *but only if you can barbell squat safely and well*. I can't squat safely with a barbell, so the comparison is irrelevant for me. For maximum productivity I don't think that anyone who can squat well with a barbell should use a Tru-Squat, *if they have the choice.* The Tru-Squat is only one of the alternatives to the barbell squat. The Tru-Squat is an expensive machine, and there are few of them around. The shrug bar/trap bar deadlift/squatlift is a far cheaper alternative, and perhaps a more productive one too. The ball squat, step-up, hip belt squat and modified straddle lift/handle squat are alternatives too, though the next tier down. The leg press, assuming a good machine is used, is also an alternative. Most of these alternatives need to be supplemented with a deadlift variation, in order to adequately work the lower back.

OTHER TOPICS 58
In BEYOND BRAWN you write about the value of "The Back Revolution®" for inversion therapy. Is it also good for back extensions?

OT58.1 The Back Revolution is a very convenient way of performing inversion therapy, which—when used properly, as described in BEYOND BRAWN—can be of great value for keeping a healthy back. It can also be used for back extensions, but a purpose-made unit for back extensions (conventional setup, as against the 45-degree version) does a better job.

OT58.2 A back extension unit can also be used for inversion therapy though it isn't as effective as the purpose-built inversion therapy unit. In my opinion, a back extension unit doubles better for inversion therapy than the Back Revolution doubles as a back extension unit.

OTHER TOPICS 59
What's your opinion of a young trainee (beginner) following John McCallum's "Keys to Progress" series all the way through?

OT59.1 "Keys to Progress" is a famous series of articles written for Bob Hoffman's/York Barbell Company's STRENGTH & HEALTH magazine from 1965 through 1972, by the late John McCallum (1926-1989). McCallum was a very talented writer and storyteller who blended information and entertainment, and acquired a tremendous following. In 1993 the "Keys" articles (along with eight others that preceded the formal start of the series) were published in book form, by IronMind® Enterprises.

OT59.2 No writer/coach is infallible. With time comes the opportunity to make corrections. I shudder at some of the advice I gave in a number of my early articles in Peary Rader's IRON MAN (in the early and mid eighties), and even a few years later in the early issues of HARDGAINER and the first edition of BRAWN.

OT59.3 In my more recent work I've corrected my earlier errors, and in some articles in HARDGAINER (especially issues #61-66) I compared my current views with some of those in my much earlier writing, and pointed out many embarrassing shortcomings. I had the opportunity to make these revisions. Of course, I'm still learning.

OT59.4 McCallum is not alive today to have an opportunity to express revised views, plug gaps and provide clarifications, etc. All we have to go on is his existing published work, and "Keys" is most of it. I've been asked about McCallum's work many times.

OT59.5 McCallum saw the connection between strength and size. He understood the value of abbreviating training routines, but he was also a product of his time. Some of McCallum's programs which today I find long, were actually short (and radical) for the time they were first published—when the drug-assisted training routines used by the "champions" were heavily promoted in the magazines of the time. A few of the programs in "Keys" would, however, be considered very abbreviated today, even in the hard gainer camp. Some of the programs in "Keys" involve a great deal of training, especially the six-days-a-week ones.

OT59.6 The reports I've heard of success from following McCallum-style training were usually not from following it exactly as written, but modified versions—usually with reduced training frequency and volume. I don't think a beginner (or any type of hard gainer) would be best served by following "Keys" as written, article by article all the way through. A selective approach would be better.

OT59.7 Many programs in "Keys" are of short duration, probably because McCallum was writing to one-month deadlines for a magazine. A flexible approach regarding the length of programs is a good idea.

OT59.8 Beginners in particular need a solid grounding in exercise technique before using routines from "Keys," as only summaries of form are included in the book. Summaries aren't enough for teaching form—in any book, not just "Keys"—especially of the core movements.

OT59.9 With "Keys" being written as a magazine column, McCallum was constrained by space limitations, and probably assumed that readers were well read in other material, for background information. For trainees who haven't much if any background information, especially beginners, "Keys" leaves some important gaps. But "Keys" by itself was probably never intended to be an exhaustive treatment of training.

OT59.10 "Keys" was relaxed in some of its form recommendations. On the press behind neck, for example: "Get a rebound and drive it back up hard and fast. Don't handle it like a crate of eggs. Be rough." McCallum promoted the hack squat: "Put a two or three inch board under your heels and go all the way down 'till you're sitting on your calves." For the stiff-legged deadlift he urged an exaggerated range of motion while standing on a bench or high block. These are just three examples of form that would cause problems for many if not most trainees when combined with the effort level McCallum urged. Personally, I'd never hack squat, put a board under my heels while performing any type of squat, or do stiff-legged deadlifts from an elevated surface, to give just three examples. I know of the perils now, but beginners and even most intermediates don't. I also know that many people have harmed themselves—often seriously—from following non-conservative and non-personalized guidelines on exercise selection and form. I'm not writing purely from personal experience.

OT59.11 Perhaps McCallum was blessed with very robust joints and could safely tolerate exercises and form which create problems for many people. He was a fireman, and I imagine firemen to be physically more robust than the average person.

OT59.12 "Keys" doesn't include many caveats and provisos, especially on exercise form and training frequency, and there's little advice on how to individualize a program. (While some people can tolerate things that most people can't, I think it best that qualifications are included to try to accommodate a large range of trainees, though this is probably beyond the scope of a magazine column.) The need for warming up is understated in "Keys," e.g., "Warm up your knees with a few free squats and then start right in on the heavy stuff." While a few people can do well on such minimal warmup work, most people can't. "Keys" notes that "Reg Park wasn't an easy gainer." In my view, anyone who could squat, row and bench press as heavily and successfully as Park did, three times a week, and prosper on six-days-a-week training, wasn't a typical trainee.

OT59.13 Some of the training frequency and volume recommendations in "Keys" are beyond the recuperative abilities of typical trainees. Here's an illustration, from one of McCallum's articles that preceded the formal start of the "Keys" series:

OT59.14 "Train on a short program. Squats, bench presses, rowing, and progressive pulls. No more, no less...

OT59.15 "Start with squats. Do a light set to warm up and then jump heavy. Do three reps. Add weight and do three more reps. Keep adding weight for each set until you can't make three reps. When you bog down add a few more pounds and do a couple of singles with that weight. Don't count the sets. Do as many as you feel like...

OT59.16 "The last exercise is progressive pulls. You start with power cleans. Start light and work up. Do three reps each set and when you can't make three then keep increasing the weight and do high pulls. Keep adding weight and when you can't make three high pulls start doing deadlifts. Do three reps in the deadlift until you can't make three. Add more weight and do a couple of singles."

OT59.17 Such heavy, low-rep and singles work is extremely demanding. Nevertheless, the reader was to perform the routine three times a week for three months.

OT59.18 McCallum did a terrific job with promoting the need to lift heavy weights, focus on the big movements, and train hard. But low-rep work and singles three times a week on each exercise in a program is excessive for almost all trainees. It may have overtrained a superman such as Bill Pearl (even on steroids), so what chance the average trainee? Pearl was one of a handful of big names regularly plugged in "Keys." I've no idea whether McCallum knew of Pearl's use of drugs.

OT59.19 In a back specialization program, for two months, "Keys" urged high-intensity stiff-legged deadlifting on a block so that the bar could be lowered "till it just clears the top of your toes" three times a week, along with rowing and power cleans, three times a week too.

OT59.20 That *alone* would have tested the recuperative limits of genetic marvels such as Grimek, Park and Pearl, in their prime. But then on *another* three days each week you were to work the rest of your body albeit with "fairly heavy weights, but not your absolute maximum." That's a six-days-a-week program (for two months), and far too much for the huge majority of trainees.

OT59.21 Some of the progression schemes in "Keys" are not progressive as I understand the principle of progressive resistance. For example, *starting* a 20-rep squat program with a weight "so heavy that the last five reps are doubtful" is a recipe for frustration for most people, if not injury. Such intensive squatting should only be performed by very proficient squatters who've *already* adapted to the rigors of high-rep squatting. I urge you to perfect your form first, using light to moderate weights, then adjust to the demands of high-rep squatting from a relatively comfortable starting poundage, and build up the weight and intensity *gradually*.

OT59.22 In some of his articles McCallum was a powerful proponent of abbreviated training. Some of the routines in "Keys" are good—though you may need to modify even those, to suit *you* so that you don't overtrain on excessive frequency and volume—but other routines are something else.

OT59.23 Perhaps the biggest strength of "Keys" is its inspirational value. It promotes a genuine love of the Iron Game, and an infectious dedication to hard training. McCallum was a master at this.

OT59.24 Beginners and intermediates don't have the ability to personalize "Keys" to suit their own circumstances. The book is most valuable as an instructional medium when it's read with a discriminating and experienced eye. Beginners and intermediates are not in a position to do this. But with experience, plenty of background study of exercise form, and understanding of one's recuperative and structural capabilities and limitations, "Keys" will be a valuable addition to your training bookshelf.

OT59.25 If you're a parent with lots of training experience behind you, and you have a teenage son who's raring to go with his weight training, give him a copy of "Keys." The book will stoke up his motivation even more. But be selective with which routines you let him choose, and in many cases you'll need to modify even those. For a few weeks now and then, let him use a program you know will overtrain him, so he can discover in practice what you should have repeatedly told him in theory. Otherwise, keep the programs abbreviated, insist on impeccable form, and put lots of emphasis on *full* recovery between workouts.

OT59.26 As noted on page 12, I promote training methods that are more conservative than those of most coaches. I explain possible if not probable dangers of certain methods or techniques, rather than ignore them, or play them down, and hope that readers don't find out about them the hard and potentially disastrous way. I also strongly promote the importance of individual variation. But I get overwhelming feedback that this produces much better results for many more people, *and* greater training longevity, than does the much less conservative, little-or-no-caveats approach that doesn't fully consider individual variation.

OTHER TOPICS 60
I've just started college. I've not been able to eat enough (the food at school is terrible), or get adequate sleep. In six weeks I lost about 10 pounds. Since then I've been able to keep my weight stable, but gaining is next to impossible. Given these circumstances, which aren't going to change for a while, how should I adjust my training to maintain as much muscle as I can, and possibly even gain a little? From your experience, where should I start?

OT60.1 Start by forgetting about your training for a bit. You need to focus on organizing your daily schedule in such a way that you *can* eat well every day, *and* sleep well every day. If you can't get those two *big* factors in good order, then your training efforts are going to go to waste even if you're doing everything right in the gym.

OT60.2 Why can't you improve your nutrition? When I was at college I got a part-time evening job at weekends to earn the money I needed to buy the extra food I needed, because the canteen fare was so lousy. Later on I moved out of college premises, at least in part so I could take full care of my own nutrition.

OT60.3 If you're really determined, you should be able to get more sleep, at least most of the time. Another reason why I moved out of college accommodation was so I could escape the noisy and inconsiderate students there, and be able to sleep better. I also cut myself off from late-night social activities because I gave my recovery a greater priority.

OT60.4 Please look at how you can reorganize your lifestyle so that you can get recovery factors put in good order. Sure there'll be problems to overcome, but life is all about overcoming problems.

I know it's easier said than done. I also know that where there's a will, there's a way. All problems exist so that human ingenuity and determination can find solutions. If you really want improved training results badly enough, you'll take the necessary action to produce the required changes.

OT60.5 No matter how demanding you think life is at college, life is likely to be even more demanding once you graduate, begin a career, and start family life. Successfully meeting the challenges of life at college is perfect training for being able to meet the greater challenges of life later on.

OT60.6 Training wise you need to work out no more than what your body can cope with and respond to. But unless you eat and sleep well you'll have such a low tolerance to exercise that you won't be able to build any significant size and strength. You need to get the factors of recovery in good order first. Then you need to get into a very abbreviated program, weight train no more than twice a week, and preferably with a different group of exercises at each of the two workouts.

OTHER TOPICS 61
I know you suggest not to use a belt, but in the squat I find it helps my form a lot. Would it really hurt my progress using a belt? I don't use a belt in any exercises other than the squat.

OT61.1 If it legitimately helps you, then stick with it. If you were using it in other exercises too, I'd be concerned, but if it's for just the one movement, then that's okay. I still think it best to train without a belt, but it's no big deal if you feel that you benefit from it for just one movement.

OTHER TOPICS 62
Who influenced you most in the Iron Game, and how?

OT62.1 Peary Rader. He got me into abbreviated training to a degree, but I also got very confused by reading his magazine, IRON MAN, because it was full of enormous contradictions. One article would be on abbreviated training, and the next might have a "champion's" routine and recommendations, which would be training suicide for the typical hard gainer. Peary allowed a huge range of training advice to be published, including a lot of material that only genetic freaks and drug users could grow on. So I never really made the change to abbreviated training while reading IRON MAN, because the mixed messages in there kept me from ever getting the *full* message about abbreviated training.

OTHER TOPICS 63
You started writing for IRON MAN in 1981, so you were around 22 years old when you started. Was it the same message you had back then?

OT63.1 The basic message was the same, but over the years it's been refined, made more safety conscious, and the training abbreviated more. I've learned a great deal since I first started writing training articles. I'm very embarrassed when I look back at some of the very first things I wrote on training, and some of my early work in the life of HARDGAINER (which I started at age 29); and even some parts of the first edition of BRAWN make me shudder because they were rough.

OTHER TOPICS 64
Some people say hard gainers are whiners and underachievers, and wimps for avoiding specific exercises. They also say we are too conservative, place exaggerated importance on overtraining, have goals that are too low, and have a limiting belief system. What do you say in reply?

OT64.1 Such people haven't understood what's in HARDGAINER and my books. It's amazing how some people come out with such statements yet have either not read my books, or have just read a few snippets of one or two of them and taken statements out of context. Some of the critics of the goals I've given are even well short of having achieved the targets themselves.

OT64.2 Most trainees are hard gainers, though in truth hard gainers are really "normal gainers." They *need* the hard-gaining perspective if they are to have a good chance of making decent gains.

OT64.3 Hard gainers have much less room for error than gifted trainees. There's less room for form "indiscretions," so form must be tight, *always*. There's less room for liberties with exercise selection, hence why high-risk exercises should be avoided. There's a much reduced capacity for coping with exercise volume and frequency, hence why training load needs to be pared back to avoid overtraining. There's much less room for cutting corners on the nutrition and sleep fronts, hence why great importance has to be given to eating and sleeping very well on an unrelenting daily basis.

OT64.4 Serious hard gainers are every bit as keen as other types of gainers. Hard gainers have to respect their limitations if they are to devise training programs that will help them. Otherwise they will go the same route that millions already have, and fail in their training.

OT64.5 It's not that hard gainers want to be different in their training habits and related factors. They just want good results. To get those good results necessitates swimming against the tide of popular training currents. It's progress you're after, not following the crowd in order to feel comfortable. Good results will make you feel very comfortable.

OT64.6 There's nothing wrong with having a very responsive physique—i.e., being an easy gainer. It's a blessing. Nor does being an easy gainer mean that somebody didn't work hard. It's simply that relative to the lot of a legitimate hard gainer, an easy gainer will grow larger and stronger faster, for a given level of effort and dedication. Some easy gainers get all uppity and aggressive when any suggestion is made that they found progress much less difficult than the average hard gainer. This doesn't, however, mean that the easy gainers don't work hard and are not dedicated; they simply have more responsive bodies. We all vary to some extent in how we respond to food, medicine and sleep—why not recognize that we all vary (in degree) to how we respond to exercise?

OT64.7 There's no harm in recognizing that if you don't get just about everything right, for year after year, you're not going to get even close to achieving your potential. The easy gainer can break at least some of the "rules" and still gain; but not so the hard gainer.

OT64.8 If you train as a hard gainer should, and if you fine-tune the basic instruction to suit you, and if you plug away for several years, you probably won't be a match for a hard-training, dedicated, easy gainer, but you *will* be a darn sight more impressive than over 95% of all experienced trainees (of your age group) in almost all gyms worldwide. That's *awesome* when you think about it. So much for a "limiting belief system."

OT64.9 The goals I've given aren't limits. They are targets. The effect of age, insufficient dedication and know-how, or some other limiting factor will mean that most trainees won't reach the 150%, 200% and 250% (of bodyweight) targets for the bench press, squat and deadlift—about 300, 400 and 500 pounds for the typical 190-pound successful trainee I've written about. But most willing, dedicated, savvy and able hard gainers *can* make one or more of the goals. Super determined hard gainers may *exceed* those goals.

OT64.10 Take a look around a typical gym, at drug-free clean trainees. How many can handle the 150%, 200% and 250% poundages? Hardly any, if any. For "underachievement," those weights (and the corresponding development that accompanies them) are some going. Once you've made it to that level of achievement, plug away at the next 5%, and so on, assuming you want to get bigger and stronger still. *I haven't set ceilings.*

OT64.11 Sure I'm conservative on exercise form and selection, because conservatism is necessary to minimize the risk of injury. This isn't wimpish. It's being sensible. What on earth is wrong with minimizing the risk of injury? If you get injured, you can't make progress. If you get injured and are unable to train for a while, then you'll know what it means to feel wimpy. If you get injured and are unable to train for a while, when you come back you'll be handling low poundages (for you) and again you'll feel wimpy. Conservatism isn't wimpy.

OT64.12 Over 25 years of training and observation, over 10 years of publishing a training magazine and dealing with its readers, and years of working with coaches who have extensive experience on the gym floor all point to the critical importance of "conservatism."

OT64.13 If you can't get big, strong and impressive from doing things the conservative way, you have little or no chance of getting big, strong and impressive. The non-conservative approaches greatly increase the risk of injuries, setbacks, frustration and failure. How's all that going to help? Abbreviated training and "conservatism" have enabled many "no hopers" to get big, strong and very impressive—though not the pro-bodybuilder interpretation of "impressive."

OTHER TOPICS 65
I've been training barefoot for a while. Is it a good idea to train without wearing shoes?

OT65.1 I used to train barefoot—in my own home gym—*but no longer*. I did it because I wanted to squat without any heel elevation relative to the balls of my feet, and couldn't find suitable shoes.

OT65.2 Feet are *highly* complex structures. Foot defects are very common, and a defect affects how the stresses placed on the feet are borne by the feet *and* the rest of the body in general. When forces on the feet are exaggerated by high-load activities such as heavy weight training, running and any competitive sport, the defects are magnified. While foot defects might not be the whole story behind foot, ankle, knee or back problems, they are highly likely to be contributing factors, perhaps major ones.

OT65.3 I recommend the use of high quality *orthopedic* shoes with molded internal soles, to compensate for structural or postural instability in the feet, *or*, in the case of defect-free feet, to *maintain* existing good condition over the *long term*. While shoes with high-quality *custom-made* molded internal soles are the ideal, off-the-shelf shoes with molded internal soles are, in most cases, far superior to regular shoes. You can even get molded internal soles that can be slipped inside your regular footwear (but you may need to remove some of the existing soles to make room for the inserts).

OT65.4 Imagine, for example, the effect on your body of heavy squatting with arches in your feet that are no longer as high and strong as they used to be in your youth. The huge forces will not be distributed in the balanced way they used to be, and your knees, for example, will have to endure skewed stress. This will apply exaggerated load on a part of each knee, eventually triggering off problems. Good support is *essential* while lifting heavy weights. It's also necessary for everyday activities if your feet have defects.

OT65.5 A molded sole with bumps, ridges and mounds in the right places can make a *huge* difference to the well-being of your feet and legs. A change in footwear, or the insertion of high-quality molded soles into your existing footwear, will help greatly to keep you lifting intensively, heavily and free of injuries. *But use reduced weights when adapting to the new footwear, and build back gradually.*

OT65.6 *Consult a podiatrist, preferably a sports podiatrist, or a chiropractor with training in orthotics.* An orthotic—i.e., a shoe insert (not merely an arch support) designed to increase the mechanical efficiency of the *whole* foot—might be prescribed. An off-the-shelf molded internal sole "insert" might, however, do a great job.

OTHER TOPICS 66
What drove you to publish, in Cyprus, an international training magazine that has no advertising?

OT66.1 I was driven by a great passion to pass on the lessons I've learned and am still learning. I had to do this—it was in my blood/or my fate in life, so to speak. Rather than just complain about the state of affairs in the training world, I had to make an effort to provide an alternative source of information.

OT66.2 Logically, the odds must have been heavily stacked against me—based in Cyprus but with my market overseas, with no sponsor or backer, no capital, and no experience of publishing.

OTHER TOPICS 67
What would you like people to remember you for?

OT67.1 As someone who made a mark for the better in the training world; who promoted healthy, practical, safe and productive training methods; who had absolutely no time for performance-enhancing drugs and the bull, dishonesty and hypocrisy rampant in the training world; and who worked to shift focus away from the competitive "elite" and towards meeting the needs of the training masses.

Why didn't you specify sets and reps?

Other than in a few illustrations, I avoided specifying numbers of sets and reps in the programs listed in BEYOND BRAWN. There's too much individual variation for a "one size fits all" dictum to be applied to sets and reps. Rather than give a best-fit "solution" (which would suit some trainees, but not others) I thought I'd serve readers' interests best if I explained the options (and not just for sets and reps), and showed how individual variation can affect many training-related factors. Readers would then be helped to understand how to personalize programs to best suit them *individually*. In BEYOND BRAWN (especially Section 2, but in the whole book in general), *and* in this book too, I've tried to teach people how to become their *own* expert personal trainers. Combine the acquired knowledge with sensible experimentation, and then you can take charge over your own training. A "one size fits all" type approach can't accommodate all individual needs.

The Success Formula

Here's another excerpt from WHY CONVENTIONAL BODYBUILDING METHODS SUCK...AND THE ALTERNATIVE APPROACH THAT REALLY DELIVERS: Contrary to what conventional bodybuilding methods would have you believe, in order to build a terrific physique...

1. you *don't* have to weight train even three times per week, let alone four, five or six times;

2. you *don't* have to use a big variety of exercises, or high-volume training;

3. you *don't* have to take "bodybuilding supplements," though some other supplements can have health benefits and be very valuable;

4. you *don't* have to get caught up in all the hoopla and hype of the bodybuilding world;

5. you *don't* have to use high-risk exercises or techniques, or any foolish macho bravado;

6. you *don't* have to copy the drug-abusing habits of the "elite" physiques.

But you *do* have to adopt a totally different approach to your training and *whole outlook* on bodybuilding. There's a huge bonus *on top* of improved results—*reduced time spent in the gym*, and a more practical approach for busy people. So you can achieve your exercise goals *without* sacrificing important aspects of your work or family life.

Shortly I'll provide a summary of what would have delivered the goods for building a big, very strong and impressive drug-free physique when I was a beginner, given a few years of consistent application. It still delivers the goods today, and for *all* types of trainees, not just beginners. In fact, it's the *only* type of training that produces decent results for most people.

Don't waste years of your life, like millions of others already have, trying to prove to the contrary.

I realize that most of the prescriptions that follow shortly are radical or even blasphemous relative to the edicts of conventional training. *Have the courage to swim against the training tide.* Always remember that popular training methods simply don't deliver the goods for most people. So why would you want to use conventional training methods?

Because I'm only interested in drug-free training, and primarily concerned with satisfying the needs of the hard-gaining masses, it's inevitable that most of the values and methods promoted in this book are heretical relative to what's customary in most gyms today.

There's no other approach to take if training methods that are practical and helpful for drug-free typical people are to be promoted. What follows is an outline only, to lay a foundation. There's much to learn about how to implement the framework in a way that's *personalized* and *appropriate* for a given individual.

Training program design needs to accommodate individual factors including goals, age, training history and experience, strengths and limitations, injury background, equipment availability, and recovery ability. In addition, exercise selection and form must be *perfect*. This is no simple matter. A look around almost any gym will provide a litany of poor exercise selection and lousy form, and demonstrate the gross ignorance that abounds on exercise selection and form. Also, recovery ability needs to be enhanced, and nutrition optimized.

While my focus has always been on meeting the needs of the drug-free and genetically typical—hard gainers (who are really "normal" gainers)—the methods I promote are also appropriate for easy gainers, i.e., people who have naturally very responsive bodies. Even easy gainers want to make progress as fast as they can, without injuries or becoming slaves to a gym. This is precisely what sensible and personalized abbreviated training delivers.

I know that the framework promotes a simple and basic approach to bodybuilding and strength training, but that's *exactly* what most people need. *One of the biggest and most destructive myths of the training world is that simple, basics-first routines are for novices only.*

It's important to get to the root of productive weight training—*building up to handling impressive weights in the big exercises in consistently perfect form.* If you want to build a terrific physique, you absolutely must build up to using big weights in the major movements. Just what's "big" varies according to the individual, due to a number of factors including goals, age, gender and training experience; but "little" weights only build little muscles. Incrementally and *consistently* increasing your exercise poundages is the name of the muscle-*building* game.

Training, nutrition and recovery all need to be geared to assist your body to build additional strength pound by pound, to work up, over a period of years, to big weights. The best way to achieve this, training wise, is to use *abbreviated* routines, *safe* exercise selection and *perfect* form. *That's* why abbreviated training is the way to go.

Getting caught up in the small exercises like most trainees do—leg extensions, leg curls, pec deck work, cable crossovers, pec flyes, lateral raises, concentration curls, triceps kickbacks, etc.—*hinders* progress on the big exercises that really matter. Why bother with those little exercises if you want to build bigger and stronger muscles? Why train in a way that hinders progress on the exercises that really matter?

There are, however, a few very important small exercises that have vital assistance value for helping to keep you injury resistant for the big exercises. But *these* small exercises *don't* include the aforementioned ones that are so popular today.

You can't refine a physique until you've first built the required muscular size. Drug-fed genetic freaks can build *and* refine simultaneously, but drug-free genetically typical trainees can't.

Here's the outline of sensible abbreviated training that's appropriate for anyone—male or female, young or not so young, hard gainer or easy gainer, beginner or very advanced. And it applies whether you want to train in a home gym, or in a public gym.

1. Simple routines of 6–8 exercises *maximum* per workout, and better still for many hard gainers, only 3–5 exercises. No single program is best—there are many interpretations that can work well.

2. Most of your exercises should be big compound movements—e.g., squat, deadlift, dip and chin—if you're at the upper end of the number of exercises, and *all* of them should be big movements if you're at the lower end of the exercise count. The harder you find it is to progress, the more you need to prune back on the exercises you perform.

3. Weight train two or *at most* three times a week.

4. Alternate two different workouts.

5. Add an *extra* day or two of rest between workouts, if necessary, for full recovery.

6. Master exercise form, and *always* use impeccable exercise technique.

7. Use a controlled rep speed of 2–3 seconds for the positive and at least 3 seconds for the negative. Put the emphasis on keeping your reps *smooth*. Explosive training greatly increases the risk of injury, *so avoid it.*

8. Warm up very well—better too much than not enough.

9. Perform no more than three work sets per exercise.

10. Make poundage progression in perfect form your training creed. Add *a little* weight to each exercise every week or two—a little weight means a pound or so on each big exercise, and no more than half of that on the smaller exercises. Use "little gems"—i.e., fractional plates or microloads. This applies during the *hard* stage of a training cycle. During the earlier "breaking in" stage you should be able to add weight faster.

11. Follow a high-quality protein-rich diet *every day* that provides a caloric and nutrient surplus. You can't build muscle without enough of the required raw materials.

12. Spread your dietary intake over five or preferably six feeds a day.

13. Experiment with protein intake—you may need large quantities to maximize results.

14. Sleep well every night—at least eight *quality* hours.

15. Conserve your energy on your off days.

Fine-tune most of this outline based on experimentation that's governed by *sticking with what helps*, and *dropping what doesn't*—to personalize the template *for you* to produce month-by-month progress.

Some factors aren't open for modification—don't compromise on perfect form, for example, though you should tweak grips and stances to find what works best for you. And for as long as you want to get stronger and bigger muscles, never compromise on the need to keep adding a little poundage to each exercise whenever possible.

With the "adjustable" factors, individual modification can make a *big* difference. Perhaps you need a lot more protein and/or calories than most people do, perhaps you need ten hours of sleep daily rather than eight, perhaps you're better off training a given bodypart three times every *two* weeks rather than once or twice a week, perhaps you're better off deadlifting only once every two weeks, or *perhaps* you can train more productively if you work each exercise a bit more frequently than most hard gainers can. *The bottom line is progress.*

Whatever adjustments you make, *be sure that they help you to make better progress than you would otherwise,* or else you have no business making them. Fine-tuning should help, not hinder progress.

Make this proven fifteen-point plan work for you by applying it with resolute dedication. Do it for a few years and you'll be so big, strong and impressive that most people will stare at you in amazement when they see you for the first time.

As I stated in the introduction to this book, I wish a wise mentor had grabbed me by the scruff of my neck as a beginner, and *forced* me to follow nothing other than simple and abbreviated training programs, with the priority being to increase my exercise poundages while always using *impeccable* form. I wish that mentor had ensured I never wavered from the sure way.

Had this happened, I'd have developed a better and stronger physique by age 20 (after five years of training) than over 95% of drug-free bodybuilders the world over.

As it happened, I gave my absolute all to bodybuilding for five years, but had little to show for it. Application and motivation are only part of the battle. Appropriate training instruction is essential. No amount of dedication and motivation (or food supplements) can make lousy training programs work.

If I'd had this imaginary mentor, and had he been an uncompromising dictator when it came to the use of perfect exercise form and abbreviated routines, and insistent on the need to keep adding a little iron to each big exercise every week or two, for year after year after year, I'd have made gains so consistently, and without injuries, that I'd have thought I was an easy gainer.

I'd have been adding a tad of iron every week or two without any perceived increase in effort needed, such would have been the gradual and intelligent nature of my progression. I'd have accumulated gains on an almost linear basis for year after year. Having discovered *The Golden Fleece*, I'd have been scratching my head wondering why so many people had trouble developing bigger muscles.

All of this doesn't apply just to me, but to all trainees who want to build stronger and better physiques, though the specific interpretation of exercises, training volume and frequency, caloric and nutritional intake, sleep needs and rate of progress varies among individuals.

Create your own imaginary wise and uncompromising mentor, and then bring him to life to ensure that from now on you never, *ever* waver from the path of productive and safe training.

Live for the moment and don't harp on about what you should have been doing in former years. No matter how many mistakes you've made, no matter how much training time you've wasted, and no matter how much you wish you could turn the clock back, what's done is done. But stop repeating past mistakes, and stop letting people cheat you!

Today is the start of the rest of your life. You'll never be as young as you are now. There'll never be a better time than today to start getting your training-related life in perfect order. So start today to get in charge of your physique!

Postscript

Many people put a great deal of time and thought into planning their training programs. But then once they get a program going, and progress accumulating (albeit slowly), they very often don't put enough into *keeping* the progress going.

Planning a program is easy *relative* to the *implementation* of it. You can study good form, and know what to do. You can practice it with relatively light weights. But holding perfect form when you're grinding out reps in new poundage territory is something else.

You can psyche yourself up to train hard, but that's not the same as actually getting out reps 17, 18, 19 and 20 in the squat, for example, when you're spent at number 16.

You can study all you want on the importance of eating every three hours or so, not skipping feeds, and eating only good food. But actually eating a good meal every three hours or so is something else.

Most people don't realize their full gaining potential. They get things going for a bit, but then don't crank up their dedication *even more* as the cycle grinds on *and the demands becomes ever greater.*

The further you go, the more dedicated you need to be in order to keep the gains coming. Not to deliver fully on what's needed to sustain progress produces the common training malaise of stagnation.

If a program can work for a few weeks—i.e., yield new pounds on the bar in good form—then it can work for a few months if not a year or more *if you play by the rules.* These rules are not mine. All I'm doing is restating them and stressing their pivotal importance.

Are you motivated enough to train really hard? Are you disciplined enough to hold perfect form *even* when training very hard? Do you go to bed early enough to get your full eight hours *minimum* of sleep? Do you feed five or six times per day of a caloric and protein intake suited to your needs? Do you really stick primarily if not exclusively with the big basic exercises? Are you really *nudging* up your exercise poundages every week or two?

"I've heard all of this before!" I can hear you shout. *But this is all there is.* The rules of training success *are* simple. *It's the implementation of the "rules" that's so demanding.* Are you really *fully* implementing the rules?

Cut yourself off from anything that hypes up many things *other than* sensible training, sensible nutrition from food (including milk), and adequate rest and sleep. "New" training "discoveries" and food supplements won't cut it. All they are designed to do is give trainees false hope and provide income for the many companies that are digging their snouts in the bodybuilding trough. *The answers to questions and concerns that people have about their training and gaining difficulties are not to be found in mainstream bull, hype and hoopla.*

When the going's going well in your training, really *crank up* your dedication to *keep* the gaining going well. Once you've done the preparatory work, dig in, hike up your resolve and dedication, and *really make the most of your training.* Make every workout, day, week and month count.

Be bold!

If you're *not* progressing towards your strength and physique goals, what you're currently doing is not working, and changes need to be made. As I've said elsewhere in this book, "More of what didn't help you over the last few months will not help you over the next few." Please recognize that you may have to make *very radical* changes before you'll see good progress. While you may be following a training program that's abbreviated by mainstream standards, it could still be too much *for you.* If you're currently "stuck," experiment for a few months with a super-abbreviated training program, and super-generous satisfaction of *all* the components of recovery. Be bold! *It may prove to be one of the most rewarding experiments of your life.*

The requirements for building a big, strong, impressive and healthy physique are simple enough. But their implementation is far from simple. Few people have the requisite resolve, courage and dedication, so inevitably they will never realize their strength and physique goals. I can explain what you need to do, and lay it out step by step, but only *you* can implement the know-how. *That's where you're on your own.* Acquire the know-how you need (and you don't need to become a walking encyclopedia), set your goals, and then *commit* to unrelenting dedication for *a period of years. Then* you'll have the chance to achieve your goals.

Know thyself

"Should I do 3 sets per exercise to not-quite failure, or a single one all the way?" "Should I do sets of 8 reps for my bench, or 5?" "Should I squat every 5, 7 or 10 days?" "Should I have 40 grams of protein per feed, or 50?" You can answer these (and many other questions) *yourself* through frank and objective analysis of your training and related factors, *along with* experimentation.

Many interpretations of abbreviated training may produce good results for a given individual, but some may work better than others. Individual variation and responsiveness can be considerable, even among typical trainees.

Once you have a good grasp of abbreviated training, and are *applying* it, get into sensible trial and error experimentation to see what works best for you. Keep all but one variable as constant as possible for a month or so, and try something different with that one variable. Retain what helps, discard what hinders. Strike a balance between looking for a better program, and not trying to "fix" something that's going well. If you know you're guilty of major shortcomings—exercise selection, program construction, training intensity, nutrition, sleep—you *must first fix them*, because no amount of tinkering with any details will make any difference *until* all the basics are in good order. No tinkering with sets, reps and training days, for example, will make any difference if you're loafing in the gym, not consuming enough food, or not sleeping well.

I promote training methods that are more conservative than those of most coaches. I explain possible if not probable dangers of certain methods or techniques, rather than ignore them and hope that readers don't find out about them the hard and potentially disastrous way. And I strongly promote the importance of individual variation. *But I get overwhelming feedback that this produces much better results for many more people, AND greater training longevity, than does the non-conservative little-or-no-caveats approach that doesn't fully consider individual variation.*

The overall picture

While you're getting on with satisfying achievement—be it physique, strength or anything else—don't be so involved that you forget to enjoy life as you go along. Take the time to observe things around you, smile more, talk less, listen more. Too many people fail to make the most of their children, the treasure of a healthy body, and the actual fruits of their labors. They also fail to appreciate the everyday good things that are taken for granted.

When life draws to a close, when you no longer see much future for yourself, and when you dwell on your past, then you'll wish you had made more of the moments as you were actually living them. Don't wait till then. Do it now!

Be obsessed, focused and consumed by your training *when you are in the gym,* and rest, eat and sleep very well while out of the gym. Then get on with the rest of your life. Don't expect even stellar physique and training achievements to bring order and happiness to your life. Great satisfaction in a limited area, yes, but nothing more. Suppose, for example, you could squat 200 pounds more than you can now, and that you have 30 pounds more muscle. As terrific as all that would be, would it make any difference to the events and relationships which have the greatest impact on your happiness?

As marvelous as training and its rewards are, never forget that they are only a small part of the big picture. Those who are obsessed with training even when they are not in the gym expose themselves to the destructive side of training—neglect of personal relationships, family life, health, education and career.

You can get the most from training *without* it consuming your life. That's what this book is about. There's even an unexpected bonus from adopting the right perspective—you're much more likely to see through hype and deception in the training world, use the rational programs that are the most productive, *and actually develop the strength and physique you're after.*

If you have serious joint limitations

I'm sometimes asked for advice by trainees who have serious joint limitations, often related to accidents or sporting injuries. I recommend trying a variety of treatments including trigger point therapy and chiropractic; but even then some trainees will still have serious limitations in one or more joints—sometimes temporary, often permanent. Abbreviated training and a focus on major exercises is still the most efficient way to go *assuming that some big moves can be used safely.* Different major exercises should be tried for the problem area(s), using *impeccable* form *and* a truly *controlled* rep cadence—and *perhaps* even a *very slow* rep speed— to find what's best. A very slow rep speed of about 6/6 (6 seconds for each phase of a rep) may be a critical factor determining whether an exercise is safe for joints that have serious limitations. It would be much better, for example, that you use leg presses (assuming you have a good leg press machine available) and partial deadlifts in a very slow cadence than leg extensions and leg curls in a conventional (or any other) rep speed. The leg presses and partial deadlifts, being big exercises, will do a lot more for you than leg extensions and leg curls, assuming you use progressive poundages. *But a very slow cadence isn't synonymous with good form.* For many people with joint limitations (and even those *without*), slow reps won't help much because their form is poor. *Perfect form and a 3/3 or so rep cadence is safer than poor form and a 6/6 speed; but for a few people, perfect form* AND VERY SLOW REPS *may be necessary.*

Your input, please

All books have room for improvement. Please provide feedback to help improve this book in a future edition. Let me know of any typos and errors you may find, and feel free to make suggestions on how to improve the book.

Got any questions?

If you have any questions that are neither covered in this text nor my other books, please let me have them.

Stuart McRobert
CS Publishing Ltd.
P.O. Box 20390
CY-2151 Nicosia
Cyprus
email: cspubltd@spidernet.com.cy

Resources

Bars and plates

1. IronMind® Enterprises, Inc., P.O. Box 1228, Nevada City, CA 95959, USA (530-265-6725), www.ironmind.com
2. Watson Gym Equipment, Unit 8, Washington Road, West Wiltshire Trading Estate, Wiltshire BA13 4JP, England (01373 859617, 0976752585), www.gymequipment.uk.com
3. York® Barbell Company, Box 1707, York, PA 17405, USA (717-767-6481), www.yorkbarbell.com

General heavy-duty equipment

1. IronMind® Enterprises, Inc. (see above)
2. Johnny Gibson Gym Equipment Co., 11 South Sixth Ave., Tucson, AZ 85701, USA (520-622-1275), www.johnnygibson.com
3. Watson Gym Equipment (see above)

Little discs

1. PDA, 104 Bangor Street, Mauldin, SC, 29662, USA (864-963-5640), www.fractionalplates.com
2. Watson Gym Equipment (see above)

Magnetic little discs

PlateMates®, Benoit Built, Inc., 12 Factory Cove Road, Boothbay Harbor, ME 04538, USA (207-633-5912, 1-800-877-3322), www.theplatemate.com

Shrug bar (trap bar alternative)

1. In the US, contact PDA (see above)
2. In the UK, contact Watson Gym Equipment (see above)

Tru-Squat

Southern Xercise, Inc., P.O. Box 412, Cleveland, TN 37364, USA (423-476-8999, 800-348-4907), www.southernxercise.com

Back Revolution

Meyer Distributing Co., 8580 Milliken Avenue, P.O. Box 3509, Roncho Cucamonga, CA 91729, USA (800-472-4221), www.meyerdist.com

Trigger point therapy

1. Bonnie Prudden Pain Erasure, P.O. Box 65240, Tucson, AZ 85728, USA (520-529-3979 and 1-800-221-4634), www.bonnieprudden.com
   Video tapes on trigger point therapy are available from here, as are Bonnie Prudden's books and a list of certified Bonnie Prudden myotherapists.

2. The Pressure Positive Company, 128 Olberholtzer Road, Gilbertsville, PA 19525, USA (610-754-6204 and 1-800-603-5107), www.backtools.com

HARDgainer

the path to physical excellence

bastion of
no-nonsense
drug-free
training

FREE magazine!

Published by Stuart McRobert, HARDGAINER is probably the most instruction-dense and hype-free training magazine on the market today, providing more practical and result-producing advice for drug-free bodybuilders and strength trainees than is available in any other magazine. It's crammed with practical advice and nuggets of wisdom to lead you to training success.

Here's some of what to expect from HARDGAINER. You'll get the undiluted truth—no exaggerated claims filled with puffery. What we say may not always sit easy with you. But you can count on one thing—it will be frank and down-to-earth. As the title implies, we speak to the hard-gaining typical individual. People like you. But average potential does not have to mean average achievements. In fact, an impressive physique and a terrific level of strength are well within your reach. The key is in the right approach. That is what HARDGAINER is about.

A 12-month/6-issue subscription costs US \$29.95 (or UK £18.95), and a 24-month/12-issue subscription costs US \$54.95 (or UK £34.95).

But you don't have to take our word for HARDGAINER being probably the most instruction-dense, practical, drug-free and hype-free training magazine on the market. Write in and we'll send you a FREE sample copy of the magazine, with no strings attached.

HARDGAINER is a subscription-only magazine. You will not find it at newsstands. *So write in today, and grab yourself a free growing experience!*

Please send me a free sample copy of HARDGAINER.

Name _____

Address _____

_____

Code/zip and country _____

Please mail to CS Publishing Ltd., P.O. Box 20390, CY-2151 Nicosia, Cyprus

Answers to thousands of questions...
and how to master your training fully

FURTHER BRAWN has given you the foundation of practical, responsible and productive training. But it's only the icing on the cake relative to what's in the books that preceded it. FURTHER BRAWN is the fourth component in a series of books that forms *The Muscle & Might Master Method*.

Many years of work went into producing these books. They all focus on meeting the needs of typical trainees who have busy lives and average genetic endowment. This is just one of the reasons why the books are so different to mainstream titles.

There's no other *set* of books that promotes practical, safety-minded, drug-free, bull-free, hype-free, independent, comprehensive and interrelated guidance for "average" people who want to develop outstanding physiques. And all the books come with a money-back guarantee. *There's no risk, but so much potential benefit.*

THE MUSCLE & MIGHT MASTER METHOD
While each component of The Master Method can stand alone as an excellent instructional tool, *together* they provide the most complete and responsible package of books for achieving physique and strength goals. FURTHER BRAWN is the fourth part of the series. Here are the first three:
BEYOND BRAWN
THE INSIDER'S TELL-ALL HANDBOOK ON WEIGHT-TRAINING TECHNIQUE
THE MUSCLE & MIGHT TRAINING TRACKER

How far do you want to go?
The Muscle & Might Master Method gives you all the tools you need to go as far *as you want* to developing your full physique and strength potential. But not everyone wants to go *all the way*. Perhaps you only want to lose 20 pounds of fat and gain 20 pounds of muscle. Perhaps a loss of 40 pounds of fat is your Holy Grail. *But perhaps you do want to go all the way to the best physique that's naturally possible for you to develop.*

You might be a hardcore bodybuilder, fitness trainee, strength athlete or powerlifter. And you can be male or female, hard gainer or easy gainer, home trainee or commercial gym user, young or not-so-young, overweight or lean. It doesn't matter which groups you belong to—The Master Method will guide you step-by-step to *your* specific goals.

BEYOND BRAWN

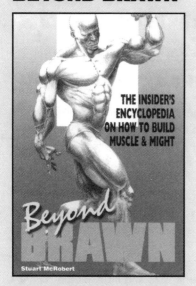

This encyclopedia contains the essential core of The Muscle & Might Master Method. It will take you all the way to your weight-training revolution. BEYOND BRAWN: The Insider's Encyclopedia on How to Build Muscle & Might—now in a *revised* edition—is 512 pages crammed with information about every facet of bodybuilding, and weight training in general.

The book is very well organized, with each chapter broken into numbered paragraphs, for easy reference. Of course, there's a comprehensive (21-page) index so you can easily return again and again to any sections you want. Here's the Table of Contents of BEYOND BRAWN:

SECTION 3: SPECIAL ISSUES

McRobert is frank and not ashamed to discuss tough issues, such as his own crippling injuries in the early 90s—and how he overcame them. The lessons you can learn from that section alone (Chapters 17 and 18), to ensure you never have to suffer like Stuart did, are worth many times the price of BEYOND BRAWN. No other book covers injury rehabilitation and prevention like this one does. Nothing ruins progress to physique and strength goals like injury does. Staying clear of injury is a priority.

This book is not just for novices. It can save you years of wasted toil regardless of your level of training experience. It will propel you into the detailed practical know-how needed to turn you into an expertly informed bodybuilder or strength trainee. You can learn all of this from just a few weeks of serious study. Then apply what you learn and you'll develop a degree of muscle and might that will make a mockery of what you would have achieved had you stayed with other training methods.

BEYOND BRAWN will take you right "inside" weight training, to study the practical reality of applying knowledge. It's not a theoretical treatise or a pack of pseudo-scientific claptrap.

"I want to say without hesitation that BEYOND BRAWN is the greatest book ever written on how to train with weights. And it's the greatest book ever written on how *to last* while training with weights. It's the greatest—period!"
– *Dick Conner, veteran strength coach and 25-year-plus proprietor of*
The Pit, a famous no-frills gym in Indiana

"For bodybuilding instruction, BEYOND BRAWN is par excellence, featuring an unprecedented depth of practical, relevant and readily applicable training information. Even more than that, the book is a training partner, companion, friend and labor of love. A truly exceptional book!"
– *Jan Dellinger*
York Barbell Company

"BEYOND BRAWN is the most comprehensive, helpful and honest book on natural strength training today. With great care and in extraordinary detail, this book covers every training-related topic you can imagine, and without any hype."
– *Bob Whelan, M.S., M.S., C.S.C.S.*
President, Whelan Strength Training

"BEYOND BRAWN is the book we all wish we had years ago. It's an absolute must read."
– *Richard A. Winett, Ph.D.*
Publisher, MASTER TRAINER

"BEYOND BRAWN is the bible of rational strength training...Page after page is jam-packed with practical real-world training information that you just cannot find anywhere else...This book has my highest endorsement—it's without a doubt the very best book on strength training I've ever read."
– *Kevin R. Fontaine, Ph.D.*
Assistant Professor of Medicine
Johns Hopkins University School of Medicine

THE INSIDER'S TELL-ALL HANDBOOK ON WEIGHT-TRAINING TECHNIQUE

You're ahead of the game as soon as you start using The Master Method, as described in BEYOND BRAWN. You need to keep that competitive edge by performing each exercise *exactly* right. How to use perfect exercise form is covered in extensive detail by THE INSIDER'S TELL-ALL HANDBOOK ON WEIGHT-TRAINING TECHNIQUE, which is now in a revised *second* edition. *Exercise form is such a serious subject that a whole book is needed to do it justice.*

As incredible as it may seem, gyms are usually the worst places to learn about perfect exercise form. The myths, fallacies and dangerous techniques that are perpetuated in most gyms are astonishing. And most training publications and "personal trainers" are no better. The foolish "no pain, no gain" maxim has wreaked havoc in the training world. It's no wonder that so many people get hurt and frustrated with weight training.

The perfect complement to BEYOND BRAWN, TECHNIQUE contains 244 photographs and over 200 fully indexed big pages showing the right and wrong ways to perform all the most productive exercises—34 different exercises, and 48 of them, in fact, if you include the variations. In addition there's extensive commentary and advice from Stuart. The book also includes a thorough flexibility program, how to use a video camera to perfect your exercise form, and how to compose form checklists.

TECHNIQUE isn't just for beginners. No matter whether you're an advanced, intermediate or novice bodybuilder or strength trainee, this book will greatly increase your grasp of safe weight-training form. *Become an expert on exercise technique.* Then your safe training longevity is almost guaranteed. Unless you can train safely over the long term, you'll never realize your goals.

"As a chiropractor with over 20 years of training experience, I can honestly say that no other book comes even close to McRobert's for teaching safe and responsible exercise technique."
– Dr. Gregory Steiner
Director of Active Chiropractic, Glasgow, Scotland

If you're a visually oriented person who learns best when you can actually see what you're studying, TECHNIQUE is an absolute must read. And even if you learn better through other methods, having the pictures in front of you as you work out will be very beneficial.

No other book on exercise form covers the subject matter so carefully, responsibly and with such attention to safety and training longevity.

Each section offers clear, concise tips for setting up the equipment properly, assuming the safe and effective positions, performing the exercises step by step, and monitoring performance, along with photographs illustrating exactly what to do, and what not to do.

Here's the Table of Contents of THE INSIDER'S TELL-ALL HANDBOOK ON WEIGHT-TRAINING TECHNIQUE:

PART 3: CRITICAL ADDITIONAL ISSUES

You can't afford to take a chance with using improper exercise form. The older you get, the more you'll realize the importance of using excellent exercise form. Don't wait until you've seriously hurt yourself before learning this critical lesson. Apply what THE INSIDER'S TELL-ALL HANDBOOK ON WEIGHT-TRAINING TECHNIQUE teaches, and then you can train safely and productively for a lifetime.

THE MUSCLE & MIGHT TRAINING TRACKER

BEYOND BRAWN is also best used with another companion volume, THE MUSCLE & MIGHT TRAINING TRACKER. This 136-page workbook contains everything you need to track your progress—day by day, week by week, month by month, year by year.

A training journal is indispensible for keeping you on track for training success. No matter where you are now—180-pound squat or 500, 13-inch arms or 17, 135-pound bench press or 350—the systematic organization and focus upon achieving goals that a sensible training journal enforces, will help you to improve your physique steadily and consistently. While most trainees are aware of the potential value of a training log, very few actually keep one; and that's one of the major reasons why they make minimal or no progress.

The front section of TRACKER highlights the most important points in designing your personal training program, then follows with sample filled-out log pages, and then detailed blank log pages for you to chart your progress. The log pages cover not only the specifics of your weight training—what exercises, how long you performed them, and a comment area to note your performance and any issues you need to address—but also nutrition, sleep and body composition.

You'll be excited to watch the numbers grow as you improve your physique and strength, and achieve the degree of brawn you've always wanted. As simple as it is to use a training log, don't underestimate the critical role it can play in helping you to maximize your training productivity.

One training log will track your bodybuilding and strength-training progress for at least 24 months—that's a cost of just $1.00 per month. And this log is built for the job it's designed to do. For example, its robust paper provides the strength to withstand heavy use, and the spiral binding enables the book to open flat for ease of use when entering data. *This is no ordinary training diary.*

HARDGAINER magazine

Though not part of the series of books that comprises The Master Method, HARDGAINER magazine reinforces the lessons given in the books. Just as you'll want to re-read the books at many stages in your training, you can always take advantage of new information. Fresh info, and the expertise and experiences of a range of contributors can arrive in your mailbox every other month.

"HARDGAINER provides serious training information for drug-free trainees— no sugar coating, just honest information."
   – Ted Lambrinides, Ph.D.
   Editor, HARD TRAINING newsletter

"Super magazine! One of the few training magazines that provides honest information for the average non-drug-using trainee."
   – Bill Starr
   Strength and conditioning coach
   Johns Hopkins University

In HARDGAINER you'll find articles by well-known experts as well as from those who are aren't household names, but who have a wealth of practical experience and important insights to share. Here you'll find lots of wisdom from those who are "in the trenches" of the training world. There's a lot of grassroots material in HARDGAINER to show you the ins and outs of the *practical reality* of applying The Muscle & Might Master Method. HARDGAINER includes such features as:

1. How-to articles about specific exercises (for instance, a 7-page article on deadlifting technique, including 15 photos)

2. Inspirational pieces on developing the right training philosophy for you

3. Sample workouts

4. Advice for new, intermediate and advanced trainers

5. An ongoing series on nutrition

6. Questions and answers

7. "From the Grassroots" articles and readers' letters

And Stuart McRobert edits and contributes to every issue.

All our back issues are available. Free details of the contents of each issue are available by mail upon request, or from our web site at www.hardgainer.com

Electronic books

We have e-books too, which can be downloaded from the internet. These e-books include an abridged edition of BEYOND BRAWN and an abridged edition of THE INSIDER'S TELL-ALL HANDBOOK ON WEIGHT-TRAINING TECHNIQUE. For details on the e-books, please visit www.hardgainer.com

BRAWN

BRAWN is the classic 1991 book that was the precursor for BEYOND BRAWN and The Muscle & Might Master Method. BRAWN focuses on genetic realities, appropriate role models, and most of the ins and outs of successful drug-free training. It's especially strong in the philosophical underpinning behind rational training. It also details how the genetically blessed are gifted, and shows why conventional training is so unproductive for typical people.

First you should read BEYOND BRAWN, THE INSIDER'S TELL-ALL HANDBOOK ON WEIGHT-TRAINING TECHNIQUE and FURTHER BRAWN, and apply what you learn. Later on you may want to read BRAWN, which is now in a revised second edition.

Ordering information

1. a) BEYOND BRAWN softcover edition costs $24.95 (£15.95).
   b) A signed and inscribed hardcover edition of BEYOND BRAWN costs $34.95 (£21.95).

2. THE INSIDER'S TELL-ALL HANDBOOK ON WEIGHT-TRAINING TECHNIQUE softcover second edition costs $24.95 (£15.95).

3. THE MUSCLE & MIGHT TRAINING TRACKER costs $19.95 (£11.95).

4. HARDGAINER magazine—a 12-month subscription costs $29.95 (£18.95), and 24 months costs $54.95 (£34.95).

Postage and handling is $5.00 (or £3.00) for single titles. If you order two or more titles there's no charge for p&h.

The books may be ordered online *or through the mail*. To order online, please go to http://www.hardgainer.com/order.html

If you're ordering through the mail, please contact
CS Publishing Ltd., P.O. Box 20390, CY-2151 Nicosia, Cyprus
email: cspubltd@spidernet.com.cy

Payment may be by personal check/cheque in US $ or sterling, bank draft drawn on a US or UK bank, UK postal order, or cash sent by registered mail. Eurocheques can't be accepted, and neither can US postal money orders or Canadian postal money orders.

Delivery time for a shipment of printed books, from the date of receipt of an order, is 2–4 weeks for the UK and mainland Europe, and 4–6 weeks for the USA and the rest of the world.

For your convenience, an order form can be found on the following page.

RISK-FREE ORDER FORM

BEYOND BRAWN softcover
❑ $24.95 US or £15.95 UK

BEYOND BRAWN hardcover (signed and inscribed)
❑ $34.95 US or £21.95 UK

THE INSIDER'S TELL-ALL HANDBOOK ON WEIGHT-TRAINING TECHNIQUE
❑ $24.95 US or £15.95 UK

THE MUSCLE & MIGHT TRAINING TRACKER
❑ $19.95 or £11.95 UK

Subscription to HARDGAINER magazine
❑ $29.95 US or £18.95 UK for 12 months
❑ $54.95 US or £34.95 UK for 24 months

For a single book, please add $5.00 or £3.00 for p&h.
Order two or more items there's no charge for p&h.
Cost of a HARDGAINER subscription includes p&h.

Name ——————————————————————————————

Address ——————————————————————————————

——————————— State & zip/code ——————— Country ————

CS Publishing Ltd., P.O. Box 20390, CY-2151 Nicosia, Cyprus
For payment options and delivery times, please see the previous page.

Money-Back Guarantee

If you're not fully satisfied that our publications give you the know-how you need to take you towards your bodybuilding and strength-training goals, return within 60 days what you bought and you'll receive a full no-questions-asked refund.

Online ordering at www.hardgainer.com

Index

To make the index as user friendly as possible, paragraph indexing was used for most of this book. For example, 51(T2.3) refers to page 51, paragraph T2.3, i.e., *Training* section, answer 2, paragraph 3. *"See"* is a cross reference from a term that is *not* used in the index to the term, usually a synonym, where the information will be found, e.g., "Dieting. *See* Weight reduction." *"See also"* is a reminder that related information is available under a different heading, e.g., "Diet. *See also* Nutrition."

Notes

Perspective

Though not written by a muscle and might buff, here are some wise words to help you keep the rigors of life in perspective.

I woke up early today, excited over all I get to do before the clock strikes midnight. My job is to choose what kind of day I'm going to have.

Today I can complain because the weather is rainy, or I can be thankful that the grass is getting watered for free.

Today I can grumble about my health, or I can rejoice that I'm alive.

Today I can lament over all that my parents didn't give me when I was growing up, or I can feel grateful that they allowed me to be born.

Today I can cry because roses have thorns, or I can celebrate that thorns have roses.

Today I can mourn my lack of friends, or I can excitedly embark upon a quest to discover new relationships.

Today I can whine because I have to go to work, or I can shout for joy because I have a job to do.

Today I can complain because I have to go to school, or I can open my mind and fill it with rich new tidbits of knowledge.

Today I can murmur dejectedly because I have to do housework, or I can feel honored because I have shelter for my mind, body and soul.

Today stretches ahead of me, waiting to be shaped. And here I am, the sculptor who gets to do the shaping.

What today will be like is up to me. I get to choose what kind of day I'll have!

Have a great day...*unless you have other plans.*

– Unknown

The Golden Fleece

If I'd been uncompromising when it came to the use of *perfect* exercise form and *abbreviated* routines, and insistent on the need to *add a little iron* to each big exercise every week or two, for year after year after year, I'd have made gains so consistently, and without injuries, that I'd have thought I was an easy gainer.

I'd have been adding a tad of iron every week or two without any perceived increase in effort needed, such would have been the gradual nature of my progression. I'd have accumulated gains on an almost linear basis for year after year. Having discovered *The Golden Fleece* I'd have been wondering why so many people had trouble developing bigger muscles.

All of this doesn't apply just to me, *but to all trainees who want to build stronger and better physiques*, though the specific interpretation of exercises, training volume and frequency, caloric and nutritional intake, sleep needs and rate of progress varies among individuals.